Distributed Leadership in Nursing and Healthcare

Distributed Leadership in Nursing and Healthcare

Theory, Evidence and Development

Edited by

Elizabeth A. Curtis, Martin Beirne, John G. Cullen, Ruth Northway and Siobhán Corrigan

Open University Press

Open University Press
McGraw Hill
8th Floor, 338 Euston Road
London
England
NW1 3BH

email: enquiries@openup.co.uk
world wide web: www.openup.co.uk

First edition published 2021

A catalogue record of this book is available from the British Library

ISBN-13: 9780335249459
ISBN-10: 0335249450
eISBN: 9780335249466

Library of Congress Cataloging-in-Publication Data
CIP data applied for

Typeset by Transforma Pvt. Ltd., Chennai, India

Printed in Great Britain by Bell and Bain Ltd, Glasgow

Praise for this book

'If you're working in the healthcare sector right now, you probably don't want to read another book about leadership. This book, thankfully, isn't about self-defined heroic organizational leaders or power-hungry political leaders – it tells the stories of the people doing leadership every day in their work to make healthcare happen. The theory, distributed leadership, is well-established and made for understanding how healthcare work is achieved; the contributors are all committed to healthcare research and education, as well as the people working to make it happen every single day. This would always have been a valuable book; Covid-19 and the leadership it's generating within healthcare settings make it both timely and timeless.'

Scott Taylor (Dr) - Business School Director of Admissions, University of Birmingham

Why do we manage the most skilled and motivated workforce in all of industry through hierarchical command and control leadership? And why and how can we develop a far more relevant and powerful distributed leadership model in nursing and healthcare. This book offers a profound and brilliant analysis of the case for distributed leadership and how we can make it happen in practice for the benefit of the communities we serve and for the dedicated professionals who work in nursing and healthcare. It is based on careful reviews of the wealth of available evidence, on the practical experience of ground-breaking pioneers, and a deep appreciation of the context of nursing and healthcare. It is a treasure chest of knowledge about how we can transform leadership in healthcare to create the conditions for the emergence of cultures of compassionate and high quality care for all.

Professor Michael West CBE - Senior Visiting Fellow, The King's Fund Professor of Organizational Psychology, Lancaster University - Emeritus Professor, Aston University

I am so pleased to see this book. For so many years in health and social care, and in nursing in particular, leadership has been taught with materials advocating very traditional models that we are all familiar with. We put leadership styles into a few different boxes, often favouring the transformational style as one to strive to achieve. However, healthcare has changed and failings in leadership have been apparent with, sadly, terrible consequences. This book claims to be 'like no other' and that is so true. The editors and authors each add quality guidance around distributed leadership to readers, providing evidence based examples,

useful websites and key reading material to support and supplement the ideas being presented. This book will be really valuable to nurses who want to adopt a more inclusive style of leadership that aligns so well with the changing ways of working in health and social care. Responsibility, power and authority to bring about and lead local change are vital and this book provides examples and insight into how to achieve this. This book is long overdue and should be essential reading for all nursing students (undergraduate and postgraduate) as they are the future leaders.

Bridie Kent, Professor in Leadership in Nursing, University of Plymouth

A timely and relevant volume focused on an issue of immense importance to all of us - leadership in the health sector. With particular attention to nursing, the authors use a distributed lens to frame their various papers, centering their analyses on leadership as a collective or social practice. Together the chapters offer useful and usable information for health sector practitioners and policymakers and, in addition, contribute to a growing body of literature that takes a distributed perspective to understanding leadership in the public sector broadly.

James Spillane, Olin Professor in Learning & Organizational Change, Northwestern University, Chicago, IL, USA.

This new book, written by an experienced group of educators and clinicians, revisits distributed leadership theories and discusses them in a wide-ranging and innovative way. It makes for a very interesting read and I particularly like the case examples, which illustrate the various concepts and theories very well as applied to various healthcare and clinical settings and situationsl. It is the first book I am aware of that delves into such depth into distributed leadership in the nursing and healthcare context and as such is a valuable addition to the field.

Professor Judy McKimm, Professor of Medical Education and Director of Strategic Educational Development, Swansea University

As health systems become increasingly more complex and pressurised, they face increased risks of failure during times of crisis, and there is a need to question where power and influence are invested in hierarchical structures. When things go wrong, as they do, we should question whether established approaches to leadership, based on hierarchies and authority gradients, always serve us well. This book invites us to consider the potential of a more distributed approach to leadership that disrupts power imbalances and establishes new possibilities concerning who can lead, who might follow, and whether this offers us a better way ahead?

Professor Daniel Kelly PhD FRCN FRSA, Royal College of Nursing Chair of Nursing Research, School of Healthcare Sciences, Cardiff University

Contents

Foreword

It is apposite that this book on distributed leadership in nursing and healthcare should arrive in the midst of a global healthcare pandemic. Conventional logic and traditional leadership theory suggest that success and failure are rooted in the characteristics of the individual leader and that during a crisis, such as Covid-19, that focus on the CEO or equivalent is ever more critical. And yet, as critical leadership scholars have noted for some time – and as this collection makes abundantly clear – neither of these assumptions is an accurate portrayal of what counts as leadership on the ground. In the first place, an analysis of individual leaders seldom provides sufficient empirical data to support the notion that these mythical heroes are sufficient to explain the trajectory of an organisation, given the complexity of the situation. Second, what counts as a crisis, and how that is constituted by those in positions of formal authority and the media, is as significant as anything that an individual might do. This is not to say that individual leaders are irrelevant: we only have to consider the impact of Johnson, Trump and Bolsonaro in their respective countries to understand that individual leaders matter. But that is not the same as explaining how leadership actually works on the ground, in hospitals, in care homes and the many organisations that make up health systems. It is as if, as Bertolt Brecht (1981: 252) asked when considering Alexander's conquest of India, 'Was he alone?' Didn't Napoleon even have a cook when he conquered Europe?

As this collection suggests, leadership is more appropriately understood as a collective effort, involving either small teams or large groups, all of whom can make a difference to the success of the organisation and the care of patients and staff. This does not mean that distributed leadership is necessarily better than individual forms of leadership in all circumstances: we do not need to have committees debating and voting on whether the existence of a fire in the hospital necessitates a research group to write an overview of the situation and report back. Nor do we need a participatory approach to standard surgical procedures – if there is a standard operating procedure that works, well then, we should let skilled staff do their jobs. But the actual leadership practice of healthcare is – as readers will discover – inherently collaborative and rooted in negotiated leadership at every level of the hierarchy. Moreover, this is not so much a political choice as a practical necessity: many of the situations facing clinicians, health professionals and all the myriad others involved in healthcare are simply beyond the capacity of any individual to 'lead', let alone control. In effect, this timely collection is not capturing a new way of *working* as much as a new way of *looking* at what we have always done. The implication of this is profound: the moral of the stories collected here is not how important it is to change the way we work in a radically collaborative way; it is not yet another change project requiring everyone to restructure everything – again. On the contrary, it is suggesting that we look more closely at how organisations actually work effectively, and how what counts as 'leadership' needs to be reinterpreted.

Keith Grint
Emeritus Professor, Warwick Business School,
Warwick University

Brecht, B. (1981) *Poems 1913–1956*, London: Eyre Methuen.

1 Introducing the collection: A leadership book like no other!

Martin Beirne

Chapter topics

- The logic behind the collection
- Purpose and ambition
- Setting the scene and explaining the context
- Shifting the focus of leadership thinking, learning and development
- An initial outline of distributed leadership
- Pointers towards positive and critical reactions
- The importance of applied scholarship and practitioner engagement
- Prioritising constructive combinations or 'configurations' of positional and local leadership behaviour

Introduction

This book is distinctive in terms of focus and approach, standing apart from the mainstream literature on leadership learning and development in healthcare. Contributing authors have expressed a strong commitment to applied research on distributed leadership, a topic that is underdeveloped, regularly unappreciated and frequently neglected in attempts to improve the performance of health organisations. The purpose here is to magnify the significance of distributed leadership as an important everyday feature of organisational life, and to promote viable ways of extending and supporting this with practical interventions and innovative leader development initiatives for health professionals.

Despite some professed practitioner interest in distributed leadership, especially among early career professionals in nursing and midwifery (Cleary et al., 2011; Beirne, 2017), much of the research writing and most of the prescriptive commentary about healthcare leaders, their impact and development is based on very conventional and conservative preoccupations with concentrated knowledge and formal authority. Leadership matters are frequently restricted to those at the top of managerial and medical hierarchies (Currie and Lockett, 2007). Executive expertise is the primary concern, especially where care levels are faltering, service standards seem to be slipping and the pressure to secure necessary improvements becomes intense (Gabel, 2013; Martin et al., 2015; Fischer, 2017). When pressing problems produce calls for better or more appropriate leadership, interest typically centres on the appointment and development of exceptional people, those with personal qualities that supposedly mark them out from the majority and equip them to occupy the most senior positions.

This collection argues for a more inclusive and less elitist understanding of leadership, associating it with influence and collective forms of reflective action rather than position or official status. It also rejects simplistic connections between executive authority and exceptional qualities. The ability to lead – to exercise judgement, show initiative, accept responsibility for addressing problems, visualise ways forward and elicit the cooperation of others to secure improvements – is not confined to the few or to a 'heroic' minority that inevitably rise to the top of work organisations on the strength of rare personal qualities. Leadership in this broader sense is more widely distributed than the mainstream literature suggests. Alternative conceptualisations and a growing body of evidence also indicate that it can have wider benefits for organisational learning and improvement (King's Fund, 2011; Günzel-Jensen et al., 2016; Beirne, 2017). The 'ordinary leadership' of frontline clinicians and the interventions of de facto leaders at different levels of formal authority and across established role descriptions are more important, and capable of potentially greater contributions to care quality and patient safety, than is generally realised (McKee et al., 2013).

The chapters that follow challenge taken-for-granted assumptions about leadership, promoting a healthy scepticism and greater propensity to question established theories and developmental programmes, especially where these have their roots in business thinking or rely on models popularised in the commercial sector and imported via consultancy companies. The growing influence of Critical Leadership Studies (CLS) is evident throughout the book (Alvesson and Spicer, 2012; Collinson, 2014), with many of the contributing authors drawing upon this movement to claim space for distributed leadership and weaken the conventional ties to hierarchy and executive expertise. This critical literature provides a compelling antidote to popular images of transformational and charismatic leadership in particular, highlighting key weaknesses in terms of the theory and evidence applied to support them (Currie and Lockett, 2007). It also demonstrates how employee self-activity and local leadership initiatives can represent an alternative, dynamic and innovative force for work organisations, at the same time revealing some of the obstacles and struggles that confront those who intervene to exercise leadership at this level (Currie and Lockett, 2011; Martin et al., 2015; Beirne, 2017).

Unfortunately, the applied relevance of CLS remains relatively underdeveloped, with the academic community behind this concentrating on theory-building, filling out the critiques of orthodoxy thinking and evaluating available empirical evidence (Beirne, 2013). A detailed practical agenda that can speak to the concerns of 'ordinary leaders' has yet to emerge from this, although some promising work on more inclusive leadership development initiatives has already been published (Carroll and Nicholson, 2014; Gagnon and Collinson, 2014). Extending the applied dimension to address the concerns of health professionals who would make more of distributed leadership is another distinguishing feature of this book.

Existing critical scholarship has prepared the ground for more inclusive approaches to leadership practice, exposing the limits of conventional thinking and identifying alternative possibilities for reconceptualising it as a distributed rather than a concentrated phenomenon. This collection makes a deliberate attempt to harness this knowledge and channel it towards fresh initiatives and focused interventions that can extend the reach of distributed leadership, while also cultivating inclinations and abilities that can make it more significant for health professionals. The chapters that follow combine considered analysis with advocacy and a practical concern to reach and support practitioners who can identify with the concept, and are open to making it more meaningful in their own work situations. Stylistically, some of the contributions also stand out from the mainstream literature by presenting their case polemically, as well as analytically, to stimulate reflection about the limits and possibilities of leadership commentary in healthcare and promote a realistic appraisal of changes that are possible in the 'here and now'.

The distributed local leadership of frontline staff in work groups, practitioner communities and social movements is often acknowledged in other areas of scholarship, and credited with making a positive contribution to organisational effectiveness (Leithwood et al., 2007; Gronn, 2008). In this respect, the narrow focus of so much of the leadership literature, within and beyond healthcare, is surprising. Attempting to correct for this and extend the focus of leadership learning and development – conceptually, empirically and with a practical agenda that engages practitioner interest – is both timely and important for the future of health organisations. It is also an ambition that differentiates this collection from the bulk of published work on leadership in healthcare.

A fresh approach to leadership learning and development

The pressures on health organisations and healthcare systems are intense, and increasingly inform debates about leadership reform and innovation to tackle persistent problems. Demographic changes, expanding demand, advances in treatment and fiscal pressures all present challenges to established ideas about effective ways of leading, managing and working. Leadership features prominently in discussions about how to cope with these environmental challenges and achieve sustainable improvements in care quality under existing constraints, although it is now more difficult to justify an orthodox approach or rehearse traditional arguments about the capacity of executive level appointments to find solutions and transform the fortunes of struggling institutions.

Leadership failures have exposed the limitations of a conventional, top-down, hierarchical approach to running health organisations. These have been widely reported and regularly investigated over the past decade, with examples identified in various countries around the world (Fischer, 2017; Beirne, 2019). Some have been linked to scandalous cases of poor performance and substandard care, including unnecessary deaths (Francis, 2013; Keogh, 2013). Explanations have typically focused on patterned behaviour and the prevailing culture of healthcare leadership, rather than the personal conduct of particular leaders or clinicians. In these cases, institutionalised preoccupations with narrow performance targets and the imposition of managerial controls on staff evidently detached health executives, or at least a core group of them, from fundamental matters of patient safety and care quality.

These findings are consistent with longer-term research on the impact of 'leaderism' and managerialism in the health sector (O'Reilly and Reed, 2010). There are regular reports of clinicians being marginalised by top-driven change initiatives that set out to re-shape their professional practice and increase efficiency while cutting treatment costs (Doolin, 2003). These were typically devised in response to the reforming policies and programmes of various governments and wider interest groups, and were solidified with the incorporation of business quality assessment models and an audit approach to judging performance. As measures were introduced across the sector to hold clinicians accountable for their practice, the prevailing logic of healthcare leadership was intimately connected (and commonly associated) with a core commitment to weaken clinical roles and undermine professional autonomy (Ham, 2008; Günzel-Jensen et al., 2016). Collaborative working relations were undoubtedly strained by this trajectory of leadership development in many health organisations, with more obvious tensions emerging between clinicians and an expanding hierarchy of formal leaders and professional managers. This created a tendency for health executives to become aloof, insular and out of touch with the everyday challenges confronting clinicians. The culture and controls placed on the clinical workplace also made it more difficult for doctors and nurses to intervene and prevent care failures (Francis, 2013; Keogh, 2013; Gordon et al., 2015).

Reactions to this pattern of leadership development and the revelations about substandard care have extended the boundaries of discussion about leaders and their role in healthcare. There is a nascent shift in leadership thinking that supports a more inclusive position. This is discernible in recent guidelines on professional conduct, as well as discussion documents and official reports. Standards issued by the Nursing and Midwifery Council (NMC, 2018) make explicit reference to leadership capabilities, and the importance of cultivating these by the point of professional registration so that frontline nurses can influence teams and take a lead in addressing care issues as they emerge. This resonates with earlier calls from the King's Fund (2011) for a devolution of leadership responsibilities to nurses and doctors, and a fresh approach that appreciates the contributions of multiple leaders working across hierarchical and functional boundaries 'from the board to the ward'.

These publications reflect a growing appreciation of local leaders and the informal and voluntary leadership behaviour of clinicians, who may not even think of themselves as leading or engaging in work that merits this label. They help to clear a path through some of the preconceived notions and recent damaging attributions of leadership to open discussion about who and what it really involves, and whether or to what extent it applies to those without executive status. There is a discernible push towards distributed leadership in this sort of literature, although it can seem rather hesitant, cautious or implicit, falling short of an unambiguous endorsement. The departure from established accounts is highly significant nonetheless, acknowledging that care quality is often dependent on leadership provided though clinical teams rather than transmitted down through hierarchies. There is an acute understanding that safety issues are more likely to be tackled and the service to patients improved if doctors and nurses at this level have the scope and confidence to share insights, anticipate requirements and accept responsibility for making work adjustments – or, in other words, involve themselves with leadership activities on a shared basis with their frontline colleagues.

Interest in distributed leadership has also gathered impetus from analyses of future trends in healthcare and reports on how best to recruit and retain clinical staff. Again, the dysfunctions of concentrated hierarchical leadership are thrown into sharp relief by the value to be gleaned from acknowledging and extending local and informal leadership behaviour. With priorities set for complex processes of service integration, telemedicine and further advances in community-based care, the ability of traditional leadership approaches to deliver meaningful progress is seriously doubted. Advances in these areas depend on numerous interconnecting layers of decision-making influence and effective means of harnessing collective insights. These are 'wicked problems' (Grint and Holt, 2011) that are beyond the understanding and control of executive teams, undermining the established logic of leadership and shifting attention towards collective intelligence and the redistribution of influence (Chreim et al., 2013).

Securing access to this expertise and to the local leadership agency of health professionals is a recurring problem, however, since the hierarchical approach is perceived to have damaged the quality of their work experience, prompting disaffection and increases in absenteeism and staff turnover. Research points to persistent and substantial shortages of clinical personnel, and to unsustainable levels of stressful working for those who remain on the front lines of healthcare (Zander et al., 2016; OECD, 2019). Increasing the scope for autonomous influence is an accepted means of improving the quality of working life (Beirne, 2013), and coincides with the case for professional role enhancement to meet future challenges and deliver more immediate improvements in quality and patient safety. While frontline professionals figure prominently in accounts of leadership reform to improve the effectiveness of healthcare systems around the world, retaining, engaging and enhancing their respective contributions should be more of a strategic and operational priority for health organisations, according to the World Health Organization (2011).

Recognising distributed leadership

Enthusiasts for distributed leadership question the value of familiar and simplistic distinctions between leaders and followers. They focus on expertise and agency rather than formal position and official standing, believing that leadership skills and contributions are not confined to those at the top of organisational or professional hierarchies. Leadership qualities and interventions are detected at different levels of formal organisation, emerging from the reciprocal interactions between groups of people as they deal with their problems and work commitments, despite traditional demarcations of rank and authority (Jones, 2014). Occasionally they have an impact spontaneously, as particular individuals step in and out of leadership activities voluntarily, sharing them with colleagues as they balance the demands on their time, energy and inclinations. At other times, local understandings and socially negotiated agreements can produce more regularised examples of informal group leadership. These can be highly functional, despite operating below the radar of conventional leadership structures, and even compensating for them via unapproved interventions that enhance performance or deliver on operational requirements (Buchanan et al., 2007; Beirne, 2017).

Research on distributed leadership aims to highlight the value of this de facto leadership behaviour and mobilise it to generate opportunities for improving job structures and levels of organisational performance. Motivated by the sense that relevant talent is being ignored or marginalised, the applied side of this is focused on tapping into the layers of expertise and capacity for leadership that lies with the initiative, vision and creativity of multiple actors, rather than just those with executive authority. Formal leaders remain significant actors within this project, certainly in most of the conceptual and practically engaged scholarship published to date. However, their role is very different, as subsequent chapters will explain in greater detail. Positional authority is considered to be vital for enabling and supporting distributed leadership, protecting space for 'ordinary leaders' to make an appreciable difference, counteracting any lingering tendencies towards executive direction and facilitating participative decision-making. Much of the applied work in this area is now channelled towards developing constructive configurations, hybrids or combinations of distributed and positional leadership, following influential work by authors such as Gronn (2009) and Collinson and Collinson (2009).

While this agenda is attracting considerable interest within healthcare, research is still limited in terms of scale and impact by comparison with other sectors, notably education. There has been some progress towards absorbing elements of it within training and professional development programmes for nurses and doctors, or at least preparing the ground for this, as already mentioned (Ham, 2008; NMC, 2018). Members of the research community are also presenting the health sector as a natural setting for distributed leadership, since care quality is now contingent upon interdisciplinary working and interdependent relations that are beyond the control of traditional leadership teams (Günzel-Jensen et al., 2016). With treatment requiring a greater diversity of frontline expertise, flatter structures and flexible forms of local leadership are ostensibly more effective than remote decision-making via directive hierarchies. These developments and interpretations are promising in themselves, although the practical implications for clinical roles and relationships remain unclear. There are also signs of nervousness and critical concerns about difficulties and potential costs arising from wider and more active leadership contributions. A number of studies have identified oppositional tendencies and a range of other obstacles to achieving a smooth rebalancing of distributed and positional leadership in practice (Martin et al., 2015; Beirne, 2017). However, research with an applied dimension that can deliver reassurance and support meaningful change from a detailed understanding of conditions, contingencies and processes that affect the nature and extent of distributed influence is underdeveloped.

This collection aims to fill this gap and encourage innovative forms of research and professional development that are capable of enhancing the leadership roles and responsibilities of health professionals. It emerged from the applied work of a Nursing Leadership Network centred at the School of Nursing and Midwifery at Trinity College Dublin. The editors and most of the authors have been highly active within this network over the last decade, delivering regular practitioner workshops and seminars, and organising a leadership conference in 2016. Most of the direct work with health professionals has been conducted in Ireland, though with contributing researchers and clinicians from across Europe, and occasionally the United States. However, an extra dimension was added in 2019, partly with funding initiatives to extend the reach into other European countries, and especially with a full day seminar and follow-on practitioner engagement sessions at Mater Dei Hospital in Malta.

Reactions to this work have been consistently positive, especially among the various cohorts of nurse practitioners who participated. It also became clear, through time, that their demands were growing, and that most of those involved were looking for something more. The case for distributed leadership was attracting enthusiasm, yet frustrations were also being expressed about the difficulties of bringing it to life in specific work situations. Our participants were demanding more focused guidance on the everyday challenges of making distributed leadership work, on limiting the adverse effects of traditional leadership, and helping them to have more of an impact as 'ordinary leaders'. This magnified the need for stronger forms of support, for additional work that encouraged people to embrace the concept, though also practise it with confidence and with enabling processes capable of embedding it as a regular feature of their professional lives. This book is part of the Network's response to this evident unease. It is concerned with capacity-building and role development so that health professionals are better equipped to enact distributed leadership, and secure lasting improvements in care and job quality as a result.

Conventional leadership theories and preoccupations

What exactly are the problems with received wisdom on leadership? It will be clear from the discussion so far that established theories and development programmes are criticised for imposing narrow boundaries on leadership ability and behaviour. Critical writers are partly concerned that attention is focused too narrowly on people who are at or near the top of formal hierarchies. This preoccupation with exclusionary and often elitist notions of leadership has also produced, and is regularly reinforced by, simplistic theorising, which has been the target for much of the critical literature. Influential critics now regularly associate the mainstream interest in executive leadership with spurious assumptions and exaggerated claims that drive an artificial wedge between the processes of leading and following (Gronn, 2008; Collinson, 2014).

Traditionally, leadership research and development has concentrated on revealing and strengthening the guiding qualities of executives, establishing explicit links with desirable outcomes, including follower behaviour, often directly and without too much attention to intervening factors. Some of the cruder versions of this conventional approach credit official leaders with the capacity to shape employee attitudes and behaviour to the extent that they internalise the approved 'mission' of their organisation and set aside any personal or sectional interests. Transformational leadership is prominent in this regard. It presents an idealised image of leadership as a one-way, top-driven process, with inspirational figures instilling shared values, aligning followers with their vision, and then orchestrating purposeful behaviour to make this a reality. Employees emerge as largely passive and dependent followers. Leadership becomes the province of highly sensitive and charismatic people, rather than something that the wider population of workers and managers can demonstrate or collectively enhance (Currie and Lockett, 2007).

Transformational leadership is now enthusiastically endorsed within healthcare. Gabel insists that it provides a 'framework for effective leadership' in the health sector (2013: 59). He also calls for it to be taught at various stages of medical education and professional development (2013: 55). Nurses and their educators have also been urged to embrace this approach. There is now a substantial literature on transformational leadership in nursing, commending it as a neutral, universally applicable and effective means of understanding the qualities and developmental needs of the sort of people who can drive improvements in patient care (Fischer, 2017; Jambawo, 2018; Collins et al., 2020). Although nurses generally enter the profession with a strong humanitarian concern to care for others, much of this reproduces the familiar managerial argument that employees need to be given a sense of mission and purpose to work effectively. They need to be transformed, to have their values and attitudes altered so that they suspend narrow personal interests and elevate their commitment through a heightened sense of obligation to their profession and organisation. Leadership and seniority are fused together as an essentially positive transformational force that energises and orchestrates useful followership.

The bifurcation of leaders and followers in this conceptualisation is inadequate, attributing qualities to leaders that are unrealistic and at odds with empirical evidence. At the same time, it perpetuates a disparaging view of employee attitudes and orientations to work, ignoring their capacity to apply a constructive, and often corrective, independent influence on organisational performance. Promotional accounts of transformational leadership give very little attention to critical reactions on the part of followers, and dysfunctional behaviour among leaders. There is no obvious inclination to question whether followers are really as susceptible as the theory suggests, or to recognise that leader behaviour can be counterproductive or negative when it sets out to condition or re-shape employee attitudes. The potency of transformational theory is largely taken for granted, or justified on the basis of anecdotal information, with insufficient attention given to available empirical evidence on the difficulties and consequences of such leadership behaviour in action.

Studies from the critical end of the leadership studies spectrum offer more nuanced insights into the nature and impact of seemingly transformative leadership initiatives, demonstrating that followers are more likely to question rather than internalise the values and mission set out by official leaders (Currie and Lockett, 2007; Beirne, 2013). Workers form their own views about leader behaviour in light of their experiences and perceptions about fair treatment, and frequently draw distinctions between the rhetoric and substance of formal leadership. Attempts to mould or change employee attitudes are not always appreciated, and can prompt a range of reactions other than those anticipated by transformational leadership theory, including distancing behaviour, resistance or a basic refusal to engage or respond. Aligning followers with the vision of the designated leader is far from straightforward, especially when such efforts are interpreted as threatening or involving a 'do as I say and not as I do' divisive culture of 'leaderism'. There is already some evidence of this within the health sector, where links between transformational leadership and managerialist reforms have been identified or perceived by hospital staff, resulting in questioning, ignoring or undermining reactions as opposed to any internalisation of reforming visions or missions (Doolin, 2003; Günzel-Jensen et al., 2016; Beirne, 2017).

The corollary is that transformational leadership is advocated on the basis of assumptions and correlations that do not stand up to scrutiny. In stressing the role of leaders in transforming follower values, orientations and behaviour, enthusiasts for this theory inflate both the capabilities of senior figures and the receptiveness of staff. They make no allowance for mediating factors between leadership and followership, especially the ability of workers to interpret events and respond in ways that are challenging and resistant rather than functional. The findings of critical studies cast doubt on the essential proposition that transformational leadership is intrinsically motivating and energising for workers. This is not to deny that positional leaders can be inspirational or capable of stimulating relatively high levels of performance among workers. Those who take a principled stand or gain the admiration of followers by representing their interests or acting to improve their wellbeing may indeed have a transformational influence, although worker agency is vital for establishing this and gauging whether any performance benefits that flow from it are sustained. These attributions and related outcomes are not in the hands of positional leaders alone.

Where follower reactions are critical or negative, empirical studies show that informal localised leadership can emerge to counteract official leader positions and resist directed change initiatives (Beirne et al., 2019). There is a large literature on trade union leadership which reveals that this can be spontaneous and grass roots based, again demonstrating the ability of official followers to become de facto leaders when they consider this to be necessary for a defence of workplace or work group interests (Darlington, 2018). Leadership and followership emerge from this critical research as fluid categories that resist hard and fast distinctions and the causal connections envisaged with the transformational view. Effective leadership development requires a better theoretical understanding of the reciprocal relationships between leading and following, and a stronger empirical appreciation of the inclinations to lead and exercise influence at different levels of formal organisation.

Distributed leadership as a fact of professional life

Once simplistic correlations between positional authority and mission-driven behaviour are cleared away, leadership can be reconceptualised as a shared capacity and regular feature of life across organisational roles and relationships. It may be perceived as positive or negative, depending upon the values and interests of those who experience leadership interventions, and that may prompt further instances of leading and following at different levels as people respond in some way (by trying to resist top-down initiatives and pursue alternative possibilities, for example). The picture that emerges is highly complex, typically incorporating multiple layers and moments of interrelated leading and following, some colliding through expressions of critical or oppositional inclinations, while others embody consistent and complementary patterns of behaviour. Even where official realms of leadership seem to be purposeful and strong, informal leaders at the workgroup or departmental level may be applying influence and engaging followers with an alternative set of priorities. By the same reasoning, individuals or groups of de facto leaders are capable of galvanising immediate colleagues (and others) to sustain collaborative working when there is no effective or easily identifiable formal leadership in place (Buchanan et al., 2007).

These cross-cutting patterns of leadership agency are evident in the way that clinical teams and wider health organisations actually function. As previously noted, empirical studies that accommodate a distributed understanding demonstrate that clinicians at the lower levels of established hierarchies are fulfilling leadership roles by influencing their colleagues and accepting responsibility for driving improvements in care quality and safety (Cleary et al., 2011; Chreim et al., 2013; McKee et al., 2013). Nurses and doctors without formal authority and official titles are delivering leadership on an everyday basis, voluntarily and as they deem appropriate, in tandem with their designated commitments, and with discernible benefits for staff engagement, supportive working relations and positive outcomes for patients and their families (Günzel-Jensen et al., 2016; Beirne, 2017). However, these instances of useful local leadership are affected, and potentially destabilised, by contrasting and competing leadership approaches, priorities and interventions. Indeed, much of the evidence points to partial gains and unrealised potential as leadership from the front line collides with more traditional impulses to lead from the top through directive positional authority.

Healthcare may be a natural setting for distributed leadership given the nature of the work, treatment and technology, although it is also a difficult context where local interventions are far from trouble-free and less than universally admired. Some studies suggest that conventional notions of leadership are so engrained within the institutional cultures of health organisations that grass roots leaders tend to exercise their influence reluctantly and precariously, when they realise that problems are pressing and services are in crisis (Günzel-Jensen et al., 2016). There is certainly a consensus among researchers that distributed inclinations to lead are generally undervalued and regularly undermined by traditionalists who occupy senior positions in health service hierarchies (Beirne, 2017). Studies of senior medical, managerial and nursing opinion suggest that conservative attitudes towards leadership and distributed influence are quite common, and likely to prompt interventions that aim to restrict local leaders or contain them within established norms and structures that have a stifling effect (Currie and Locket, 2011; McKee et al., 2013; Martin et al., 2015). These can be a source of frustration, disaffection and staffing difficulties, as indicated earlier, sapping the energy of local leaders or channelling it towards more challenging or compensating behaviour that has a short-run, episodic and curtailed impact on work performance.

Subsequent chapters will offer more detailed insights into these competing leadership tendencies, both conceptually and empirically. As might be anticipated from the title of the collection, most are written with a concern to enhance the experiences and contributions of local leaders. They offer candid evaluations of established leadership theories and the legacy of entrenched hierarchical thinking within health organisations and professions. The theoretical sections of the book encourage critical reflection about the continuing and unhelpful influence of common assumptions and taken-for-granted notions that make it difficult to appreciate the value of distributed leadership. Together with the case studies and empirical content in Section Three, they illuminate inhibiting and enabling factors, channelling this towards a deeper understanding of practitioner responses and inclinations to engage in distributed leadership. The final section examines the educational and developmental significance of this collective review of theory and evidence, mapping ways forward and considering the prospects for achieving more constructive combinations of distributed and positional leadership in practice.

Conclusion

Healthcare systems are facing challenges that require more active clinical contributions to leadership, especially on a collective basis at the point of delivery. At this level, 'ordinary leaders' in multiskilled teams frequently accept responsibility for leading on quality and patient safety, albeit informally, occasionally and temporarily. As subsequent chapters will demonstrate, many frontline clinicians regularly step in and out of leadership activities, balancing these with their other work and sharing them with colleagues as they find ways of responding to contextual pressures together. Though highly significant in terms of organisational performance, this realm of leadership behaviour is frequently neglected or considered to be something other than leadership, even by those involved. Mainstream theories and discussions reinforce this tendency by equating leadership with seniority, concentrated authority and inflated images of exceptional expertise. Leadership in the wider sense – of ability to exercise influence and engage others in a collective approach to resolving problems through an explicit sense of purpose and shared responsibility – is too often sidelined by the narrow assumptions and limited agenda set by conventional literature and related executive education programmes.

The expanding field of Critical Leadership Studies provides a compelling corrective to exclusive, 'heroic' and elitist notions of leadership, offering a more inclusive conceptualisation and basis for alternative thinking about leader development (Carroll and Nicholson, 2014; Gagnon and Collinson, 2014; Alvesson and Spicer, 2012). Although the applied side of this remains relatively thin by comparison with published critiques of orthodox thinking, ideas about distributing and redistributing leadership influence are attracting greater interest and innovative activity (Günzel-Jensen et al., 2016; Beirne, 2017). This reaffirms the importance of leadership, though demonstrates that effective leaders are not always in positions of authority, and that people who do occupy senior positions are capable of creating problems and engaging in counterproductive behaviour that damages their organisations. This is hardly a revelation for health professionals, given recurring concerns about underperforming hospitals and prominent enquiries into scandalous care failures over the last decade (Francis, 2013; Keogh, 2013). However, it does underline the need for alternative ways of identifying, developing and supporting leaders in healthcare, adding to the sense of unease with conventional logic and engrained assumptions.

Distributed leadership provides a means of acting on these concerns and channelling critical arguments towards more innovative forms of practice. It loosens the connection with seniority and shifts the focus of developmental activity from executive skill-building to nurturing, supporting and harnessing 'ordinary leadership' interventions within wider communities of health professionals. Positional authority remains important for securing and sustaining these contributions, for extending and protecting the space that larger populations of leaders require to exercise their influence effectively and in a coordinated fashion (Gronn, 2009; Günzel-Jensen et al., 2016). In this respect, distributed and concentrated forms of leadership are mutually significant, although they need to operate in tandem rather than in tension, as subsequent chapters will demonstrate.

If the benefits associated with distributed leadership are to be realised, leaders across the different levels of health organisations need to develop conducive inclinations, insights and abilities. They also need to reach confident judgements about their own and others' contributions, and the support that is available to work across established boundaries and layers of formal responsibility. The knowledge-sharing, capacity-building and practitioner outreach activities of the Nursing Leadership Network that laid the foundations for this book tapped into an appetite for this sort of change, though also recognised reservations about the likelihood of securing distributed leadership as a regular feature of organisational life. Available evidence reinforces this sense of enthusiasm and caution, indicating that clinicians, especially nurse practitioners, are looking for more focused guidance on the everyday challenges of making distributed leadership work, on limiting the constraints posed by traditional leadership thinking, and helping them to make more of available opportunities (Beirne, 2017). It seems clear that the case for (re)distributing leadership influence strikes a chord with significant numbers of clinicians, and also that expressed concerns about the rate of change and options for negotiating obstacles to progress call for more focused applied research. This collection makes a constructive attempt to meet this challenge, and ensure that health professionals are more supported and better placed to practise distributed leadership.

Key concepts discussed

- This chapter explained the significance of contextual pressures and challenges to traditional thinking about leadership.
- It also underlined the importance of looking beyond conventional preoccupations with seniority, hierarchy and controversial assumptions about exclusive executive abilities.
- Leadership influence can be applied in the absence of formal authority.
- Transformational leadership theory exaggerates executive capabilities and oversimplifies the relationship between leading and following.
- Clinicians without formal leadership roles are also de facto leaders. Many of them balance activities on this front with their other work, and through informal arrangements share them with colleagues.
- Distributed leadership is a fact of life in health organisations, with recognised benefits for patient care and job quality.
- There is evident enthusiasm for distributed leadership among health professionals, although this is tempered by an acute sense of inhibiting factors and appetite for more effective forms of support.
- Distributed leadership has greater relevance for the modernisation of healthcare than is generally acknowledged, although organisational changes and new leader development programmes will be needed to make the most of this potential.

Key readings

- Alvesson, M. and Spicer, A. (2012) Critical leadership studies: The case for critical performativity, *Human Relations*, 65 (3): 367–390.
  This article provides some excellent insights into critical leadership studies, associated critiques and ongoing debates. It also includes some controversial and contested comments about distributed leadership.
- Günzel-Jensen, F., Jain, A. and Kjeldsen, A. (2016) Distributed leadership in health care: The role of formal leadership styles and organizational efficacy, *Leadership*, 14 (1): 110–133.
  This article presents the results of one of the most detailed quantitative studies of distributed leadership in healthcare to date. It is consistent with some of the most influential research on distributed leadership, notably the work of Peter Gronn (2008, 2009) on constructive configurations of informal and positional influence.
- King's Fund (2011) *The Future of Leadership and Management in the NHS: No More Heroes*, London: The King's Fund.
  This report is significant for encouraging progressive thinking about leadership in healthcare, and more active questioning of established theories and approaches to leader development.
- Nursing and Midwifery Council (NMC) (2018) *Future Nurse: Standards of Proficiency for Registered Nurses*, London: NMC.
  These standards reflect recent thinking about the qualities and abilities of nurses at their point of professional registration, including explicit references to leadership in the delivery of care.

Examples of conventional leadership theory applied to healthcare

- Collins, E., Owen, P., Digan, J. and Dunn, F. (2020) Applying transformational leadership in nursing practice, *Nursing Standard*, 35 (5): 59–66.
- Fischer, S. (2017) Developing nurses' transformational leadership skills, *Nursing Standard*, 31 (51): 54–63.
- Gabel, S. (2013) Transformational leadership and healthcare, *Medical Science Educator*, 23 (1): 55–60.
- Jambawo, S. (2018) Transformational leadership and ethical leadership: Their significance in the mental healthcare system, *British Journal of Nursing*, 27 (17): 998–1001.

Useful websites

- The King's Fund: https://www.kingsfund.org.uk/
  Provides a range of literature and advice sheets on leadership in healthcare, including advocacy on distributed leadership.
- NHS Leadership Academy: https://www.leadershipacademy.nhs.uk/
  A developmental agency, offering programmes and resources, including a Healthcare Leadership Model that aims to be inclusive and relevant, even for health workers who are not in formal leadership roles.
- Nursing and Midwifery Council: https://www.nmc.org.uk/
  This is the professional regulatory body for nursing and midwifery in Britain, setting standards that have an explicit leadership element.

References

Alvesson, M. and Spicer, A. (2012) Critical leadership studies: The case for critical performativity, *Human Relations*, 65 (3): 367–390.

Beirne, M. (2013) *Rhetoric and the Politics of Workplace Innovation*, Cheltenham: Elgar.

Beirne, M. (2017) The reforming appeal of distributed leadership: Recognising concerns and contradictory tendencies, *British Journal of Healthcare Management*, 23 (6): 262–270.

Beirne, M. (2019) Beyond controversy in change management: Rethinking options for intellectual disability services, in F. Sheerin and E. Curtis (eds.) *Leadership for Intellectual Disability Services: Motivating Change and Improvement*, Abingdon: Routledge, 139–162.

Beirne, M., Hurrell, S. and Wilson, F. (2019) Mobilising for equality? Understanding the impact of grass roots agency and third party representation, *Industrial Relations Journal*, 50 (1): 41–56.

Buchanan, D., Addicott, R., Fitzgerald, L., Ferlie, E. and Baeza, J. (2007) Nobody in charge: Distributed change agency in healthcare, *Human Relations*, 60 (7): 1065–1090.

Carroll, B. and Nicholson, H. (2014) Resistance and struggle in leadership development, *Human Relations*, 67 (11): 1413–1436.

Chreim, S., Langley, A., Comeau-Vallée, M., Huq, J.-L. and Reay, T. (2013) Leadership as boundary work in health care teams, *Leadership*, 9 (2): 201–228.

Cleary, M., Horsfall, J., Deacon, M. and Jackson, D. (2011) Leadership and mental health nursing, *Issues in Mental Health Nursing*, 32 (10): 632–639.

Collins, E., Owen, P., Digan, J. and Dunn, F. (2020) Applying transformational leadership in nursing practice, *Nursing Standard*, 35 (5): 59–66.

Collinson, D. (2014) Dichotomies, dialectics and dilemmas: New directions for critical leadership studies, *Leadership*, 10 (1): 36–55.

Collinson, D. and Collinson, M. (2009) Blended leadership: Employee perspectives on effective leadership in the UK further education sector, *Leadership*, 5 (3): 365–380.

Currie, G. and Lockett, A. (2007) A critique of transformational leadership: Moral, professional and contingent dimensions of leadership within public service organisations, *Human Relations*, 60 (2): 341–370.

Currie, G. and Lockett, A. (2011) Distributing leadership in health and social care: Concertive, conjoint or collective?, *International Journal of Management Reviews*, 13 (3): 286–300.

Darlington, R. (2018) The leadership component of Kelly's mobilisation theory: Contributions, tensions, limitations and further development, *Economic and Industrial Democracy*, 39 (4): 617–638.

Doolin, B. (2003) Narratives of change: Discourse, technology and organisation, *Organisation*, 10 (4): 751–770.

Fischer, S. (2017) Developing nurses' transformational leadership skills, *Nursing Standard*, 31 (51): 54–63.

Francis, R. (2013) *Report of the Mid Staffordshire NHS Foundation Trust Public Enquiry: Executive Summary*, London: HMSO. Available at: https://www.gov.uk/government/publications/report-of-the-mid-staffordshire-nhs-foundation-trust-public-inquiry (accessed 14 October 2020).

Gabel, S. (2013) Transformational leadership and healthcare, *Medical Science Educator*, 23 (1): 55–60.

Gagnon, S. and Collinson, D. (2014) Rethinking global leadership development programmes: The interrelated significance of power, context and identity, *Organization Studies*, 35 (5): 645–670.

Gordon, L., Rees, C., Ker, J. and Cleland, J. (2015) Dimensions, discourses and differences: Trainees conceptualising health care leadership and followership, *Medical Education*, 49 (12): 1248–1262.

Grint, K. and Holt, C. (2011) *Followership in the NHS*, London: The King's Fund.

Gronn, P. (2008) The future of distributed leadership, *Journal of Educational Administration*, 46 (2): 141–158.

Gronn, P. (2009) Leadership configurations, *Leadership*, 5 (3): 381–394.

Günzel-Jensen, F., Jain, A. and Kjeldsen, A. (2016) Distributed leadership in health care: The role of formal leadership styles and organizational efficacy, *Leadership*, 14 (1): 110–133.

Ham, C. (2008) Doctors in leadership: Learning from international experience, *International Journal of Clinical Leadership*, 16 (1): 11–16.

Jambawo, S. (2018) Transformational leadership and ethical leadership: Their significance in the mental healthcare system, *British Journal of Nursing*, 27 (17): 998–1001.

Jones, S. (2014) Distributed leadership: A critical analysis, *Leadership*, 10 (2): 129–141.

Keogh, B. (2013) *Review into the Quality of Care and Treatment Provided by 14 Hospital Trusts in England: Overview Report*, London: HMSO.

King's Fund (2011) *The Future of Leadership and Management in the NHS: No More Heroes*, London: The King's Fund.

Leithwood, K., Mascall, B., Strauss, T., Sacks, R., Memon, N. and Yashkina, A. (2007) Distributing leadership to make schools smarter: Taking the ego out of the system, *Leadership and Policy in Schools*, 6 (1): 37–67.

Martin, G., Beech, N., MacIntosh, R. and Bushfield, S. (2015) Potential challenges facing distributed leadership in health care: Evidence from the UK National Health Service, *Sociology of Health and Illness*, 37 (1): 14–29.

McKee, L., Charles, K., Dixon-Woods, M., Willars, J. and Martin, G. (2013) 'New' and distributed leadership in quality and safety in health care, or 'old' and hierarchical? An interview study with strategic stakeholders, *Journal of Health Services Research and Policy*, 18 (suppl. 2): 11–19.

Nursing and Midwifery Council (NMC) (2018) *Future Nurse: Standards of Proficiency for Registered Nurses*, London: NMC.

OECD/European Observatory on Health Systems and Policies (2019) *State of Health in the EU – United Kingdom: Country Health Profile 2019*, Paris: OECD Publishing/Brussels: European Observatory on Health Systems and Policies, Brussels. Available at: https://www.euro.who.int/__data/assets/pdf_file/0006/419478/Country-Health-Profile-2019-United-Kingdom.pdf (accessed 14 October 2020).

O'Reilly, D. and Reed, M. (2010) Leaderism: An evolution of managerialism in UK public service reforms, *Public Administration*, 88 (4): 960–978.

World Health Organization (WHO) (2011) *Strengthening nursing and midwifery*, WHA64.7. Available at: https://apps.who.int/gb/ebwha/pdf_files/WHA64/A64_R7-en.pdf?ua=1 (accessed 14 October 2020).

Zander, B., Aiken, L., Busse, R., Rafferty, A.M., Sermeus, W. and Bruyneel, L. (2016) The state of nursing in the European Union, *Eurohealth*, 22 (1): 3–6.

2 Context and the case for reconceptualising leadership in healthcare

Ruth Northway

Chapter topics

- The current context of healthcare
- The limitations of traditional leadership approaches
- The potential for alternative approaches including distributed leadership

Introduction

Figueroa et al. (2019) note that whilst there is no standard agreed definition of healthcare leadership, a number of key elements can be identified. These include the ability to identify priorities, provide strategic direction, and create commitment across the healthcare sector to address these priorities in order to improve health services. This suggests that what constitutes appropriate and effective leadership needs to be considered through an understanding of the context within which health services (and hence healthcare leaders) currently operate, since it is from this context that priorities will emerge, and within which services need to respond.

At the time of writing this chapter, the Covid-19 pandemic was impacting on populations and healthcare systems globally. This significantly challenged and changed the context within which such healthcare systems operate and posed important questions to which both political and healthcare leaders had to try to respond. Given its likely impact on the future of healthcare leadership, consideration will also be given in this chapter to its immediate effects and possible future consequences.

The aim of this chapter is therefore to set the scene for subsequent chapters and discussion in this book. It will explore the current context within which healthcare organisations and health professionals operate and explore the limits of positional authority and executive control within this context. An argument for exploring alternative approaches, with a particular focus on distributed leadership, will be presented.

The current context of healthcare

In the literature published over the past decade or so there is consensus that globally healthcare systems are facing many changes and challenges. Having undertaken a rapid review of such literature, Figueroa et al. (2019) argue that these challenges can be identified at three levels: the macro-system context, the meso-organisational context and the micro-context where it is related to the individual healthcare leader. Of course, there is interaction between these levels with, for example, challenges at a macro level impacting on the responses required at the organisational and individual levels.

One of the key factors impacting on healthcare systems is demographic change and this exerts an influence in two areas: the demand for healthcare and the healthcare workforce. As Figueroa et al. (2019) note, many countries are experiencing population growth, increased life expectancy leading to an increasing proportion of the population being of older age, and an increased burden of disease and illness. Indeed, whilst ageing is not always associated with ill health some health problems are age related and the likelihood of older people experiencing multiple long-term health conditions is increased compared with younger age groups. This means that whilst people are living longer, they may be spending an increased number of years with health problems that require support from healthcare systems. Furthermore, many of these conditions are long term in nature and require ongoing support within community settings, placing a high level of demand on primary care services. The demand for health services is thus increased across the system and at the same time the expectations of both the public and healthcare staff are changing and increasing (McIntosh and Layland, 2020), resulting in increased demands in terms of quality as well as quantity of provision.

To meet this increased demand requires that healthcare systems have sufficient staff with the right knowledge and skills in the right place at the right time. However, shortages of such staff have been noted (McIntosh and Layland, 2020). In addition, challenges in terms of achieving the optimum skill mix amongst healthcare professionals, difficulties in collaboration between professions, and ineffective use of human and other resources and staff burnout, all further exacerbate this situation (Figueroa et al., 2019). There is thus a mismatch between demand for healthcare and the availability of appropriate staff to meet this demand.

A further major factor impacting on healthcare is the availability (or not) of sufficient financial resources. However, many healthcare systems have been subject to financial pressures over recent years (West et al., 2014; McIntosh and Layland, 2020). In the face of the increased demands noted above, this has caused considerable strain on many healthcare systems and the staff working within them. It has also led to calls for greater productivity and innovation (West et al., 2014) and also for a different approach to leadership (discussed later in the chapter).

Cameron et al. (2019) argue that some of these pressures on healthcare systems are relatively well known but that less attention has been paid to others such as technology, climate change and austerity. Moreover, some of these factors are outside of the immediate control of healthcare systems and yet impact on them. Nonetheless it can be seen that, for example, wider governmental policies that guide the economy and influence the population's living standards will impact on the health and wellbeing of populations and hence on the demand for health services. It is thus argued that if sustainable health systems are to be developed, leaders need to focus on the wider factors that impact upon health and health services (Cameron et al., 2019).

In many ways the factors outlined above might be viewed as a 'perfect storm' in which more is being expected of healthcare systems and those who work within them whilst at the same time resource constraints make it challenging to meet such demands. In such circumstances effective leadership is required more than ever and it is perhaps therefore to be expected that where there are failures in healthcare a lack of leadership is cited as a key contributory factor. This issue will be returned to later in this chapter. However, it is also evident that the provision of healthcare is becoming increasingly complex, that this shapes the context in which health services are provided, which in turn places different demands upon healthcare leaders.

Healthcare and complexity

In everyday language reference is often made to 'healthcare systems' and increasingly these are recognised as being 'complex' systems. However, what does it mean to be a 'complex' system and what are the implications for leadership within such systems?

Whilst much has been written about complexity, Mitchell (2009) suggests that complex systems share three key properties:

1. Complex collective behaviour
2. Signalling and processing information
3. Adaptation.

Each of these will be considered in turn below.

Complex systems comprise many networks, which, in turn, comprise many elements that operate according to various rules without central control or leadership making it difficult to predict patterns of behaviour (Mitchell, 2009). At first sight this view might give rise to concerns in the context of healthcare since there is a need to predict (so far as possible) patterns of behaviour and this, in turn, requires that there is some central control. However, it cannot be disputed that healthcare systems comprise many elements and that there is a need for these elements to work together in order to achieve desired outcomes.

For example, if we just take the example of one hospital, then that organisation alone will comprise many departments in which many different professionals work. They need to work in a coordinated manner in order to provide timely and effective care. If the Human Resources Department does not work effectively with the Finance Department it is unlikely that there will be sufficient staff available to provide the services required. If the Housekeeping Department does not work effectively with those that manage the operating theatres, then even if the correct staff are available to perform an operation that operation will not be able to go ahead if the theatre has not been cleaned to the standards required. Even at the level of the individual patient, a high level of coordination and collaboration can be required particularly where an individual has complex and multiple health problems. For example, it may be necessary to coordinate efforts across different specialisms in order to achieve optimum outcomes but even within one clinical department there will be professional groups who have different values and priorities (Goodwin, 2019).

This fictional hospital, however, does not operate in isolation and is itself part of a wider system which both impacts on its functioning and which it influences by its actions. For example, patients are generally referred to hospitals through primary care systems, which means that there needs to be effective ways of working with such systems. Likewise, when it is time for someone to be discharged this may be reliant on the ability of both primary and social care systems to provide the required support. Indeed, it is not uncommon to hear news reports (particularly in winter) of pressures being placed on hospitals due to an inability to safely discharge patients. Working across traditional organisational boundaries is thus required (King's Fund, 2011).

However, acute health services, primary care services and social care services are themselves dependent upon political decisions regarding policy and funding, thus highlighting other elements of what is a very complex system that is required to provide effective and safe healthcare. Indeed, the current Covid-19 pandemic has further shown how the healthcare system itself needs to be seen as part of a wider system, the elements of which need to work together in order to ensure that health services can be delivered safely and effectively. For example, it has highlighted the reliance upon international supply chains for the provision of key equipment, the impact of systems such as public transport on public health and the economic impact of healthcare challenges.

In relation to signalling and processing information, Mitchell (2009) argues that complex systems produce information and signal that information both internally and from their external environment. As can be seen from the discussion above there are many elements within the healthcare system and each of these is reliant upon receiving and sharing information in a timely and appropriate manner. For example, a failure to provide correct information at the point of discharge could lead to a breakdown in care and a readmission to hospital. Similarly, a failure by a hospital to report key data can lead to ineffective planning at a policy level, which, in turn, can lead to the appropriate financial support not being available.

Mitchell (2009) argues that the final key property of complex systems is that they adapt in order to survive and enhance success: they evolve through learning and changing their behaviour. As Figueroa et al. (2019) note, healthcare systems are continually changing at all levels and across contexts. Indeed, some key factors that give rise to the need for constant change were noted in the previous section of this chapter. At the time of writing, however, the Covid-19 pandemic was challenging healthcare systems internationally to adapt and change at a very quick pace whilst dealing with high levels of uncertainty.

Undoubtedly this pandemic posed many leadership challenges and is likely to shape future leadership practices in healthcare. When there is time for reflection on developments in this area it will be interesting to note exactly what adaptations were made during this period, what learning took place, and how much of this learning is used to inform future delivery of healthcare. However, within the UK work commenced quite early to identify what challenges health services would face in the wake of the pandemic. In submitting evidence to the Health and Social Services Committee of Inquiry into Delivering Core NHS and Care Services During the Pandemic and Beyond, the Health Foundation,

Nuffield Trust and the King's Fund (2020) in their joint submission identified five key challenges:

- managing infection prevention and control
- determining how the healthcare system can understand unmet need
- reducing public fear of using health services
- looking after and growing the workforce
- looking to see how the system can improve as it recovers.

The first of these challenges is perhaps the most obvious since the threat of infection rates rising again was uppermost in people's minds. However, whilst health services were focusing much of their efforts on managing Covid-19, there was a fear that other health conditions might have gone undetected and/or unmet and hence that there could be a high level of unmet need that would subsequently place significant demands on health services. Some of this unmet need is likely to have arisen due to a reluctance on the part of individuals to access health services for fear of putting themselves at increased risk of infection and hence rebuilding public confidence and trust was identified as a major challenge.

It is also evident that the crisis placed huge pressures on health staff, as not only were workloads increased but staff had also had to deal with extremely harrowing situations with, in some instances, colleagues losing their lives to the virus. In amongst this many staff voiced fears regarding a lack of personal protective equipment (PPE) and felt hat they were being placed in an extremely vulnerable situation without appropriate support. All of these factors are likely to have a lasting and significant impact on the health and wellbeing of staff and may, for some, lead to burnout and long-term sickness further exacerbating the workforce issues noted earlier in the chapter.

Each of these factors presents leadership challenges to be addressed. For healthcare systems to recover from this crisis it is likely to take some time but it important to note that in their response, the Health Foundation, Nuffield Trust and the King's Fund (2020) also suggested that in this process of recovery there was a need to look for potential improvements. The basis of this argument was that the crisis exposed some weaknesses within the system that need to be remedied.

It can thus be seen that healthcare systems are complex and this is a theme that will be returned to elsewhere in this book (see, for example, Chapter 15). Mitchell (2009) asserts that within complex systems there is little central control or leadership but, as will be seen in the next section, leadership is required within healthcare systems since its absence has been identified as a key contributing factor to failures in healthcare. The question thus arises as to what form of leadership is required: a point that will be explored later in the chapter.

Limitations of traditional leadership approaches

Many models of leadership have been proposed over the years and these have been categorised in various ways. One such form of categorisation is that offered by Northouse (2019), who argues that leadership approaches can largely be placed into two broad categories – namely those that primarily focus on the characteristics or traits that are required by leaders, and those that focus on the process of interactions that occur between those who lead and those who follow. Northouse's framework will be used to explore some of the various leadership approaches along with what he considers to be some of their strengths and weaknesses.

If people are asked to name great leaders, their responses often include reference to those personal characteristics which they feel exemplify why the individuals they identify deserve such an accolade. This is the basis for those leadership theories that are based on traits. These theories have identified characteristics which are required by leaders and these include intelligence, self-confidence, determination and integrity. Whilst this has been a popular approach to the understanding of leadership a number of limitations have been noted. For example, whilst there is some agreement regarding those traits required of leaders, such views are inevitably based on subjective opinions, they fail to take account of the context within which leaders operate and the outcomes that are achieved.

In contrast, situational leadership approaches are based on the interaction between leadership style and the situations within which leaders operate, acknowledging that different situations are likely to require different leadership styles. For example, in emergency situations where safety is a key consideration, a more autocratic style may be appropriate but where there is a need to build consensus and effect change, then a supportive, facilitative style may achieve more. Northouse (2019) argues that such approaches have a number of strengths such as their practicality, their focus on flexibility and the fact that they encourage leaders to respond to the individual needs of their teams differently dependent on the task at hand. However, limitations have also been noted, not least the limited evidence base and the fact that such approaches do not fully address one-to-one versus group leadership in the context of organisations.

Transformational leadership focuses on leaders engaging with others to effect change and transformation through building and sustaining motivation and commitment. Northouse (2019) suggests that such an approach has a number of strengths due to its focus on the process of leadership, its broader focus, and its emphasis on the needs, values and morals of followers. He also argues that it has a strong evidence base and that there is evidence of it being effective. However, as with other approaches there are also some criticisms of transformational leadership, including the fact that it lacks conceptual clarity, concerns that it views leadership as a personality trait rather than as a behaviour that can be learnt, limitations in evidence base and that it can be elitist with a 'heroic' bias. It is important to note that concerns have been raised regarding 'heroic' leadership in the context of healthcare (King's Fund, 2011).

These are just a few of the many leadership theories and approaches that have been proposed. However, each can be seen to have strengths and weaknesses and they tend not to focus on who is/can be a leader, meaning that leadership can be viewed as a role only people in key organisational positions perform. Weberg (2012) argues that traditional leadership approaches and preparation of leaders are inadequate to address the complexity of current healthcare systems due to three key factors:

- linear thinking
- lack of awareness of organisational culture
- being unprepared for innovation.

Weberg's arguments in relation to each of these three areas will be considered.

First, he argues that linear approaches to leadership do not take account of a systems capacity to change, adapt and innovate – instead, they assume that any input to a system leads to a predetermined output. Indeed, he argues that their focus is on management rather than leadership, viewing the role of the leader as being to control uncertainty and to achieve stability. As has already been seen earlier in this chapter, the complexity of current healthcare systems means that such an approach may not be effective since healthcare systems influence and are influenced by other systems.

The second problem as identified by Weberg (2012) is that traditional leadership approaches tend to have a limited focus on organisational culture and that this is challenging in the context of healthcare services where leaders need to be aware of both the formal and informal organisational cultures. Such a view might itself be challenged – for example, Gill (2010) cites a body of research that explores the links between leadership and culture. Nonetheless, as will be seen in the next section of this chapter, a failure to take account of organisational culture has had extremely serious effects on the delivery of healthcare. It may thus be that whilst there has been a focus on culture and leadership this has been insufficient.

The final limitation of traditional leadership approaches is, according to Weberg (2012), that they do not provide the necessary preparedness for the levels and type of innovation that are required in the current context of healthcare. In part this may be due to the focus on stability noted above but, in addition, he argues that such approaches support a power dynamic in which followers lack the motivation to meet both their own and the organisation's needs. This means that leaders need to exert control and determine the direction of travel. However, this is in contrast to what appears to be required – namely, for organisational vision to emerge from collaboration between all involved.

Taken together Weberg (2012) argues that these shortcomings make traditional leadership approaches unsuitable for today's healthcare organisations. Beirne (2017) goes further and suggests that traditional leadership approaches which focus on leadership knowledge being concentrated in a small elite group are both unrealistic and 'potentially damaging'. The next section will examine some evidence of failures in healthcare provision and the role that leadership (or lack of leadership) has played in them before arguing for a different approach to leadership and presenting an alternative approach.

The case for change

It is sad to note that in 2019 a seminar was held in the UK by the Health Foundation to reflect on fifty years of NHS inquiries. Powell (2019) argues that these inquiries span a long period of time, they relate to different types of hospital and they focus on different issues. However, despite these differences there are some recurring themes and one of these is the role that leadership (or a lack of leadership) played in the situation being investigated. This observation is not a new one since back in 2010 the King's Fund established a commission to review current leadership and management within the NHS and to make recommendations for future development in the context of challenges facing healthcare systems. The report of that commission noted that these inquiries demonstrated 'painfully and acutely what can happen when leadership and management fail' (King's Fund, 2011: 12).

These inquiries, which were all conducted in the UK, will be used as an example here to explore how leadership 'failed'. Nonetheless, it is important to note that similar failures and inquiries have occurred in other countries.

As West et al. (2014) observe, it was the values and norms of behaviour apparent in many of the settings on which these inquiries focused that created the conditions for what happened. They argue that culture shapes everything that occurs within an organisation and that leadership is a key factor that shapes culture. Writing about three of the inquiries into failures in healthcare (Bristol Royal Infirmary, Mid Staffs and Morecambe Bay), Goodwin (2019) identifies that culture was identified as a key contributory factor, but that the culture in each of these settings varied.

According to Goodwin (2019), in the Bristol Royal Infirmary it was noted that the power to make decisions was vested in too few individuals and that a rigid distinction was made between clinical and managerial issues. At Mid Staffs the culture was a negative one in which bullying was reported as a recurring issue: where individuals attempted to raise concerns they were met with responses that were defensive of leadership within the Trust. A leadership culture that was based on bullying and intolerance was also noted in Morecambe Bay. Hierarchical relationships were identified as being problematic in both Bristol and Morecambe Bay, whilst a lack of clinical involvement in decision-making was noted in both Bristol and Mid Staffs. Whilst many factors can influence culture, Goodwin (2019) identifies leadership as one of these factors and it is perhaps not unsurprising that a need for 'inspirational leadership over a sustained period of time' was identified as a key recommendation in the first Francis Report concerning Mid Staffs (Francis, 2010: s. 136).

These inquiries highlight failures in care that had a negative impact on healthcare provision that gave rise to patient safety concerns and, in some instances, patient deaths. However, there is also a suggestion that the current situation in healthcare is not working for those in senior leadership positions either. Anandaciva et al. (2018) identify current pressures on healthcare systems, many of which were noted in an earlier section of this chapter. However, they also add that an approach to service performance and financial pressures that is increasingly personalised is adding to the 'cocktail' of pressures. They argue that individual leaders are more commonly being blamed for failures in care and financial problems and that this is making senior leadership posts in the NHS less attractive. This in turn leads to increased turnover of people in such posts, which places further strain on the system due to a lack of leadership.

West et al. (2014) also argue that a leadership approach focused on command-and-control in which there is a tendency to scapegoat individuals leads to a culture in which failure is feared and there is no appetite for innovation. In the context of complex healthcare systems where innovation and adaptation to rapidly changing situations is required, this is clearly not an effective or sustainable approach. It would seem, then, that there is a need to reconsider leadership within the context of healthcare services and to explore potential alternative approaches.

An alternative approach?

As was highlighted earlier in this chapter the delivery of healthcare is complex and this presents some specific challenges for healthcare leadership. Weberg (2012) argues that leadership in the context of complexity requires systems thinking in which leaders move within the organisation fostering interactions between different parts of the system that impact upon each other. Such an approach enables practitioners to become involved in decision-making, which enables the system to evolve more effectively as well as dispersing responsibility throughout the organisation and taking the 'burden' of complexity from those in traditional, formal leadership roles (Weberg, 2012).

Dougall et al. (2018) also argue that the combination of increased demands for healthcare, constrained resources and the realisation that delivering effective healthcare requires coordination with systems outside of health services means that a collaborative approach and distributed leadership is required. They further suggest that there is a need to move from power being vested in a few people within healthcare organisations to 'new' power that enables those at a grassroots level to engage in shaping and leading the organisation. Again this is not a new observation since the King's Fund Commission observed back in 2011 that the traditional model of 'hero' leaders (in which power is vested in a few people in senior position) is not fit for purpose in current healthcare organisations. They argued a need to move towards more distributed forms of leadership in which there is leadership 'from the board to the ward'.

Distributed leadership (the focus of this book) has therefore been suggested as an appropriate approach to leadership in the context of the current global challenges experienced by healthcare systems (Figueroa et al., 2019). Indeed, it has been suggested that it is the 'only' way to ensure that such systems are able to work effectively both within the organisation and with other organisational systems (McIntosh and Langland, 2020). However, what does such an approach mean in practice? In their report, the King's Fund (2011) make reference to a paper by Turnbull James (2011) produced to inform the work of the Commission. In that paper a number of features of distributed leadership were identified, namely:

- It involves multiple actors taking up formal and informal leadership roles within an organisation.
- It requires collaborative working across organisational and professional boundaries.
- The distribution of leadership requires new practices and innovation not just people at lower organisational levels assuming traditional leadership roles.

- It needs to be understood in terms of leadership practices and organisational interventions.
- The focus is on organisational relations, connectedness, interventions in organisational systems, and on changing practices and processes. (adapted from Turnbull James, 2011)

It can be seen, therefore, that it offers the potential to address some of those challenges identified earlier in this chapter – namely, the need for working across traditional boundaries and a focus on complex systems and the interactions within and between these systems. However, it is also an approach that requires looking beyond just those in formal leadership positions and beyond the behaviours of leaders: a fundamental change in practices is necessary.

Whilst distributed leadership thus appears to offer a potential solution to current leadership challenges, Anandaciva et al. (2018) also offer a note of caution. They argue that the boards of healthcare organisations often experience difficulties in balancing strategic and operational issues and hence whilst there may be discussion regarding a systems leadership approach, operational pressures may mitigate against this translating into support for its development in practice. Furthermore, Martin et al. (2015) undertook a review of three healthcare organisations that had adopted distributed leadership as part of their strategic approach and identified three key 'disconnects'. The first related to power, and they found that despite distributed leadership aiming to support empowerment of leaders at all levels within these organisations there remained issues relating to the perceptions of power held by others within those organisations. A second disconnect related to distance and this had two dimensions: within large and complex organisations physical distance between elements of those organisations can mean that there is limited interaction, but even where groups are working in physical proximity professional differences or 'distance' can lead to problems. Finally, they argue that there can be a disconnect in relation to values wherein difficulties arise due to perceptions of the values held by others such as 'clinical' or 'managerial' values.

Elsewhere it has been suggested that the educational preparation of clinicians such as medical staff does not enable them to develop the skills required for distributed leadership (Zafar, 2020). This may be one of the factors that impact on the translation of the principles of distributed leadership into practice in healthcare organisations. To embed distributed leadership therefore requires organisational commitment, appropriate educational provision, and support for leaders at all levels.

Conclusion

This chapter has explored some of the challenges that are currently facing global healthcare systems and has presented an argument that traditional leadership approaches are no longer fit for purpose within today's complex healthcare organisations. Distributed leadership has been suggested as an alternative that recognises this complexity, enables working across traditional boundaries, and supports a systems approach. The subsequent chapters in this book will enable readers to review the emerging evidence of the translation of the principles of distributed leadership into practice and to consider evidence of its effectiveness.

Key concepts discussed

- factors impacting on healthcare delivery
- healthcare as a complex system
- leadership models
- limitations of leadership models
- distributed leadership.

Useful websites

- The Health Foundation: https://www.health.org.uk
  Provides policy analysis and research related to the development of healthcare.
- The King's Fund https://www.kingsfund.org.uk
  Health and care policy with a particular focus on leadership.

References

Anandaciva, S., Ward, D., Randhawa, M. and Edge, R. (2018) *Leadership in Today's NHS: Delivering the Impossible*. London: The King's Fund.

Beirne, M. (2017) The reforming appeal of distributed leadership: Recognising concerns and contradictory tendencies. *British Journal of Healthcare Management* 23 (6): 262–270.

Cameron, G., Alderwick, H., Bowers, A. and Dixon, J. (2019) *Shaping Health Futures: Preparing for Tomorrow's Possibilities Today*. London: The Health Foundation.

Dougall, D., Lewis, M. and Ross, S. (2018) *Transformational Change in Health and Care: Reports from the Field*. London: The King's Fund.

Figueroa, C.A., Harrison, R., Chauhan, A. and Meyer, L. (2019) Priorities and challenges for health leadership and workforce management globally: A rapid review. *BMC Health Services Research* 19: 239. Available at: https://doi.org/10.1186/S12913-019-4080-7 (accessed 14 October 2020).

Francis, R. (2010) *Independent Inquiry into Care Provided by Mid Staffordshire NHS Foundation Trust, January 2005–March 2009 (The Francis Report)*. London: The Stationery Office. Available at: https://www.gov.uk/government/publications/independent-inquiry-into-care-provided-by-mid-staffordshire-nhs-foundation-trust-january-2001-to-march-2009 (accessed 14 October 2020).

Gill, R. (2010) *Theory and Practice of Leadership*. London: Sage.

Goodwin, D. (2019) NHS inquiries and the problem of culture. *The Political Quarterly* 90 (2): 202–209.

Health Foundation, Nuffield Trust and King's Fund (2020) *Joint letter to the Health and Social Care Select Committee for the evidence session on delivering core NHS and care services during the pandemic and beyond*. Available at: https://www.health.org.uk/sites/default/files/2020-05/Joint_letter_to_Health_and_Social_Care_Select_Committee.pdf (accessed 15 May 2020).

King's Fund (2011) *The Future of Leadership and Management in the NHS: No More Heroes*. London: The King's Fund.

Martin, G., Beech, N., MacIntosh, R. and Bushfield, S. (2015) Potential challenges facing distributed leadership in health care: Evidence from the UK National Health Service. *Sociology of Health and Illness* 37 (1): 14–29.

McIntosh, B. and Layland, A. (2020) Change management in the NHS: Distributed leadership. *British Journal of Healthcare Management* 25 (7): 1–10.

Mitchell, M. (2009) *Complexity: A Guided Tour*. Oxford: Oxford University Press.

Northouse, P.G. (2019) *Leadership Theory and Practice*, 8th edition. London: Sage.

Powell, M. (2019) Inquiries into the British National Health Service. *The Political Quarterly* 90 (2): 180–184.

Turnbull James, K. (2011) *Leadership in Context: Lessons from New leadership theory and current leadership development practice*. London: The King's Fund. Available at: www.kingsfund.org.uk/leadershipcommission (accessed 14 May 2020).

Weberg, D. (2012) Complexity leadership: A healthcare imperative. *Nursing Forum* 47 (4): 268–277.

West, M., Eckert, R., Steward, K. and Pasmore, B. (2014) *Developing Collective Leadership for Healthcare*. London: The King's Fund.

Zafar, A. (2020 *Why Doctors Need to be Leaders*. USA: Purpleye Press.

3 Acknowledging and nurturing complementary leadership contributions

Marie Elizabeth Ward and David Vaughan

Chapter topics

- Distributing leadership practices, while not new, are certainly a challenging idea in healthcare given the current dominance of traditional hierarchical medical-led models.
- The chapter lays out some lessons that have been learned in the field of patient safety that can help support the development of distributed leadership in other areas of healthcare.
- The examples given focus in particular on what we believe is the area that has been most neglected in healthcare patient safety – safety culture.

Introduction

Traditional hierarchical models of leadership have been found wanting in healthcare over the last number of years with no shortage of scandals and cover ups exposed (Kennedy, 2001; Harding Clark, 2006; Madden, 2008; Francis, 2013; HIQA, 2015). It is clear that there are diverse cultures in healthcare, not all of which are conducive to leading and improving safety. As Sullenberger (2012) notes, there are islands of excellence in a sea of system failures. Vize (2019) notes that each high-profile enquiry in the NHS has revealed layer upon layer of systemic failings, including the breakdown of teamwork, poor leadership, lack of respect between professional groups, a tolerance of poor standards, defensiveness, dishonesty, failure to assess risks, and repeated failures to recognise and investigate serious incidents.

Despite twenty years of effort since Lucian Leape first highlighted the issue of patient safety in the famous report 'To Err is Human' (IOM, 1999), rates of patient harm have at least remained stable if not increased (Rafter et al., 2017; Wears and Sutcliffe, 2020). This has in part been put down to failures to understand the complexity of healthcare (Cook, 2013; Braithwaite, 2018). We would add that patient safety initiatives to date have not systematically tackled the culture in healthcare. The culture in healthcare (and its marked diversity even within a single organisation) is quite unique:

- Healthcare systems were not designed, rather they evolved to meet changing needs. This has the benefit of flexibility, as was seen during the Covid-19 pandemic, but also has downsides.

- Healthcare systems are so stretched that staff within them spend most of their time and resources on firefighting.
- There is a lack of acceptance among healthcare professionals and healthcare systems that neither the staff nor the systems are perfect and that mistakes will occur.
- There is a lack of acceptance among the public that mistakes will happen and are a part of most healthcare services – perfection is demanded (the recent Irish Supreme Court Cervical Check Case, for example, ruled that screeners should have 'absolute confidence' before passing a sample as clear (Clarke, 2020)).
- Some subcultures in healthcare are not supportive of staff admitting to mistakes; this is in part down to traditional leadership styles and traditional 'rite of passage' culture where staff have to prove they can be as 'tough' as their predecessors.
- Leadership in healthcare is also siloed with leadership 'triumvirates' of medical, nursing and business staff emerging to try to counteract the silos.

Leadership theory in general has been fraught with arguments and dichotomies: Are great leaders born? Do men and women have different leadership skills?, etc. Hosking, writing as early as 1988, argued that we do not understand the terms 'leader' and 'leadership' and we should move towards understanding *leadership as a process* rooted in an organisational system. Leadership, she argues, is not the purview of those in 'leadership roles' but an organising activity central to the dynamics of any organisation. Different names have been given to the new style of leadership that seeks to involve staff more in these types of organising activities, including participative leadership (Nystrom, 1990), collective leadership (West et al., 2011, 2014; McAuliffe et al., 2017) and distributed leadership (Bolden, 2011). Bolden provides an excellent account of the development of the theory and ideas of distributed leadership and also argues that for the field to develop, we need to provide real and concrete examples of when leadership is most appropriately shared, address how to develop distributed leadership, how to deal with the political nature of leadership within organisations and the age old issue of 'imbalances in the distribution of power and influence' (2011: 264).

This chapter will focus on approaches to help acknowledge and nurture distributed leadership practices for patient safety, and in the following three areas in particular:

- psychological safety at an individual level and a just culture at the group/organisational level
- openly disclosing when things go wrong
- principles of high reliability organisations, in particular deference to expertise (and not role/position).

Psychological safety and just culture

Edgar Schein (1986) defined an organisation's culture as a pattern of shared basic assumptions learned by people as they work together. He noted that when it comes to organisational culture, there are parts of the culture that we see all around us (e.g. posters displaying vision and mission statements, portraits of founders, or what he referred to as 'artefacts'); there are the beliefs and values of ourselves and our colleagues that we are willing to express; and finally there are the underlying assumptions or unconscious 'taken-for-granted' beliefs and values that might be more difficult to access.

The term 'safety culture' was first introduced by the International Nuclear Safety Group in its Summary Report on the Chernobyl Accident (IAEA [1986] 1992), where it was noted that there was a lack of commitment on the part of individuals and the organisation to the priority of safety. They went on to clarify that a safety culture involved 'an inherently questioning attitude, the prevention of complacency, a commitment to excellence, and the fostering of both personal accountability and corporate self-regulation in safety matters' (IAEA, 1991). Safety culture has become a key priority within safety-critical industries and despite a lack of agreed definition (O'Donovan et al., 2019), there are models of essential components or elements of a safety culture. In the largest EU project on aviation safety, a seven-component model was developed by Lei and Ruishan (2014) building on the work of James Reason. The seven components are:

1. Commitment to safety as the number one organisational priority
2. Commitment to achieving reliability and excellence through applying an evidence-based approach to safety
3. Commitment to flexibility and resilience to deal with safety issues
4. Culture of learning
5. Culture of team working and developing resilience
6. Culture where all staff are supported in reporting any safety issues
7. A 'just culture'.

It is these elements of safety culture and just culture in particular that healthcare has struggled with. In a review of patient safety efforts, Pronovost et al. (2015) noted that healthcare has not fully embraced safety as a science and in particular has not recognised the importance of safety culture:

> Many health systems talk about the importance of creating a 'safe culture' and attempt to measure culture and cultural improvements. However, the changes are largely superficial, seeking quick fixes often without the deeper qualitative understanding of staff concerns or the desired behavior changes. Culture in healthcare can appear punitive, focusing on judging rather than learning and improving the system. (2015: 11)

In an analysis of why healthcare is 'still not safe', Wears and Sutcliffe (2020) have similarly argued that healthcare has been unable to change and adapt to take on board the messages coming from patient safety (which they also note are often not framed in a way the healthcare system can identify with, as they came from other industries). They note that although

> . . . initially challenged by patient safety, [the healthcare system] embraced and ultimately swallowed it, effectively fending off the challenge of fundamental reform . . . patient safety has been medicalized; brought under the authority and control of health professionals in ways that channel it into more familiar and less threatening pathways. (2020: vii)

In recent times and following the much publicised Google study of team performance codenamed Project Aristotle, the work of Amy Edmondson in relation to psychological safety has achieved even greater prominence. She highlights the importance to psychological safety of a 'shared belief held by members of a team that the team is safe for interpersonal risk-taking', and of 'a sense of confidence that the team will not embarrass, reject or punish someone for speaking up' (Edmondson, 1999: 354). Her work builds on that of Schein and Bennis (1965), who noted that people need to feel psychologically safe if they are to feel secure and able to change. The team environment is characterised by interpersonal trust and mutual respect in which team members are comfortable being themselves. These teams were found to be the most productive, with psychological safety being referred to as the 'X factor' of team performance.

For healthcare teams battling in the traditional hierarchical ways of working, such questioning is not always accepted. In the current healthcare setting this would require significant changes in leadership practices. Some suggestions are included here to change and nurture leadership practices in everyday settings.

Nurturing contribution at meetings and ward rounds

Nembhard and Edmondson (2006) and Edmondson (1996) studied the impact of leadership practices on psychological safety. They found that leader inclusiveness – that is, words and deeds by leaders that invite and appreciate all contributions – helped staff to develop psychological safety and to feel more able to speak up even within the traditional hierarchy in healthcare. They also found the opposite to be true. If a leader takes an authoritarian, unsupportive or defensive stance, team members are more likely to feel that speaking up in the team is a risky strategy. Meetings take up a huge amount of our working lives and simple leadership practices in the workplace setting can develop psychological safety among team members, including inviting comments and questions at meetings, seeking assurances from people that they understand what has been said and how it relates to them and their work, encouraging a 'no stupid questions' attitude, encouraging a healthy questioning of decisions while they are being made, and being able to comment critically on decisions and outcomes of work practices. A useful practical reference in relation to this, see Tourish (2005).

Nurturing contribution – the special case of ward rounds

Ward rounds are an essential organisational process in hospitals, providing a link between a patient's admission to hospital and their discharge or transfer elsewhere. They serve as the locus of decision-making, care planning and communication for all inpatients. The outputs of the ward round influence operations throughout the hospital for the day. In the absence of ward rounds there would be inertia in patient flow. Best practice indicates that ward rounds should include the multidisciplinary team (MDT) of doctors, nurses, health and social care professionals (HSCPs), and the patient or their carer coming together to review a patient's condition and develop a coordinated plan of care, while facilitating full engagement of the patient in shared decision-making about their care (RCP/RCN 2012).

Despite the centrality of ward rounds to hospital work processes and their importance to patients there is huge variation in what purpose they serve, where they take place and who takes part in them. They can be ineffective or even dysfunctional (Francis, 2013; Shaughnessy and Jackson, 2015). Ward rounds involve large amounts of information that must be communicated in a time-limited environment with many competing interests. This has the potential to reduce effective communication and risk patient safety (Sharma and Peters, 2013). Trimble found that with its 'poor structure, often chaotic environment and frequent time pressures' ward rounds do not support good decision-making (2015: 6). One Danish study found that ward rounds took up to six hours, causing frustration to consultants and with the result that neither nursing staff nor patients were able to plan for or attend them (Enslev Jensen et al., 2016).

A nurse's ability to contribute to the patient's treatment plan is generally via the ward round (Busby and Gilchrist, 1992). However, research literature over the last 20–30 years shows nurses being excluded from the ward round (Busby and Gilchrist, 1992; Liu et al., 2013) and having to go to extraordinary lengths and to employ non-verbal behaviours to have a 'voice' at the round (Hill, 2003).The positive impact of shared decision-making on health outcomes is well documented (e.g. Parissopoulos et al., 2013). However, patients report a number of negative associations with matron ward rounds, including a lack of information, discussions being rushed or inaccessible, and feelings of disempowerment (O'Hare, 2008; Swenne and Skytt, 2014).

A number of different frameworks and checklists have been developed and tested in the UK, USA, Sweden and Australia in an attempt to improve the quality of ward rounds. These structured approaches to ward rounds, which provide an opportunity for different 'voices' to be heard, include:

- The Considerative Checklist (Herring et al., 2011)
- UK Royal College of Physicians/Royal College of Nursing framework (RCP/RCN, 2012)
- UCL Hospital Ward Round Safety Checklist (Amin et al., 2012)
- Ward Round Room Approach (Bååthe et al., 2016)
- Measuring Ward Round Quality for Urology (Darbyshire et al., 2015)
- Structured Interdisciplinary Bedside Rounds (Gausvik et al., 2015).

Similar to other checklists and structured communication tools in healthcare these approaches to ward rounds provide an opportunity for leadership practices to be distributed among key personnel, especially senior nurses and junior doctors who have a key role in ward rounds. Through supporting and nurturing distributed leadership practices, barriers in relation to implementation and in particular to culture and process issues surrounding the ward rounds, including 'disconnect between medical and nursing staff', lack of ring-fenced time for nurses to attend, junior doctors being unprepared for active participation (Darbyshire et al., 2015) can be overcome.

Building trust among the team

The trust literature shows that if we know our colleagues on a personal level we are far more likely to trust them and, should there be a breach of trust, we are more likely to get over it (Lewicki and Bunker, 1996). Healthcare teams, however, are a matrix of many smaller siloed teams (e.g. nursing, medical, HSCPs, support staff) who may or may not know each other. Lyubovnikova et al. (2015) coined the term 'pseudo-teams' in healthcare – that is, teams whose members do not really know their purpose, role or each other. The Kate Granger #hellomynameis campaign helped staff as much as patients with learning each other's names. Leaders must engineer time and space for all staff to get to know each other. This demands changes in practice and as time is so short in healthcare, it must be seen as a priority. If staff do not trust each other, they cannot begin to trust and rely on each other's skill base, which is absolutely necessary in safety-critical industries. Interventions to allow healthcare staff to get to know each other, to build trust and to clarify the goals of the team; to develop individual and shared role clarity; and to understand the role of the team in the wider organisation were all part of a study to develop open-source interventions to introduce collective leadership to healthcare teams (for a list of co-designed interventions, see Ward et al., 2018).

Encouraging others to speak up about safety

The Francis Report identified staff that were afraid to speak out, and when they did, senior staff were hostile towards them and defensive of existing practices (Francis, 2013). Hilton (2016: 327) notes this 'fits with the old adage [in healthcare] that staff should "give in or get out": giving in and accepting the *status quo* is easier than getting out'. In her account of whistleblowing in the NHS, Hilton notes that 'if sub-standard practices develop, they may become accepted as the norm and pass unnoticed except by new staff or visitors' (p. 329).

The Francis Report found that staff demonstrated 'loyalty to the organisation' within the NHS and Social Care Inspectorate, as well as to the hospital they worked in. However, Hilton argues that the 'etiquette of loyalty to an organisation rather than to patients can affect staff perspectives on speaking out' (Hilton 2016: 329). She also stresses that '"best in the world" statements support complacency to criticism. They reinforce practices of ignoring whistle-blowers and misjudging them as unreasonable' (p. 329).

In the UK, organisations have now been 'mandated to appoint "Freedom to Speak Up Guardians" (conduits for concerns about facilities, quality of care, or colleagues' behaviour) and must fund the role themselves' (Martin et al., 2019: 153). Martin et al. (2019) argue, however, that where speaking up is still considered a 'high risk: low benefit act' (Attree 2007), then 'new procedures and the appointment of figures such as Freedom to Speak Up Guardians [are] seen as unlikely to provide reassurance' (Martin et al., 2019: 157). These type of actions need to be supported by more radical change at the system level.

Referring to Barbara Robb's book *Sans Everything: A Case to Answer* (1967), Hilton noted that 'most . . . whistle-blowers were new to the hospital, idealistic about the well being of their patients, and lacked formal health service related professional qualifications' (2016: 329). Hilton continues:

> In other hospitals, *Sans Everything* inspired students to blow the whistle, but their allegations were generally ignored. Unqualified staff, and students who had not yet acquired the views which their professions were *meant* to hold, provided a 'new pair of eyes' and enlightened insights into quality of care. Yet these groups were, and are, the least likely to be asked for their views. (2016: 329).

A recent project brought together Health Systems and Human Factors researchers to co-design a 'serious game' to encourage junior doctors (who have 'fresh eyes' on the system) to speak up about safety and report safety concerns (Ward et al., 2019). The game, entitled 'PlayDecide: Patient Safety', involved role-playing in relation to real patient safety cases, and proved successful in enabling staff to discuss their thoughts and feelings about patient safety. This game has since been adapted for all healthcare workers and is openly available for healthcare teams to download at http://patientsafetydiscussions.ie/. Following playing of the game, but only in tandem with changes in leadership practices (where leaders were educated on the importance of speaking up and encouraging junior doctors to speak up), there was a significant increase in reporting behaviour of junior doctors. Psychological safety is also highly dependent on the organisational culture and must be supported by what is referred to as a 'just culture'.

Developing a just culture

In healthcare as well as in other industries, a culture of blame has existed when something goes wrong (Wilson et al., 2008; Braithwaite et al., 2010; Pronovost et al., 2015). Within the aviation industry there were significant efforts to move from a blame to a no-blame culture following the Tenerife disaster of 1977 in which over 550 people lost their lives. However, this initiative began to be questioned by staff who came to feel that deliberate harm or damage to aircraft was not being appropriately dealt with and staff who had made genuine mistakes were being blamed or punished in other ways – for example, by being sent for re-training. Colloquially in some organisations the policy became known as 'blame and train' rather than a no-blame policy. In his study of aviation culture, Professor James Reason argued that:

> What is needed is a *just culture*, an atmosphere of trust in which people are encouraged, even rewarded, for providing essential safety-related information – but in which they are also clear about where the line must be drawn between acceptable and unacceptable behaviour. (1997: 195)

Professor Sydney Dekker (2009), building on this work, notes that a just culture is meant to balance learning from incidents with accountability for their consequences. His advice for creating the basis for a just culture is that incidents need to be normalised and legitimised. Incidents should be seen not as failures or shameful, but a learning opportunity to improve an organisation. Both Reason's and Dekker's work is reflected in just culture algorithms that have recently been developed for the way in which healthcare organisations should deal with staff who make mistakes (HSE 2018; NHS Improvement 2018). These algorithms support quality and patient safety managers in determining, together with the staff involved, if the incident occurred as a result of intention to cause harm or systemic failings of the organisation. These types of algorithms and policies must be supported by systemic change in the whole approach to patient safety in healthcare. The International Civil Aviation Authority (ICAO), for example, recommends that each of their member organisations commit to the following (adapted from ICAO, 2016):

- All staff should be recognised for the role they play in delivering a safe service to customers.
- Each organisation must provide staff with the appropriate environment, tools, training and procedures required to perform their job.
- Each organisation must encourage all staff to demonstrate the appropriate safety attitude and safe behaviour at all times.
- Organisations will be managed in such a way that staff will not be exposed to situations in which safety is compromised because of organisational factors.
- All staff are encouraged to voluntarily report instances of safety risk and possible hazards without fear of reprisal.
- A just culture will be visibly supported by the highest organisational levels and visibly endorsed at the workforce level (e.g. by unions or workers' representatives).

Within healthcare as in all other organisations this make demands of leadership and challenges old styles of leadership. Khatri et al. (2009) found that a blame culture is more likely to blossom in healthcare organisations that rely predominantly on hierarchical, compliance-based functional management systems and that a just culture is more likely to be fostered in health organisations that encourage greater employee involvement in decision-making.

In their interviews with senior leaders in healthcare, Martin et al. (2019) noted that without cultural and infrastructural change, initiatives to develop openness in healthcare can become legalistic, compliance driven and at worst 'punitive'. They made two main recommendations, the first of which was 'to make aspirations of openness relevant to sharp-end clinicians working in pressured environments, for whom compromises and work-arounds are a taken-for-granted feature of routine work, and who may see such interventions primarily as blame-allocation devices' (2019: 158). For leadership practice this means that 'actions must match words, especially in environments where initiatives purportedly intended to prompt learning and improvement have a tendency to metamorphose into tools of performance management' (ibid.).

Second, and this relates very much to the reasons for lack of achievement in the patient safety movement, Martin et al. noted that

> [t]he word 'openness' is perhaps too passive a term to describe what is desired here. A major barrier to openness identified by participants was not concealment or opacity among their colleagues but rather a kind of normalised incuriosity. Intervening in such contexts is challenging: established routines of explanation and rationalisation may over time become institutionalised as

legitimate ways of dealing with problems; it is difficult to disrupt these routines without the disruption itself being deemed deviant. (2019: 158).

A just culture requires a rich flow of information about operational practice, including: normal everyday activities; when things go wrong – errors, adverse events, near-misses; when we achieve excellence (e.g. the Learning from Excellence movement, https://learningfromexcellence.com); and a clear shared understanding of standards of professional practice across disciplines and contexts incorporating team behaviours, risk avoidance and safe practices.

A particular challenge in healthcare is that incidents tend to be examined in silos. For example, medical staff review incidents at their 'Morbidity and Mortality' (M&M) meetings, while organisations may have different quality, safety, risk or incident managers reviewing other incidents. Not all staff have training in understanding safety science, an understanding of the systemic causes of some incidents or insight into how healthcare really works, to fully analyse and understand the underlying systems issues that can conspire to cause incidents. As Dekker (2009) and Cromie and Bott (2016) argue, a just culture relies on an openness across all leaders in the organisation to come together and begin to define what is acceptable or unacceptable behaviour (e.g. when can a patient death be deemed preventable or unpreventable), otherwise we have to ask ourselves who is getting to draw the 'line in the sand' as to acceptable and unacceptable behaviour.

Open disclosure and patient and family experience

Creating an environment where healthcare staff can be open about mistakes among themselves is one challenge – being open with patients and the public is quite another. Open disclosure, known as duty of candour in the UK and communication/resolution programs in the US, is increasingly seen as both an ethical requirement for caregivers in the event of an adverse event and a means of reducing the likelihood of litigation by families and patients following an adverse event. Reference to the requirement for physicians to acknowledge errors to patients and families first appeared in 1980 in a legal journal (Vogel and Delgado, 1980).

Open disclosure is defined as an open, consistent, compassionate and timely approach to communicating with patients following patient safety incidents. It includes expressing regret for what has happened, keeping the patient informed and providing reassurance in relation to ongoing care and treatment, learning and the steps being taken by the health services provider to try to prevent a recurrence of the incident (HSE 2019).

In Ireland open disclosure of a patient safety incident has been policy since 2013 but is not mandatory. It includes:

- a factual explanation in relation to what has happened and how/why it happened
- listening to and hearing the patient's story, i.e. their understanding of what has happened and their description of the impact of the patient safety incident
- demonstrating empathy, kindness and compassion towards all those involved in and/or affected by the patient safety incident that has occurred to include the patient, their relevant person(s) and staff

- an apology/expression of regret (as appropriate to the situation) – this must be sincere and personal to the patient and/or their relevant person and to the given situation
- shared decision-making in relation to on-going care and treatment and the management of the patient safety incident that has occurred. (HSE, 2019)

However, open disclosure does not routinely happen in Ireland or indeed in other countries. All of the issues discussed in this chapter so far point to the complexities of openly disclosing mistakes in healthcare: a blame culture, fear of litigation, lack of a just culture, failure to support staff who are sometimes referred to as the second victim in these incidents, and a lack of clarity regarding who is responsible for making a disclosure and offering an apology. Patient representative groups for families do have some reservations about the term 'second victim', noting that *they* are the second victims and that healthcare staff should be referred to as third victims.

Open disclosure demands distributed leadership for safety; there is now permission and an expectation on all healthcare staff to openly disclose mistakes and to deal directly with patients and their families when doing so. For this to happen, however, healthcare organisations need to invest in training and support of all their staff in carrying out open disclosure.

Below we present a case study, where we can see that these issues are not new to healthcare. It is a case study of a child's death in 1886 in Sir Patrick Dun's Hospital, following her admission with a femoral fracture. By reviewing both internal and external correspondence as well as newspaper reports, we describe the repeated efforts on the part of her father to seek an explanation for her death from the hospital, culminating in reporting in the national press.

Case study: Open disclosure – the case of Elizabeth Sheridan

A five-year-old girl, Elizabeth Sheridan, was admitted to Sir Patrick Dun's hospital, Dublin on 15 March 1886 with a fractured femur. In early April she died from 'scarlatina', which she appears to have picked up in the hospital. Over a period of seven months, there are numerous references to the case in both internal hospital documents and in national newspapers. The Board of Governors oversaw the operations and strategy of the hospital, while the Medical Board of the hospital consisted of all seven physicians working there. Each year the court of the Queen's Bench sat to discuss funding for all Dublin hospitals.

According to the hospital board minutes (11 May 1886), a letter was received from the father, alleging neglect by the hospital in the treatment of his child, and what concerned him particularly was the poor state in which he had received the child's body, to him 'barely recognisable', following her post-mortem. The Medical Board of the hospital responded to the claims in the letter to the Board of Governors stating that in their opinion charges of neglect had no foundation, and they had not contacted the father as requested about his child's imminent death as there was no indication of approaching death and noted that 'far from being a healthy child, it was an example of rickets in a severe degree' (17 May 1886). In September a reply was issued to Mr. Sheridan to the same effect from the Board of Governors to note 'The Board were perfectly satisfied that your child was treated with every kindness and consideration and that all possible efforts were made to save her life' (14 September 1886).

Mr. Sheridan was not satisfied with this response and attended the court of the Queen's Bench that year to object to the hospital receiving a grant given annually by the city towards the running of the hospital (*Irish Freeman's Journal*, 15 November 1886). In the press report it is noted that Mr. Sheridan had respectfully asked for some explanation as to the state of his child's body following the post-mortem but had received none. In the court it emerged that Mr. Sheridan had called for the police to come to the morgue and the doctor who was treating his child to provide an explanation and to explain to him why he had not been asked for consent to carry out a post-mortem on his daughter. He noted the doctor's reply was that he did not need consent. Mr. Sheridan also noted in the court that he asked the doctor to show him signs of scarlatina but there were none – his daughter died of bronchitis. The news article ended by noting that Mr. Sheridan was still seeking an explanation. In the reports of the court hearing it is noted that the Board had responded to all of Mr. Sheridan's issues and felt that his daughter's care was not wanting. The judge queried the lack of isolation facilities to which a representative of the hospital responded, 'There is no doubt, unfortunately that the want of isolation (facilities) exists, although it is right to add that [all] possible precautions are taken. I may mention that all the hospitals in Dublin recognise the necessity for isolation, and we in Sir Patrick's hospital have collected £1000 for the purpose, and hope soon to have £2000 for the purpose of having isolated fever wards'. Mr. Sheridan responded: 'I am very glad to hear it, but was it not hard that I never got an answer for four months'.

The judge goes on to note: 'The man lays great stress on the post mortem examination having been performed on the body of his child without his sanction'. The reply here is 'that in Ireland at the time there was deemed no need to seek consent especially where the cause of death is "obscure"'. The hospital representative goes on to note that in London 'hospitals have been reduced to the painful necessity of refusing to receive patients without a formal consent from the relatives enabling them to carry out a post mortem examination. This is worse than the worst medicine that could be given to any patient. I can only repeat that in this case we sympathise with Mr. Sheridan, but can assure the court that the hospital can fearlessly face inquiry'. Mr Sheridan replied to this: 'I am grateful to your lordship for allowing me to state the facts and if the hospital authorities only answered my complaints, there would be no need for me to come here'.

It appears that Mr. Sheridan is satisfied here but the doctor who carried out the post-mortem writes subsequently to the Medical Board (18 November 1886) demanding the Medical Board stand up to the Board of Governors as he felt that 'the Board in ignoring the [most] important charges in the man's letter – namely that his child was killed in the hospital by ill treatment and neglect tacitly admit this truth'. He felt this would be all the public would remember of the case. The Board of Governors convened a special meeting and published the outcome in the *Irish Times* (26 November) where they noted: 'That in consequence of the statements made by Thomas Sheridan, in the court of the Queen's Bench, on Thursday last, respecting the treatment of his child, who had been a patient in the hospital, the case was reconsidered, and the Board continues to hold the opinion formed by them in May last, that a post-mortem examination was essential, in order to certify the cause of death, in consequence of the obscure nature of the symptoms manifested by the child. The examination was conducted by Dr. X, with his invariable regard to decency and the feelings of the relatives. The Board express their regret that the answer to Mr. Sheridan's letter was so long delayed'.

This case dates from 1886 and while it is unclear from all the documents, and in the absence of any independent review of the case difficult to draw conclusions, it does seem extraordinary, having had such a public case in Ireland and many more like it since, that openly disclosing patient safety incidents to patients and their families is still not standard practice more than 100 years later. Even in the absence of an independent enquiry many failures of leadership are evident here: physicians not taking the time to discuss with Mr. Sheridan his concerns about his daughter's care and failure of the Medical Council and the Board of Governors to work together in responding to Mr. Sheridan's letters. Remarkably, there appears to have been a two-month delay between receipt of Mr. Sheridan's letter in September and the Board stating they had received it in November. The case demonstrates the importance of distributed leadership and accountability for safety, the timely and open communication between clinicians and management structures, and the need for open disclosure, kindness and empathy between hospitals and families. Legislation has moved on significantly in this regard as patients and their families now have a right to request access to their care records. New legislation is also in train in Ireland to make open disclosure mandatory in the event of a pre-defined set of patient safety incidents (Patient Safety Bill, 2019).

High reliability organisations, collective mindfulness and deference to expertise

High reliability organisations (HRO) are organisations that have succeeded in avoiding catastrophes in safety-critical industries where normal accidents can be expected because of the risk factors and complexity involved. Weick and Sutcliffe (2007) studied HROs and found them to have a unique structure but more importantly that HROs think and act differently from other organisations. The authors' key finding was that HROs use what they called 'mindful' organising for the unexpected as well as the expected. They defined mindfulness as a mental orientation that continually evaluates the environment as opposed to mindlessness, where a simple assessment leads to choosing a plan that is continued until the plan runs its course. They found five defining features of this collective mindfulness at work in HROs.

Cincinnati Children's Hospital and the James M. Anderson Center for Health Systems Excellence have been on an HRO journey for nearly ten years and are striving to achieve zero harm in their hospitals. They are unique in healthcare to have adapted and strove to emulate an HRO. The following extract is from their website where they outline what trying to be an HRO in healthcare means. This is mapped onto the five defining features of HROs (Weick and Sutcliffe, 2007). Striving to become an HRO makes serious demands on the leadership practices of all staff in relation to patient safety. These demands and changes in leadership practice are noted here.

Becoming a high reliability organisation – the case of Cincinnati Children's Hospital

1. *Preoccupation with failure*: In the hospital *all staff* are focused on errors and near-misses, learning from them and figuring out how to prevent them from happening again. Attention to detail is crucial. Finding and fixing problems is everyone's responsibility and is encouraged and supported by leadership.

   In some organisations this is the remit of M&M meetings or the incident manager.
2. *Reluctance to simplify interpretations*: *All staff* are required to constantly ask the 'why' question and invite others with diverse experience to express their opinions. The belief is that the more you are immersed in something, the harder it is for you to objectively observe and question things that need questioning. Staff are encouraged to leverage new thinking to get the right answer. The 'fresh eyes' perspective of new staff is actively sought.

   In some organisations new staff are there to learn from the 'expertise' of those who have built up years of service.
3. *Sensitivity to operations (an HRO distinguishing characteristic)*: *All staff* are encouraged to have an ongoing concern with the unexpected. All staff are encouraged to close the loopholes in processes where there is potential for patient harm, to maintain situational awareness (having an understanding of what has been happening; what is happening now and what might happen next) at all levels in the organisation. All staff and team leaders are encouraged to develop teams that feel psychologically safe to speak up and pay particular attention to the frontline – which in Cincinnati Children's Hospital is primarily nurses, patient care attendants, technical and support staff.

   In some organisations healthcare assistants, caterers, cleaners and porters are voiceless when it comes to patient safety.
4. *Commitment to resilience*: The organisation's leadership accepts that things will happen that they cannot predict; mistakes will be made, and

they will get into trouble. However, *all staff* are encouraged to quickly identify issues and have structures in place so they can immediately respond and minimise any harm to patients.

In some organisations there is a blame culture where staff are afraid to speak up about mistakes they have made or poor performance they have witnessed from others.

5. *Deference to expertise*: *All staff* are encouraged to find and use *experts* for the given problem in the given time. These experts are the ones who understand the work situation the most and not necessarily those with the most qualifications. Cincinnati Children's Hospital engages in leadership practices that empower frontline staff to make decisions when a critical issue arises acknowledging that this will result in quicker mitigation of harm.

In HROs, senior leaders conduct frequent safety walk rounds to reinforce safety behaviours and find and fix critical safety issues. They also meet in daily operational briefs, with a selection of staff from different areas, where they look back to learn from failures and look forward to predict and lessen risk or harm.

Frontline leaders (for example, nursing managers) round with staff every day, giving 5:1 positive to negative feedback, conducting daily safety huddles/briefings and modelling expected safety behaviours. HRO leaders manage by anticipation and prediction rather than reaction. Frontline leaders are focused on predicting events in the next 24 hours and making real-time adjustments to keep patients, families, employees and visitors safe.

In some organisations there is deference to expertise based on titles and qualifications sometimes to the neglect of those closest to the process that might understand it best.

Adapted from: https://www.cincinnatichildrens.org/research/divisions/j/anderson-center/safety/methodology/high-reliability

Through adopting these principles Cincinnati Children's Hospital believe they have spared nearly 7,000 children from harm and saved $130,696,700 over six years between 2012 and 2018 (Kotogal, 2019). Initiatives such as operational briefings and safety huddles are being widely adopted now in healthcare and are proving to be a great way to nurture distributed leadership. Staff report learning more about how their organisation works, how care is coordinated, and being more willing to share resources with other areas as a result of having a greater understanding of the pressures they are under (Ryan et al., 2019).

Conclusion

This chapter has highlighted how lessons learned from the field of patient safety can help support the practice of distributed leadership in healthcare. We have explored in particular patient safety initiatives that reflect or relate to safety culture. The importance of psychological safety and the development of a just culture in healthcare were reviewed. In order to create a just culture in healthcare all staff need to feel psychologically safe to speak up about safety, and leadership practices in healthcare need to change to enable this to happen. Openly disclosing patient safety incidents requires distributed leadership practices – yet this is still a challenge and not yet mandatory 100 years on from the case study presented. The story of Cincinnati Children's Hospital's efforts to be harm-free by adopting the principles of high reliability organisations is told in their own words, and highlights the radical changes they have made in leadership practices to bring about extraordinary savings in both financial terms and reduction in harm to children.

Key concepts discussed

- The ability of all staff to lead needs to be acknowledged, especially when it comes to issues of patient safety; all staff, including those most new and 'with fresh eyes' on the system, have a critical role to play.
- Leadership practices, including inviting contributions, developing curiosity about patient safety, questioning the status quo, and questioning siloed approaches to care, need to be developed, distributed and supported across all healthcare roles and grades.
- Organisational structures and systems need to change to support these distributed leadership practices.
- Examples from patient safety can shed some light on both how to do this and the importance of doing this for the safety of healthcare.

Key readings

- Berwick, D. and National Advisory Group on the Safety of Patients in England. *A promise to learn – a commitment to act.* Available at: https://assets.publishing.service.gov.uk/government/uploads/system/uploads/attachment_data/file/226703/Berwick_Report.pdf (accessed 20 March 2020).
- O'Donovan, R., Ward, M., De Brún, A. and McAuliffe, E. (2019) Safety culture in healthcare teams: A narrative review of the literature. *Journal of Nursing Management* 27 (5): 871–883.
- Pronovost, P.J., Ravitz, A.D., Stoll, R.A. and Kennedy, S.B. (2015) *Transforming Patient Safety: A sector-wide systems approach.* Report of the WISH Patient Safety Forum 2015. Qatar: World Innovation Summit for Health. Available at: https://www.wish.org.qa/wp-content/uploads/2018/01/WISH_PatientSafety_Forum_08.01.15_WEB-1.pdf (accessed 3 April 2020).
- Tucker, A. and Edmondson, A. (2011) Case study on Cincinnati Children's Hospital. *Harvard Business Review.* Available at: https://www.academia.edu/34523677/Cincinati_Hospital (accessed 4 April 2020).
- Vincent, C. and Amalberti, R. (2016) *Safer Healthcare, Strategies for the Real World.* Available at: https://link.springer.com/book/10.1007/978-3-319-25559-0 (accessed 20 March 2020).

- Wears, R.L. and Sutcliffe, K.M. (2020) *Still Not Safe: Patient Safety and the Middle-managing of American Medicine*. New York: Oxford University Press.

Examples of studies

- Rafter, N., Hickey, A., Conroy, R.M., Condell, S., O'Connor, P., Vaughan, D. et al. (2017) The Irish National Adverse Events Study (INAES): The frequency and nature of adverse events in Irish hospitals – a retrospective record review study. *BMJ Quality & Safety* 26: 111–119.
- Ward, M.E., De Brún, A., Conway, C., Cunningham, U., English, A., Fitzsimons, J. et al. (2018) Using co-design to develop a collective leadership intervention for healthcare teams to improve safety culture. *International Journal for Environmental Research and Public Health* 15 (6): 1182.
- Ward, M.E., Ní Shé, É., De Brún, A., Korpos, C., Hamza, M., Burke, E. et al. (2019) The co-design, implementation and evaluation of a serious board game 'PlayDecide patient safety' to educate junior doctors about patient safety and the importance of reporting safety concerns. *BMC Medical Education* 19: 232. Available at: https://pubmed.ncbi.nlm.nih.gov/31238936/

Useful websites

- Amy Edmondson Podcast on Psychological Safety: https://diversity.lbl.gov/2019/09/24/tedx-talk-on-psychological-safety/
- Professor Sidney Dekker's resources on Just Culture: https://sidneydekker.com/just-culture/
- Cincinnati Children's Journey to becoming a High Reliability Organisation: https://www.cincinnatichildrens.org/research/divisions/j/anderson-center/safety/methodology/high-reliability
- HSE Resources on Open Disclosure: https://www.hse.ie/eng/about/who/qid/other-quality-improvement-programmes/opendisclosure/
- Dr. Marie Ward (2019) Webinar on Introduction to Human Factors and Safety Science for Healthcare: https://www.hse.ie/eng/about/who/qid/resourcespublications/qitalktime-ergonomics-presentation-121119.pdf
- Pilot Martin Bromiley, Founder and Current Chair of the charity Clinical Human Factors Group: https://chfg.org/

References

Amin, Y., Grewcock, D., Andrews, S. and Halligan, A. (2012) Why patients need leaders: Introducing a ward safety checklist. *Journal of the Royal Society of Medicine* 105 (9): 377–383.

Attree, M. (2007) Factors influencing nurses' decisions to raise concerns about care quality. *Journal of Nursing Management* 15 (4): 392–402.

Bååthe, F., Ahlborg, G., Jr., Edgren, L., Lagström, A. and Nilsson, K. (2016) Uncovering paradoxes from physicians' experiences of patient-centered ward-round. *Leadership Health Services* 29 (2): 168–184.

Bolden, R. (2011) Distributed leadership in organizations: A review of theory and research. *International Journal of Management Reviews* 13 (3): 251–269.

Braithwaite, J. (2018) Changing how we think about healthcare improvement. *British Medical Journal* 361: k2014. Available at: https://doi.org/10.1136/bmj.k2014 (accessed 14 October 2020).

Braithwaite, J., Westbrook, M.T., Travaglia, J.F. and Hughes, C. (2010) Cultural and associated enablers of, and barriers to, adverse incident reporting. *Quality and Safety in Health Care* 19 (3): 229–233.

Busby, A. and Gilchrist, B. (1992) The role of the nurse in the medical ward round. *Journal of Advanced Nursing* 17 (3): 339–346.

Clarke, C.J. (2020) Morrissey & anor v Health Service Executive (Approved) [2020] IESC 43 (23 July 2020). Available at: https://www.bailii.org/ie/cases/IESC/2020/2020IESC43_0.html (accessed 4 April 2020).

Cook, R. (2013) Resilience, the second story, and progress on patient safety, in E. Hollnagel, J. Braithwaite and R.L. Wears (eds.) *Resilient Health Care*. Farnham: Ashgate.

Cromie, S. and Bott, F. (2016) Just culture's 'line in the sand' is a shifting one: An empirical investigation of culpability determination. *Safety Science* 86: 258–272.

Darbyshire, D., Barrett, C., Ross, D. and Shackley, D. (2015) Measuring ward round quality in urology. *International Journal of Risk and Safety in Medicine* 27 (1): 23–33.

Dekker, S.W.A. (2009) Just culture: Who gets to draw the line? *Cognition, Technology and Work* 11 (3): 177–185.

Edmondson, A.C. (1996) Learning from mistakes is easier said than done: Group and organizational influences on the detection and correction of human error. *Journal of Applied Behavioural Science* 32 (1): 5–28.

Edmondson, A.C. (1999) Psychological safety and learning behavior in work teams. *Administrative Science Quarterly* 44 (2): 350–383.

Enslev Jensen, B., Found, P.A., Williams, S.J. and Walley, P. (2016) Improving the efficiency and effectiveness of ward rounds. *International Journal of Quality and Service Sciences* 8 (3): 279–297.

Francis, R. (2013) *Report of the mid Staffordshire NHS Foundation trust public inquiry*. London: The Stationery Office. Available at: https://www.gov.uk/government/publications/report-of-the-mid-staffordshire-nhs-foundation-trust-public-inquiry (accessed 20 March 2020).

Gausvik, C., Lautar, A., Miller, L., Pallerla, H. and Schlaudecker, J. (2015) Structured nursing communication on interdisciplinary acute care teams improves perceptions of safety, efficiency, understanding of care plan and teamwork as well as job satisfaction. *Journal of Multidisciplinary Healthcare* 8: 33–37.

Harding Clark, M. (2006) *The Lourdes Hospital Inquiry: An inquiry into peripartum hysterectomy at Our Lady of Lourdes Hospital, Drogheda*. Report of Judge Maureen Harding Clark. Dublin: Department of Health and Children. Available at: https://www.lenus.ie/bitstream/handle/10147/42922/2679.pdf?sequence=1&isAllowed=y (accessed 3 April 2020).

Health Information and Quality Authority (HIQA) (2015) *Report of the Investigation into the Safety, Quality and Standards of Services Provided by the Health Service Executive to Patients in the Midland Regional Hospital, Portlaoise*. Dublin: HIQA. Available at: https://www.lenus.ie/bitstream/handle/10147/620054/PortlaoiseInvestigationReport.pdf?sequence=1&isAllowed=y (accessed 3 April 2020).

Health and Safety Executive (HSE) (2018) *Incident Management Framework*. Dublin: HSE. Available at: https://www.hse.ie/eng/about/qavd/incident-management/hse-2018-incident-management-framework-guidance-patient-staff-stories.pdf (accessed 4 April 2020).

Health and Safety Executive (HSE) (2019) *Open Disclosure: Communicating with patients following patient safety incidents*. Dublin: HSE. Available at: https://www.hse.ie/eng/about/who/qid/other-quality-improvement-programmes/opendisclosure/hse-open-disclosure-full-policy-2019.pdf (accessed 4 April 2020).

Herring, R., Caldwell, G. and Jackson, S. (2011) Implementation of a considerative checklist to improve productivity and team working on medical ward rounds. *Clinical Governance: An International Journal* 16 (2): 129–136.

Hill, K. (2003) The sound of silence – nurses' non-verbal interaction within the ward round. *Nursing in Critical Care* 8 (6): 231–239.

Hilton, C. (2016) Whistle-blowing and duty of candour in the National Health Service: A 'history and policy' case study of the 1960s and 2010s. *Journal of the Royal Society of Medicine* 109 (9): 327–330.

Hosking, D.M. (1988) Organising, leadership and skilful process. *Journal of Management Studies* 25 (2): 147–166.

Institute of Medicine (IOM) (1999) *To Err is Human: Building a Safer Health System*. Washington, DC: National Academy Press.

International Atomic Energy Agency (IAEA) (1991) *Safety Culture: A report by the International Nuclear Safety Advisory Group*. IAEA Safety Series No. 75-INSAG-4. Vienna: IAEA. Available at: https://www-pub.iaea.org/MTCD/publications/PDF/Pub882_web.pdf (accessed 3 April 2020).

International Atomic Energy Agency (IAEA) ([1986] 1992) *INSAG-7 – The Chernobyl Accident: Updating of INSAG-1*. IAEA Safety Series No. 75-INSAG-7. Vienna: IAEA. Available at: https://www-pub.iaea.org/MTCD/publications/PDF/Pub913e_web.pdf (accessed 3 April 2020).

International Civil Aviation Organization (ICAO) (2016) *Improving Just Culture*. Working Paper A39-WP/193. Available at: https://www.icao.int/Meetings/a39/Documents/WP/wp_193_en.pdf (accessed 4 April 2020).

Kennedy, I. (2001) *The Report of the Public Inquiry into Children's Heart Surgery at the Bristol Royal Infirmary 1984–1995*. London: Department of Health. Available at: https://navigator.health.org.uk/content/report-public-inquiry-children%E2%80%99s-heart-surgery-bristol-royal-infirmary-1984%E2%80%931995-2001 (accessed 3 April 2020).

Khatri, N., Brown, G.D. and Hicks, L.L. (2009) From a blame culture to a just culture in health care. *Health Care Management Review* 34 (4): 312–322.

Kotogal, U. (2019) *Ten Years Toward Zero Harm: A report on our safety journey*. Presentation to Children's Health Ireland, Dublin.

Lewicki, R.J. and Bunker, B.B. (1996) Developing and maintaining trust in work relationships, in R.M. Kramer and T.R. Tyler (eds.) *Trust in Organisations: Frontiers of Theory and Research*. Thousand Oaks, CA: Sage.

Liu, W., Manias, E. and Gerdtz, M. (2013) Medication communication during ward rounds on medical wards: Power relations and spatial practices. *Health* 17 (2): 113–134.

Lyubovnikova, J., West, M.A., Dawson, J.F. and Carter, M.R. (2015) 24-Karat or fool's gold? Consequences of real team and co-acting group membership in healthcare organizations. *European Journal of Work and Organizational Psychology* 24 (6): 929–950.

Madden, D. (2008) *Building a Culture of Patient Safety – Report of the Commission on Patient Safety and Quality Assurance*. Dublin: The Stationery Office. Available at: https://www.gov.ie/en/publication/5d9570-building-a-culture-of-patient-safety-report-of-the-commission-on-pat/ (accessed 4 April 2020).

Martin, G.P., Chew, S. and Dixon-Woods, M. (2019) Senior stakeholder views on policies to foster a culture of openness in the English National Health Service: A qualitative interview study. *Journal of the Royal Society of Medicine* 112 (4): 153–159.

McAuliffe, E., De Brún, A., Ward, M.E., O'Shea, M., Cunningham, U., O'Donovan, R. et al. (2017) Collective leadership and safety cultures (Co-Lead): Protocol for a mixed-methods pilot evaluation of the impact of a co-designed collective leadership intervention on team performance and safety culture in a hospital group in Ireland. *BMJ Open* 7: e017569. Available at: https://bmjopen.bmj.com/content/7/11/e017569 (accessed 14 October 2020).

Nembhard, I.M. and Edmondson, A.C. (2006) Making it safe: The effects of leader inclusiveness and professional status on psychological safety and improvement efforts in health care teams. *Journal of Organizational Behavior* 27 (7): 941–966.

NHS Improvement (2018) *A Just Culture Guide*. Available at: https://improvement.nhs.uk/resources/just-culture-guide/ (accessed 4 April 2020).

Nystrom, P.J. (1990) Vertical exchanges and organizational commitment of American business managers. *Group and Organization Management* 15 (3): 296–312.

O'Donovan, R., Ward, M., De Brún, A. and McAuliffe, E. (2019) Safety culture in healthcare teams: A narrative review of the literature. *Journal of Nursing Management* 27 (5): 871–883.

O'Hare, J.A. (2008) Anatomy of the ward round. *European Journal of Internal Medicine* 19 (5): 309–313.

Parissopoulos, S., Timmins, F. and Daly, L. (2013) Re-exploring the ritual of the ward round. *Nursing in Critical Care* 18 (5): 219–221.

Patient Safety (Notifiable Patient Safety Incidents) Bill (2019) Dublin: Government of Ireland. Available at: https://www.gov.ie/en/publication/9e2562-patient-safety-bill (accessed 30 April 2020).

Pronovost, P.J., Ravitz, A.D., Stoll, R.A. and Kennedy, S.B. (2015) *Transforming Patient Safety: A sector-wide systems approach*. Report of the WISH Patient Safety Forum 2015. Qatar: World Innovation Summit for Health. Available at: https://www.wish.org.qa/wp-content/uploads/2018/01/WISH_PatientSafety_Forum_08.01.15_WEB-1.pdf (accessed 3 April 2020).

Rafter, N., Hickey, A., Conroy, R.M., Condell, S., O'Connor, P., Vaughan, D. et al. (2017) The Irish National Adverse Events Study (INAES): The frequency and nature of adverse events in Irish hospitals – a retrospective record review study. *BMJ Quality & Safety* 26: 111–119.

Reason, J. (1997) *Managing the Risks of Organizational Accidents*. Aldershot: Ashgate.

Robb, B. (1967) *Sans Everything: A Case to Answer*. London: Nelson.

Royal College of Physicians and Royal College of Nursing (RCP/RCN) (2012) *Ward Rounds in Medicine: Principles for best practice*. Available at: https://www.rcplondon.ac.uk/projects/outputs/ward-rounds-medicine-principles-best-practice (accessed 4 April 2020).

Ryan, S., Ward, M., Vaughan, D., Murray, B., Zena, M., O'Connor, T. et al. (2019) Do safety briefings improve patient safety in the acute hospital setting? A systematic review. *Journal of Advanced Nursing* 75 (10): 2085–2098.

Schein, E.H. (1986) *Organizational Culture and Leadership*. San Francisco, CA: Jossey-Bass.

Schein, E.H. and Bennis, W. (1965) *Personal and Organizational Change via Group Methods*. New York: Wiley.

Sharma, S. and Peters, M.J., on behalf of the PICU/NICU Risk Action Group (2013) 'Safety by DEFAULT': Introduction and impact of a paediatric ward round checklist. *Critical Care* 17 (5): R232.

Shaughnessy, L. and Jackson, J. (2015) Introduction of a new ward round approach in a cardiothoracic critical care unit. *Nursing in Critical Care* 20 (4): 210–218.

Sullenberger, T. (2012) *5 Questions: Sullenberger on applying lessons of airline safety to health-care practices*. Available at: https://med.stanford.edu/news/all-news/2012/09/5-questions-sullenberger-on-applying-lessons-of-airline-safety-to-health-care-practices.html (accessed 30 April 2020).

Swenne, C.L. and Skytt, B. (2014) The ward round – patient experiences and barriers to participation. *Scandinavian Journal of Caring Sciences* 28 (2): 297–304.

Tourish, D. (2005) Critical upward communication: Ten commandments for improving strategy and decision making. *Long Range Planning: International Journal of Strategic Management* 38 (5): 485–503.

Trimble, M. (2015) The thinking doctor's ward round. *Ulster Medical Journal* 84 (1): 3–7.

Vize, R. (2019) Latest NHS maternity scandal is product of toxic 'can't happen here' mentality, *The Guardian*, 22 November. Available at: https://www.theguardian.com/society/2019/nov/22/nhs-maternity-scandal-toxic-mentality (accessed 4 April 2020).

Vogel, J. and Delgado, R. (1980) To tell the truth: Physicians' duty to disclose medical mistakes. *UCLA Law Review* 28: 52–94.

Wang, L. and Sun, R. (2014) A new safety culture measurement tool and its application. *International Journal of Safety and Security Engineering* 4 (1): 77–86.

Ward, M.E., De Brún, A., Conway, C., Cunningham, U., English, A., Fitzsimons, J. et al. (2018) Using co-design to develop a collective leadership intervention for healthcare teams to improve safety culture. *International Journal for Environmental Research and Public Health* 15 (6): 1182.

Ward, M.E., Ní Shé, É., De Brún, A., Korpos, C., Hamza, M., Burke, E. et al. (2019) The co-design, implementation and evaluation of a serious board game 'PlayDecide patient safety' to educate junior doctors about patient safety and the importance of reporting safety concerns. *BMC Medical Education* 19: 232. Available at: https://pubmed.ncbi.nlm.nih.gov/31238936/ (accessed 2 November 2020).

Wears, R.L. and Sutcliffe, K.M. (2020) *Still Not Safe: Patient Safety and the Middle-managing of American Medicine.* New York: Oxford University Press.

Weick, K. and Sutcliffe, K. (2007) *Managing the Unexpected: Resilient Performance in an Age of Uncertainty.* San Francisco, CA: Jossey-Bass.

West, M., Dawson, J., Admasachew, L. and Topakas, A. (2011) *NHS Staff Management and Health Service Quality.* London: Department of Health. Available at: https://www.gov.uk/government/publications/nhs-staff-management-and-health-service-quality (accessed 6 April 2020).

West, M.A., Lyubovnikova, J., Eckert, R. and Denis, J.-L. (2014) Collective leadership for cultures of high quality health care. *Journal of Organizational Effectiveness: People and Performance* 1 (3): 240–260.

Wilson, B., Bekker, H.L. and Fylan, F. (2008) Reporting of Clinical Adverse Events Scale: A measure of doctor and nurse attitudes to adverse event reporting. *Quality and Safety in Health Care* 17 (5): 364–367.

What is leadership about and what does it involve in practice?

John G. Cullen

Chapter topics

- What is leadership?
- Established approaches for researching leadership
- Do new societies, organisations and forms of work require new approaches to studying leadership?
- Ethical leadership
- The growing role of followers
- New problems – new forms of leadership practice

Introduction

According to Freud, leadership and leaders are on our minds all the time. In a short work titled *Group Psychology and the Analysis of the Ego* (1922) he postulated that individuals draw together and form into groups as a result of their shared identification of an individual, who often represents an 'ego-ideal' (or the image of themselves that they would ideally like to become). When we are drawn to a leader, or see somebody who we work with (or for) as a practitioner of leadership who demonstrates leadership qualities, psychoanalytic theory would propose that we are projecting our need for particular types of parental figures onto somebody else.

It has often been claimed that there is more written about leadership than any other field in management and organisational studies (Cullen, 2008), so what does it mean when somebody identifies an individual as a leader or an exemplar of leadership? Until relatively recently, this identification would involve investigating:

- the 'traits' of the leader to ascertain what observable characteristics made them more of a leader than others (Walter and Scheibe, 2013; Taylor, 2019)
- the behaviours or 'styles' which the leader demonstrated (Lewin, 1947)
- how the individual navigated the changing 'situations' or the various organisational and group 'contingencies' (Larson et al., 1976; Nystrom, 1978; Powell and Butterfield, 1984)

- the types of relationships and 'exchanges' which exist between leaders and followers (Chang and Johnson, 2010; Le Blanc and Gonzalez-Roma, 2012; Tse et al., 2012; Harris et al., 2014)
- how their 'charisma' influenced their ability to motivate others (Weber, 1947; Campbell et al., 2008; Bligh and Kohles, 2009; Bligh and Robinson, 2010; Clark and Greatbatch, 2011; Davis and Gardner, 2012), or
- how ethical or moral they appear (Brown et al., 2005; Brown and Trevino, 2006; Ciulla, 2014).

In their fantastic short book on leadership (which is discussed below), Brad Jackson and Ken Parry (2008) claim that the three questions that are most asked about leadership are: 'Are leaders born or made?', 'What makes an effective leader?' and 'What's the difference between leadership and management?' The first two questions highlight the idea that leadership is something an individual does (or learns to do) to other people. This sets leaders apart in a way that distinguishes leadership from other areas of organisational life. Writers such as Zaleznik (1977) propose that the practice of leadership is different from management in that it is somehow more people-oriented and motivational than run-of-the-mill administration. This again elevates leadership into something that is different and somehow more sacred than other managerial duties. Perhaps it suggests that leaders are a moral and intellectual elite who are better equipped to make decisions on behalf of, or for, the rest of us?

In the sections below, we'll examine the manner in which the 'new leadership' approaches of the early 1980s, which celebrate heroic forms of charismatic leadership, still remain the way that many people think about the practice of leadership. Although these new versions of theories, such as 'transformational leadership', were put forward as ways of making organisations more efficient *and* moral, the chapter will look at the work of critics who examine how their proponents play down the demands that these made on employees. One person's 'culture change' is another's 'colonisation'. Many of the new 'celebratory' theories of leadership ignore the psychological, sociological, political, critical or theoretical roots of leadership or distributed leadership theory. The sections below will explore these. We'll end with an examination of the challenges to leaders and distributed leadership that are presented by the emergence of new technologies (such as artificial/augmented intelligence), new work platforms (such as the 'gig economy') and leadership development approaches (such as 'agonistic governance').

Problematising leadership

Critical approaches to the study of leadership try to draw back the curtain on the claims of leadership theorists, researchers and self-proclaimed leadership gurus, some of whom will be discussed below. The influence of critical theory expanded in the field of cultural studies in the late 1960s and 1970s, and in the 1990s had begun to exert an influence in the social sciences. Critical leadership studies focus on the methods that are used to research a subject and, in turn, to develop theories about it. When we consider that a large proportion of research that has been conducted on leadership was developed through surveys and experiments conducted amongst students, we have to question whether the behaviours they celebrate actually have much to do with the lived experiences of professionals in workplaces. There is a significant difference between participating in a classroom-based simulation, and in working in a long-term engagement with a colleague where the stakes, rewards and punishments are very different.

One example of this is the concept of 'transformational leadership', which was first proposed by James McGregor Burns in 1978 and was introduced to management and organisational studies by Bernard Bass. McGregor Burns originally stressed that ethical behaviour was central to practice of transformational leadership, but Bass initially downplayed the importance of morality in organisational studies. It remains one of the most researched, cited and written about fields in management and leadership studies and the amount of peer-reviewed research published has shown no sign of abating for decades (Cullen, 2019). In summary, transformational leadership is presented as the opposite of 'transactional leadership'. Transactional leaders reward followers through incentives for work; transformational leaders change their organisation through creating the conditions in which employees reassess and re-evaluate what it is they get from work. Such 'personal' transformations mirror the organisational changes that the leader wishes to attain for their organisation. The popularity of this theory (amongst researchers and teachers in any case) may be due to the manner in which it appeals to the ego of would-be corporate saviours, or the need for people to get something more than mundane rewards from their work. It is often used to describe 'heroic' attempts at change, whilst glossing over the hidden cost of such initiatives to employees. Dennis Tourish's work on the *Dark Side of Transformational Leadership* (2013) highlights the dangers of engaging in fantasies about the transformative power of leaders. This theory can encourage narcissistic beliefs amongst leaders about their own power to change things, which leads to a lack of a sense of responsibility when things go wrong. Such behaviours will then go on to be replicated in the next organisation that they lead, and employees may suffer from low-tone 'brainwashing' that occurs when somebody tries to change an employee's very sense of self.

Following the hardship inflicted by many in positions of authority through 'austerity' measures in order to fix broken social and economic systems, there is evidence of a much more healthy form of cynicism in the field of leadership studies. Rather than asking what makes some people more 'leader-like' than others (a question which often demands that we ignore the financial and social advantages which these individuals bring with them into their jobs), critical leadership scholars are more likely to ask: why do people think that these individuals would make good leaders, or what is it about their behaviour that we associate with leadership. In many ways, we are returning to Freud's idea that leaders and leadership are *socially constructed at the unconscious level.*

We can see this in approaches such as 'social identity theory' (Luhrmann and Eberl, 2007; van Knippenberg, 2011), which proposes that groups tend to choose their leaders on the basis of how 'prototypical' they are of other group members, rather than being exemplars of excellent communication, analytical or motivational skills. In other words, groups tend to select members who are most like the rest of the group, rather than those who are the best. It is also found in approaches such as 'implicit leadership theory', which sees leadership as something that an individual unconsciously defines for themselves over time, but in reference to their social experiences in the real world (Alabdulhadi et al., 2017).

When we ask what the demands are that people make of leaders in the contemporary world, we are really testing the boundaries of the social and ethical world that we inhabit at the current moment. Earlier, I mentioned the austerity measures which were inflicted on large parts of populations in some of the wealthiest countries on earth following the global financial crisis in the last decade. Many of the measures taken were presented in an almost medicalised language that promised they would restore the 'health' of a financial system. The medicine, however, tasted many times more bitter to the poorest and most vulnerable sections of populations who had to endure the side-effects of other more prosperous sectors' recovery.

After leadership?

This chapter has been drafted in the early months of 2020 where boorish politicians who have often never experienced real hardships continue to be elected to leadership positions or exert undue influence on the political soul of some of the leading liberal democracies in the world.

For example, the dust jacket of former mayor of New York, 'Rudi' Giuliani's co-written book (titled *Leadership*) claims that the work is 'the definitive American leader's personal guide to his principles of leadership' (Giuliani and Kurson, 2002). One of the leadership lessons which takes an entire chapter in the book is titled 'Stand Up To Bullies'. At the time of writing this chapter, Giuliani is one of President Donald Trump's lawyers and frequently defends him in the media.

In our highly 'mediatised' world, being famous and holding positions of authority can often be confused with leadership. The abuse of power by powerful men such as Harvey Weinstein led to the emergence of the #MeToo movement, which exposed the extent of abusive, degrading, bullying and criminal behaviour that was allowed to fester in many organisations and sectors. Often the victims of this abuse did not speak up because they felt that would not be believed as a result of the power and influence wielded by these 'charismatic leaders'. In common parlance, 'charismatic leadership' has come to be generally understood as stemming from the motivational aspects of working with somebody who has a highly engaging personality. However, this does not take into account Max Weber's original attribution of charisma to the idea that when somebody has been placed in a position of authority above us, we unconsciously assume that they are somehow better than us, or blessed with God's grace (or 'Charism').

The fact that business and political leaders have entered public discourse about what leadership is, has led many to assume that because they are the 'head' of a service, corporation or other socially constructed entity that they somehow are equipped to advise others on how to achieve their sacred status. Something very strange has happened to how the world sees leaders and understands what leadership is. Manifestations of this emerge in the excellent aforementioned book by Jackson and Parry titled *A Very Short, Fairly Interesting and Reasonably Cheap Book about Studying Leadership* (2008), which expertly demonstrates how decades of research and writing have left us in a situation where we have many more, but infinitely better, questions about the field than perhaps at any other stage in history.

The crisis in leadership and leadership studies has opened up many new avenues to those interested in both developing new understandings of leadership, and those bravely who still want to lead in increasingly difficult times. A fascinating recent edited collection titled *After Leadership* (Carroll et al., 2019) begins by reflecting on Alasdair MacIntyre's (1981) opening assessment of the field of moral philosophy in the mid- to late twentieth century, which is emblematic of our broken understanding of what leadership is. Few researchers are capable of conducting a root-and-branch reappraisal of what leadership is and what it means, but *After Leadership* brings together some of the leading critical voices on leadership to do exactly this. Two chapters in particular are relevant to the topic of distributed leadership.

The first is Steve Kempster and the late Ken Parry's 'After leaders: A world of leading and leadership . . . with no leaders' (2019), which is a rich discussion of how leadership should happen without the distortion of existing approaches to understanding what makes leaders or what one should do without them. The attention in such scenarios turns from trying to understand people and onto the actions that get things done. The purpose of what organisations do and the value they create, and the meaningfulness of the work of individuals and groups moves to the fore. Instead of focusing on leaders, leadership becomes about getting things done in responsible ways.

The second, 'Post-leadership leadership: Mastering the new liquidity' (2019) by Stewart Clegg and Miguel Pina e Cunha builds on the concerns raised by Kempster and Parry in their focus on the way that new modes of work have fundamentally changed the ways that organisations work. Rather than the solid, stable hierarchical structures of old, organisations are becoming increasingly 'fluid', which means that individual workers are less reliant on the value that they create for leaders, and more reliant on what they create for their clients, and also how to establish new forms of career capital for themselves. Liquid leadership is distributed and flows throughout an organisation.

This is especially important when one looks at the emerging field of what is known as the future of work. Although sociologists of work and employment economists have long studied emerging and future skills needs, scholars of the future of work are increasingly concerned about the ways in which advances in machine learning and artificial or augmented intelligence are changing, and will continue to change, the next generations of workplaces. The enhanced capabilities which future employees will bring to the workplace may provide evidence-based and data-driven alternatives to the 'inspired' decision-making skills of leaders who traditionally remained above and apart from their employees in traditional workplaces.

With the world of work and organisations changing, and increases in the empowerment of employees who would previously be thought of only as followers, we might begin to ask: 'Has distributed leadership's time finally come?' In order to determine if this is the case, we have to look back to its theoretical roots and its emergence.

The theoretical roots of distributed leadership

Richard Bolden's (2011) review of distributed leadership in organisations draws attention to the fact that, although it appeared to emerge as a practice and topic of research in its own right around the year 2000, its roots as a practice and subject of study go way back. He notes that the idea that leadership as something that is done by groups of people was occasionally found in the leadership literature in the early years of the twentieth century. This was doubtlessly influenced by many of the new sociological and psychodynamic theories that had emerged to provide new explanations for individual actions from a social lens.

For example, Emile Durkheim's study of suicide (1970) was perhaps the first great contribution to modern sociology. In this work he articulates how suicide was often perceived as the sad result of deeply experienced pain by an individual. However, he proposed that although suicide is something that an individual does to themselves, it is the result of larger changes in social structure. Our attempts to understand and prevent suicide can be greatly assisted by examining how changes in social circumstances impact on individuals in the world. When an economic system, for example, undergoes a 'boom', many of the pre-existing social structures that assisted individuals to understand their place in the world change or disappear, which leaves individuals to experience a state of being morally unanchored from the world they live in.

Similarly, Freud's work increasingly turned towards studying the social rather than the individual as his intellectual career progressed, but the psychoanalytic theorist who most clearly engaged with the idea of distributed leadership is Carl Jung. He posited that our unconscious was something that was shared, rather than completely individually formed. The nature of the 'collective unconscious' according to Jung could be demonstrated through shared psychological motifs found around the world in the form of folklore, myths, religion and art (Jung, 1984). In other words, we are primed for leadership through the significant symbolic system that has developed in our shared, collective reservoir of unconscious energy over the evolution of our psychological history. This shared understanding is embedded in how we *internalise* cultural cues from an early age (Vygotsky, 1978), learn the norms which guide how we behave in social situations (Lave and Wenger, 1991) and unconsciously *teach* these norms to others (Shweder, 1991) in a way that ensures that our understanding of leadership and its outcomes are widely understood.

Although ideas related to the concept of distributed leadership had been evolving in the social sciences since the latter half of the nineteenth century, Bolden (2011) says that it has only really been embraced by scholars in the last two decades. Prior to 2000, it had been periodically mentioned as a concept since the 1980s, but was overshadowed by the growth of literature on what became known as the 'new leadership'. This 'new leadership' is not one thing but might loosely be described as work on transformational and charismatic leaders as people 'who define organizational reality through the articulation of a vision, and the generation of strategies to realize that vision' (Jackson and Parry, 2008: 28). It is perhaps not difficult to see why the idea of leadership as something that is shared and distributed throughout organisations may have been lost in almost messianic re-affirmation of a central leader in new leadership theory.

Bolden (2011) writes that the development of concepts such as 'distributed cognition' and 'activity' contributed to the emergence of distributed leadership. The former links human thought processes directly to the environment in which they occur, and the latter highlights the inescapable inter-linkages between our activities and the material and intellectual world in which we find ourselves. In a frequently cited classic article on the difference between managers and leaders, Zaleznik (1977) suggested that leaders often felt as if their work was something that is done outside the work environment that they were responsible for. This 'separateness', according to Zaleznik, was a key factor in their success. The theories which underpin the development of distributed leadership suggest the opposite: being part of, and committed to, the environment that one works in is natural and critical for responsible growth and change. The idea of distributed leadership, then, is incompatible with the notion of an individualised, heroic leader.

Much of the appeal of distributed leadership is that it speaks directly to new forms of complex, matrix-based organisations where a 'traditional' centralised leadership approach will simply not work. For example, the advent of 'platform' organisations (such as Airbnb, Deliveroo and Uber) effectively removes centralised authority with accessible apps and standardised guidelines. Traditional leadership is effectively 'managed out' of the workplace relationship. Although these models have been highly successful in commercial terms, they have not been without problems. One of the elements of traditional leadership is the extent to which an individual was identifiable with a set of decisions and a strategy, which meant that responsibility for mistakes could be clearly associated with one person. When difficulties arise for workers and managers in platform scenarios, the responsibility for addressing these is passed to the employees who must resolve them. However, healthcare and public service bodies do not (yet!) work on platform models, and the benefits of distributed leadership can be more clearly articulated when one considers the continuing recurrence of problems and challenges that are unstructured and unprecedented.

This is particularly the case when facing the issues that arise with 'wicked problems' – that is, problems that an organisation has never encountered before, are unstructured (which means that the precise nature of the difficulty the organisation faces is difficult to understand) and there is a lack of certainty if the solution that is provided to resolve the problem will create additional, or more severe, difficulties in the future (Grint, 2005). Wicked problems are ones which create difficulties for leaders who simply do not know what the right thing to do is. This, more than any other scenario, stresses the need for good leadership. Francis Ford Coppola's war film *Apocalypse Now* studies what happens when leadership is missing or compromised during a political conflict that is rapidly disintegrating into a 'wicked' situation. An army captain is assigned to a boat crew to travel by river to the headquarters of a colonel who has 'gone rogue'. During this trip various types of leaders and leadership are encountered. Robert Duval's regiment commander Kilgore is an example of a centralised, heroic leader who is also self-delusional and disconnected from the chaos impacting his soldiers around him. As the river boat crew draws closer to their target, they encounter a leaderless outpost on the Do Lung bridge, which has descended into anarchic anomie;

the terrified soldiers have no sense of how they should react to attacks and are completely starved of direction and purpose.

Fraher and Grint (2016) theorised that a leadership mindset known as 'agonistic governance' is required in such situations. Agonistic governance involves embracing uncertain and complex situations and recognising that these *are* the natural challenges of leadership. Understanding and accepting failure is thus a key component of this form of leadership. Fraher and Grint studied how elite military units such as the Navy Seals train their officers and soldiers in a manner that familiarises them with ambivalent situations and failure, in a way which acknowledges that imposing any other form of leadership on a wicked problem will often result in short-term success. The reasons for this are that wicked situations are highly complex and multifaceted. Because of the interconnected and interrelated nature of problems such as climate change, for example, it is not possible to solve these centrally from one point or position. Wicked problems are 'systemic' and broad solutions that resolve issues throughout the system are required. Wicked problems, in other words, can best be resolved through leadership approaches which recognise that solutions are distributed throughout the organisational or social setting in which they are located.

Critiquing distributed leadership

Why, then, is it important to critique distributed leadership? Leadership theory often addresses its failings when the approaches adopted by a proponent or exemplar of it are subsequently found out to have created more difficulties than they solved. Critical approaches are primarily philosophical, in that they address the underlying assumptions that are held within a theoretical framework. They are expressly the opposite of 'clinical' approaches, which are concerned with how something is done is practice. Rather than being a theoretical abstraction, though, critical approaches often help to clarify areas which are ignored by 'dominant accounts' of leadership spectacles (Elmes and Frame, 2008).

Popular accounts of disasters, which are often used in management education or leadership development programmes, regularly highlight individual or corporate heroes and villains; the truth-tellers and whistleblowers are exonerated and the toxic leaders are vilified, but the systemic nature of the problem is often ignored and the distributed voices who sustained the development of the problem are also ignored. There are many examples of this, of course, but Dianne Vaughan's account of the *Challenger* Space Shuttle disaster (1996) exemplifies the manner in which strategic political decisions to change the core logic of an important space exploration organisation (NASA) resulted in deep reverberations throughout an entire sector. The drive to make NASA more financially self-sufficient resulted in responsibility for leading the development of various spacecraft components to be distributed. When a conflict arose between institutional pressures and the cultural beliefs at NASA, and the producer of an important element of *Challenger*'s solid rocket boosters, the company personnel who were charged with developing that component were effectively instructed to change their directive not to launch, even though they knew that it would malfunction and risk the loss of life and the spacecraft.

Leadership, like power, *is* distributed throughout organisations and social settings. Michel Foucault's brilliant study of the nature of power, *Discipline and Punish* (1977), demonstrated that power is never what we think it is. Power is not done to us: we distribute it in a way that ultimately serves our individual needs. If somebody with power uses it to curtail our needs too much, we will not accept it and eventually work against those who we perceive as working against our needs through resistance. If we understand distributed leadership as something which flows throughout an organisation or social system, that 'leadership is more appropriately understood as a fluid and emergent, rather than as a fixed, phenomenon' (Gronn 2000: 324), we must be conscious of the potential dangers that arise from such situations, as well as the many benefits that could possibly accrue to the broader system if it was permitted to flourish.

Conclusion

> Leadership is widely seen as both the problem and solution to all manner of contemporary issues: from ending world poverty to addressing global warming; from turning around ailing corporations to regenerating local communities; from reviving schools to creating scientific breakthroughs. The hunger and quest for leadership knowledge appears to be insatiable. (Jackson and Parry, 2008: 9)

It has been over ten years since Brad Jackson and the late Ken Parry wrote these words, and we can add new workplace, organisational and social problems to the list of issues that require effective leadership: refugee crises, the climate emergency, populist political movements, the growing wealth divide, racism, sexism, the rise of the far right, pandemics, violence against women and children, the rise of augmented and artificial intelligence (and the impact of these on current occupations), overpopulation, discrimination, etc. Once, leaders were seen as sacralised embodiments of the solutions to these issues; now, the idea that one person or a few people can and should heroically lead people out of these difficulties is viewed with a very healthy cynicism. This retreat from the 'hero-leader' notion has opened up many important opportunities to understand how leaders might encourage and facilitate new forms of change.

For example, many leaders in the financial sector (in both its private and public manifestations) are increasingly vocal about the need to take social and environmental sustainability seriously and put in place measures that require all companies to report clear metrics on how they perform in relation to these (Elkington, 1997). The textbooks and 'official histories' and congratulatory accounts of self-proclaimed leaders are becoming less favoured than leadership accounts which draw attention to the failures of leaders, and the steps they took to remedy them (Anderson, 1998). These are not the typical accounts of the crucible experiences of leaders (Bennis and Thomas, 2002; Byrne et al., 2018; Taylor, 2018), where a leader becomes stronger through negotiating and overcoming personal adversity, but ones where they address their moral failings to other people, and attempt to fix these by creating systems and structures that will deliver social and environmental justice.

The systemic, interrelated nature of society means that it is increasingly difficult to generate benefits for one group at the expense of others in a sustainable way. This is why the principles of organisational sustainability involve developing strategies that seek to deliver social, cultural and environmental benefits for all as well as economic benefits for an organisation and its workers. However, organisational sustainability requires that these four elements be treated as 'co-equal', and one cannot be sacrificed for another (Werbach, 2009; Cullen, 2017). We can see manifestations of this in the environmental activism of leaders in the financial sector and the companies who paid to air Super Bowl advertisements that celebrated diversity, migration and compassion in the aftermath of the Trump election and inauguration.

Perhaps, most importantly, the liberating effects of thinking about leadership in new ways has the potential to yield many benefits to those who realise that it is critical to solving the new social and environmental problems that are presenting. Academic journals such as *Leadership* and *Human Relations* have recently taken an unusual stance in inviting research articles on leadership (and other organisational topics) that are written in ways that are applicable to real problems, and meaningful for readers who might have to actually do this work in practice (i.e. practitioners rather than researchers!). This is a very welcome recognition that leadership research is something, like distributed leadership, that is achieved in communities-of-practice, rather than by communities-of-'knowledge' that study the field they wish to contribute to from an isolated, detached and often, it must be said, irrelevant position (Tourish, 2015; Learmonth, 2020).

Key concepts discussed

- established approaches to studying leadership: trait theories; behavioural approaches; situational leadership; contingency-based approaches to leadership; charismatic leadership
- toxic leadership and its causes and effects
- new organisational forms and social influences: populism, the 'gig economy', the future of work. Implications for leadership
- ethical leadership. Transformational leadership
- followership (and toxic followership in a post-truth environment)
- new problems, new forms of leadership practice: agonistic governance and wicked problem-solving.

Key readings

- Carroll, B., Levy, L. and Richmond, D. (2008) Leadership as practice: Challenging the competency paradigm, *Leadership*, 4 (4): 363–379.
  This article moves discussions away from abstracted research on what leadership is, to examine how it is done in practice.
- Carroll, B., Ford, J. and Taylor, S. (eds.) (2019) *Leadership: Contemporary Critical Perspectives*, 2nd edition, London: Sage.
  This text provides an extensive broad overview of established leadership theory, and compares these with contemporary critical leadership approaches.

- Fraher, A. and Grint, K. (2016) Agonistic governance: The antinomies of decision-making in US Navy SEALs, *Leadership*, 14 (4): 395–414.
  This article looks at a highly relevant practical case for how leadership is learned and accomplished in high-pressure situations.
- Gabriel, Y. (1997) Meeting God: When organizational members come face to face with the Supreme Leader, *Human Relations*, 50 (4): 315–342.
  A psychoanalytic account of how followers project fears and fantasies onto leaders.
- Grint, K. (2005) Problems, problems, problems: The social construction of 'leadership", *Human Relations*, 58 (11): 1467–1494.
  A key article for understanding a critical practice of contemporary leadership: engaging with 'wicked problems'.
- Jackson, B. and Parry, K. (2008) *A Very Short, Fairly Interesting and Reasonably Cheap Book about Studying Leadership*, London: Sage.
  First published in 2007, this is a short overview of some of the concerns of contemporary leadership studies.

References

Alabdulhadi, A., Schyns, B. and Studigl, L.F. (2017) Implicit leadership theory, in E.A. Curtis and J.G. Cullen (eds.) *Leadership and Change for the Health Professional*, London: Open University Press, 20–36.

Anderson, R.C. (1998) *Mid-course Correction: Toward a Sustainable Enterprise – The Interface Model*, Atlanta, GA: Peregrinzilla Press.

Bennis, W.G. and Thomas, R.J. (2002) Crucibles of leadership, *Harvard Business Review*, 80 (9): 39–45.

Bligh, M.C. and Kohles, J.C. (2009) The enduring allure of charisma: How Barack Obama won the historic 2008 presidential election, *Leadership Quarterly*, 20 (3): 483–492.

Bligh, M.C. and Robinson, J.L. (2010) Was Gandhi 'charismatic'? Exploring the rhetorical leadership of Mahatma Gandhi, *Leadership Quarterly*, 21 (5): 844–855.

Bolden, R. (2011) Distributed leadership in organizations: A review of theory and research, *International Journal of Management Reviews*, 13 (3): 251–269.

Brown, M.E. and Trevino, L.K. (2006) Ethical leadership: A review and future directions, *Leadership Quarterly*, 17 (6): 595–616.

Brown, M.E., Trevino, L.K. and Harrison, D.A. (2005) Ethical leadership: A social learning perspective for construct development and testing, *Organizational Behavior and Human Decision Processes*, 97 (2): 117–134.

Byrne, A., Crossan, M. and Seijts, G. (2018) The development of leader character through crucible moments, *Journal of Management Education*, 42 (2): 265–293.

Campbell, S.M., Ward, A.J., Sonnenfeld, J.A. and Agle, B.R. (2008) Relational ties that bind: Leader–follower relationship dimensions and charismatic attribution, *Leadership Quarterly*, 19 (5): 556–568.

Carroll, B., Firth, J. and Wilson, S. (eds.) (2019) *After Leadership*, New York: Routledge.

Chang, C.H. and Johnson, R.E. (2010) Not all leader–member exchanges are created equal: Importance of leader relational identity, *Leadership Quarterly*, 21 (5): 796–808.

Ciulla, J. (2014) *Ethics: The Heart of Leadership*, Santa Barbara; CA: Praeger.

Clark, T. and Greatbatch, D. (2011) Audience perceptions of charismatic and non-charismatic oratory: The case of management gurus, *Leadership Quarterly*, 22 (1): 22–32.

Clegg, S. and Pina e Cunha, M. (2019) Post-leadership leadership: Mastering the new liquidity, in B. Carroll, J. Firth and S. Wilson (eds.) *After Leadership*, New York: Routledge, 175–193.

Cullen, J. (2008) *Communication and Knowledge Sharing at Work*, Dublin: Blackhall Publishing.
Cullen, J.G. (2017) Educating business students about sustainability: A bibliometric review of current trends and research needs, *Journal of Business Ethics*, 145 (2): 429–439.
Cullen, J.G. (2019) Leading through contingencies, in B. Carroll, J. Ford and S. Taylor (eds.) *Leadership: Contemporary Critical Perspectives*, 2nd edition, London: Sage, 68–92.
Davis, K.M. and Gardner, W.L. (2012) Charisma under crisis revisited: Presidential leadership, perceived leader effectiveness, and contextual influences, *Leadership Quarterly*, 23 (5): 918–933.
Durkheim, E. (1970) *Suicide: A Study in Sociology*, translated by J.A. Spaulding and G. Simpson, London: Routledge & Kegan Paul.
Elkington, J. (1997) *Cannibals with Forks: The Triple Bottom Line of 21st Century Business*. Oxford: Capstone.
Elmes, M. and Frame, B. (2008) Into hot air: A critical perspective on Everest, *Human Relations*, 61 (2): 213–241.
Foucault, M. (1977) *Discipline and Punish: The Birth of the Prison*, translated by A. Sheridan, London: Allen Lane.
Fraher, A. and Grint, K. (2016) Agonistic governance: The antinomies of decision-making in US Navy SEALs, *Leadership*, 14 (4): 395–414.
Freud, S. (1922) *Group Psychology and the Analysis of the Ego*, London: International Psycho-Analytical Press.
Giuliani, R.W. and Kurson, K. (2002) *Leadership*, New York: Hyperion.
Grint, K. (2005) *Leadership: Limits and Possibilities*, Basingstoke: Palgrave Macmillan.
Gronn, P. (2000) Distributed properties: A new architecture for leadership, *Educational Management and Administration*, 28 (3): 317–338.
Harris, T.B., Li, N. and Kirkman, B.L. (2014) Leader–member exchange (LMX) in context: How LMX differentiation and LMX relational separation attenuate LMX's influence on OCB and turnover intention, *Leadership Quarterly*, 25 (2): 314–328.
Jackson, B. and Parry, K. (2008) *A Very Short, Fairly Interesting and Reasonably Cheap Book about Studying Leadership*, London: Sage.
Jung, C.G. (1984) *The Spirit in Man, Art and Literature*, London: Ark.
Kempster, S. and Parry, K. (2019) After leaders: A world of leading and leadership . . . with no leaders, in B. Carroll, J. Firth and S. Wilson (eds.) *After Leadership*, New York: Routledge, 64–80.
Larson, L.L., Hunt, J.G. and Osborn, R.N. (1976) The great hi-hi leader behavior myth: Lesson from Occam's Razor, *Academy of Management Journal*, 19 (4): 628–641.
Lave, J. and Wenger, E. (1991) *Situated Learning: Legitimate Peripheral Participation*, Cambridge: Cambridge University Press.
Learmonth, M. (2020) Editorial: Reading for interest, *Human Relations*, 73 (5): 627–630.
Le Blanc, P.M. and Gonzalez-Roma, V. (2012) A team level investigation of the relationship between leader–member exchange (LMX) differentiation, and commitment and performance, *Leadership Quarterly*, 23 (3): 534–544.
Lewin, K. (1947) Frontiers in group dynamics: Concept, method and reality in social science: Social equilibria and social change, *Human Relations*, 1 (1): 5–41.
Luhrmann, T. and Eberl, P. (2007) Leadership and identity construction: Reframing the leader–follower interaction from an identity theory perspective, *Leadership*, 3 (1): 115–127.
MacIntyre, A.C. (1981) *After Virtue: A Study in Moral Theory*, Notre Dame, IN: University of Notre Dame Press.
Nystrom, P.C. (1978) Managers and the hi-hi leader myth, *Academy of Management Journal*, 21 (2): 325–331.
Powell, G.N. and Butterfield, D.A. (1984) The female leader and the 'high-high' effective leader stereotype, *Journal of Psychology*, 117 (1): 71–76.

Shweder, R.A. (1991) *Thinking through Cultures: Expeditions in Cultural Psychology*, Cambridge, MA: Harvard University Press.

Taylor, S. (2018) Forming character in business school leadership education: Rejoinder to 'The development of leader character through crucible moments', *Journal of Management Education*, 42 (2): 301–305.

Taylor, S. (2019) Trait theories of leaders and leadership: From Ancient Greece to twenty-first-century neuroscience, in B. Carroll, J. Ford and S. Taylor (eds.) *Leadership: Contemporary Critical Perspectives*, 2nd edition, London: Sage, 49–67.

Tourish, D. (2013) *The Dark Side of Transformational Leadership: A Critical Perspective*, New York: Routledge.

Tourish, D. (2015) Some announcements, reaffirming the critical ethos of *Leadership*, and what we look for in submissions, *Leadership*, 11 (2): 135–141.

Tse, H.H.M., Ashkanasy, N.M. and Dasborough, M.T. (2012) Relative leader–member exchange, negative affectivity and social identification: A moderated-mediation examination, *Leadership Quarterly*, 23 (3): 354–366.

van Knippenberg, D. (2011) Embodying who we are: Leader group prototypicality and leadership effectiveness, *Leadership Quarterly*, 22 (6): 1078–1091.

Vaughan, D. (1996) *The Challenger Launch Decision: Risky Technology, Culture, and Deviance at NASA*, Chicago, IL: University of Chicago Press.

Vygotsky, L.S. (1978) *Mind in Society: The Development of Higher Psychological Processes*, translated by M. Cole, V. John-Steiner, S. Scribner and E. Souberman, Cambridge, MA: Harvard University Press.

Walter, F. and Scheibe, S. (2013) A literature review and emotion-based model of age and leadership: New directions for the trait approach, *Leadership Quarterly*, 24 (6): 882–901.

Weber, M. (1947) *The Theory of Social and Economic Organization*, New York: Free Press.

Werbach, A. (2009) *Strategy for Sustainability: A Business Manifesto*, Boston, MA: Harvard Business School Press.

Zaleznik, A. (1977) Managers and leaders: Are they different?, *Harvard Business Review*, 55 (3): 67–78.

5 Hybrids of positional authority, personal principles and collective leadership contributions

Martin Beirne

Chapter topics

- Restrictions on leadership thinking and learning
- Challenging connections between exceptionalism and top-driven leadership
- Responding to critiques of distributed leadership
- Different levels and dynamics of leadership contribution
- Socially informed leadership thinking
- Resistance leadership as an alternative source of knowledge
- Leadership alignment issues
- Recognising distributed *and* positional leadership roles
- Combinations of leadership influence
- Encouraging and extending distributed leadership

Introduction

Distributed leadership questions the simplistic yet commonplace notion that people in work organisations, political institutions and social movements can be allocated, on an either/or basis, to the binary categories of leader or follower. It starts from the basic proposition that influence, power and the expertise to draw maximum advantage from collective behaviour are distributed through work groups and communities, rather than confined to talented or 'heroic' elites. Interest in the subject has grown largely as a reaction to exclusionary and elitist accounts of what leadership involves and requires in mainstream literature and popular consciousness. It reflects a deep sense of unease about the aggrandisement of formal leadership positions, and a widespread dissatisfaction with the exaggeration of executive capabilities by writers and consultants who channel their interests towards the top of organisational and professional hierarchies.

Concerns about principled and responsive behaviour at this level (or the lack of it) are undoubtedly important, as indeed are executive education programmes that counteract elitism and the negativity that can be triggered by images of exceptionalism and insularity. However, these are insufficient in themselves for leadership learning and effective development. What is required alongside the executive focus is an explicit appreciation of the initiative and influence of 'ordinary leaders' (McKee et al., 2013) in galvanising cooperation among workers and service providers at the local level. The promise with distributed thinking is that work organisations and social movements can draw benefits from openly acknowledging, and more effectively supporting, multiple levels of leadership agency. It offers a more inclusive understanding of leader behaviour, and potentially an agenda for leadership reform, though not in a straightforward or uncontested fashion (Torrance, 2013; Woods, 2016). Discussions of distributed leadership frequently reach beyond matters of performance and effective functioning to address wider questions about the running and governance of work organisations. This is constructive, so far as it goes, though also controversial.

This chapter supports an expansion of applied research that aims to de-monopolise and rebalance leadership learning, development and practice. It defends distributed leadership against some dismissive reactions, while also sounding a cautionary note about the folly of equating corrective arguments and the assault on orthodox thinking with an anti-hierarchy stance, or attempt to diminish the significance of formal leadership roles in theory or everyday life. Recognising developments in the arguments and literature covering distributed leadership, the discussion here concentrates on alignment issues and the progressive potential to bring informal and hierarchical elements together in more constructive blends (Collinson and Collinson, 2009; Currie and Spyridonidis, 2018) or complementary configurations of leader behaviour (Gronn, 2009, 2016). The final section considers the implications of this for applied work that may be capable of encouraging more inclusive approaches, and sustaining mutually supportive forms of 'ordinary' and positional leadership into the future.

Addressing dismissive reactions and negativity

Distributed leadership has attracted some disparaging comments – and negative judgements – about whether it adds anything substantial to the analysis and development of leadership theories and capabilities. Some of the more cutting evaluations see nothing other than loose and woolly rhetoric that empties the subject of any reasonable meaning by casting anyone and everyone as a leader. Alvesson and Spicer are among the most dismissive of commentators, claiming that the writing on distributed leadership obstructs rather than illuminates the nature and extent of leadership behaviour:

> Distributed theories of leadership point out that it can be found almost anywhere with the result of nearly any coordinating process becoming considered as 'leadership'. (2012: 383)
>
> . . . the quest to find leadership that is distributed throughout the organization has only made matters worse. It means nearly anything and everything can be viewed as leadership. According to this approach, influencing your boss ('upwards leadership'), working with a co-worker ('peer leadership') and even motivating yourself ('self-leadership') are all kinds of leadership. As the concept has been applied to increasingly varied processes it has become ever more blunted. (2012: 369, 370)

These comments are unduly harsh and unhelpful, signalling an impatience with some of the work in this area and a willingness to debunk more serious scholarship on this basis. With these remarks, Alvesson and Spicer reduce a range of committed research to the quality of the weakest contributions and the crudest prescriptive rhetoric. They also deflect attention from the valuable learning that is possible when scrutinising telling studies of distributed leadership in action, as the next section will demonstrate.

There is no doubt that some of the most enthusiastic advocates of distributed leadership lost track of hierarchical authority, and marginalised the continuing influence of formal leadership behaviour with their analyses. However, this is in the nature of scholarly debate, and provides insufficient grounds for such a strident rejection of the entire field. It is not unusual for corrective writing to recoil so far from the targets of legitimate critique that matters of importance seem to be downgraded or neglected as momentum builds. The social sciences are constantly oscillating between research that prioritises human agency over structural constraint, and vice versa, although debates across these familiar dividing lines frequently advance the overall stock of knowledge and the collective understanding of these mutual influences on work and life.

With the enthusiasm for distribution and anti-leaderism (O'Reilly and Reed, 2010) in prominent areas of applied research – notably in education, though also in healthcare – the continuing influence of concentrated, positional influence slipped into the background, at least for a while. This has been acknowledged by Gronn (2008, 2009) in two of the most frequently cited articles on distributed leadership. He concedes that the appeal of challenging exceptionalism coincided with a tendency to treat pluralities of leaders as being much the same in terms of their influence. This was a mistake, which Gronn and others have corrected with the attention now given to leadership hybrids and configurations, though without giving up on the distributed approach, which '. . . provides part of the picture of practice but by no means the entirety of it' (2009: 383).

Positional leadership and formal authority remain important, though not on their own or without accounting for the reactions of wider organisational communities, including opposition to executive decisions, and with that forms of resistance which themselves involve instances of leadership. Studies of informal worker behaviour through episodes of industrial action provide the most obvious means of defending space for a distributed understanding of leadership, and answering the criticism from Alvesson and Spicer (2012). The industrial relations literature on disputes, especially unofficial strikes, offers valuable insights into the leadership capabilities of frontline workers. There are detailed accounts of spontaneous and emergent leadership among factory workers (Zoller and Fairhurst, 2007; Atzeni, 2009), and even employee-led resistance movements to oppose the decisions of trade union leaders and their negotiated agreements with employers, for example, on compensation for gendered pay inequality (Beirne et al., 2019).

This scholarship shows that workers are not as passive in their followership, or as susceptible to official leader behaviour as conventional leadership theories suggest (especially those of the charismatic and transformational variety). There is a creative capacity for leadership on the shop floor, although this is frequently overlooked, or regarded as something that effective positional leaders should be able to contain:

> . . . even within the initiation of what appears on the surface to be 'spontaneous' strike activity – where there is no official or easily identifiable activist leadership – that does not mean there are no leaders, even though this may not be recorded. Some form of leadership takes place because an individual person or group takes the initiative to walk off the job and then bring the actions and demands of a determined minority to the mass of workers to do likewise. Drawing on pre-existing informal communication networks, an apparently spontaneous action creates varying levels of conscious leadership and organisation as workers' basic sense of discontent is articulated, amplified and actualised. (Darlington, 2018: 624)

Of course, positional leadership represents more to workers than a source of inequality and target for resistance. Officials in work organisations, professions and trade unions are often genuinely admired. Some formal leadership behaviour can be reasonably described as transformational, and even heroic, although these words have been tarnished by their excessive usage in mainstream theory and the delivery of executive development programmes (Carroll and Nicholson, 2014). Nonetheless, research on employee perceptions of their leaders, and on work group evaluations of individual leader performance, regularly captures appreciative comments, when a stand has been taken against discrimination and for equality or fair treatment, for instance. Studies of nursing opinion have recorded widespread support for senior figures within the profession and across health organisations who exhibit value-driven behaviour, and act on their personal morality or decency to 'speak up' for staff and promote constructive employee relations (Anonson et al., 2014; Wing et al., 2015). Such attributions of constructive, progressive or good leadership are usually qualified, however, with attention drawn to the contrasting behaviour of others or the difficulties that admired leaders face in trying to sustain their approach. Positive attributions can co-exist with more negative views of prevailing patterns of leadership, and shift rapidly depending upon ongoing experiences.

All of this underlines the importance of taking distributed leadership seriously and looking at the interplay between concentrated and local leader behaviour. To understand leadership in practice, the various layers of leadership contributions need to be scrutinised together, with attention given to the working out of different inclinations to lead, and to tensions alongside elements of overlapping and complementary activity. The distributed approach breaches the conventional boundaries of leadership studies by calling attention to de facto leader behaviour. It removes hierarchy and formal authority from the list of essential criteria for deciding what counts as leadership. There is nothing in this that undermines leadership research, or renders it impotent by diverting attention onto mundane behaviour, as Alvesson and Spicer (2012) contend. Nor is there any denial that effective leaders have a talent for reading situations, responding to events and influencing people around them. Distributed leadership breaks the linkage between exceptionalism, superiority and legitimate influence that have restricted the impact of traditional leadership theories and related executive development programmes. Instead of giving up on concentrated leadership and formal authority, the writing on distribution poses questions about what is acceptable and effective in the behaviour of official leaders.

Alvesson and Spicer (2012) are also interested in the sort of choices that are available to improve leadership in practice. 'Deliberated leadership' is the label they use to encourage debate about the scope for changing role descriptions, and essentially redrawing the boundary lines between leaders and others. Unfortunately, the value in this seems to be reduced by the application of a rigid dividing line between hierarchical leaders and others. Their discussion is organised around the possibilities for achieving a better or more equitable balance between the necessary activities of formal leaders and alternative 'non-leadership' forms of participative group working and autonomous decision-making. This removes established ideas about team leading and attributions of informal local leadership from their agenda. Employee perceptions about the leadership qualities of influential colleagues (shop stewards, for example), positive or negative, have no obvious significance within this approach to deliberated leadership, making it difficult to understand how the 'non-leadership' element can work, or even engage the interests of those who might be involved. Such practical matters of local leading and the legacy effects of established team interactions seem to be as easily dismissed as distributed leadership itself. The treatment of formal authority is also a worry with deliberated leadership.

Alvesson and Spicer (2010: 384) entertain the possibility that autocratic leadership is appropriate, or likely to be considered so among some people in certain circumstances. The strong probability that this is the unrepresentative view of authority figures who are concerned about defending their prerogatives, or of dominating personalities who project the image that 'they know best', is not an obvious source of concern. However, this jars with the normative side of distributed leadership thinking, which aims to recognise and support talent, initiative and constructive influence wherever it lies within social movements, work organisations and professions. There is an aspiration with much of this literature to rebalance inequalities of influence so that de facto grassroots leadership is not merely acknowledged, but actually strengthened to contain autocratic tendencies and mitigate the effects of authoritarian inclinations. Again, this should not be equated with anti-authority posturing or the permissive use of language, since positional influence is seen as potentially enabling, as well as inhibiting, and likely to benefit from greater accountability (Torrance, 2013; Jones, 2014).

Leadership as initiative and capacity to make a difference may have a positive impact at one level or another, whatever the orientation of those involved and their route into such a role. However, these constructive aspects may co-exist with, or give way to, more conservative, insular, combative and even cliquish tendencies that affect the course of particular initiatives, especially with struggles between official and informal leaders and their supporters. Theoretically, effective leadership development requires a better understanding of how these complex lines of influence are distributed and redistributed as organisational life unfolds.

Accounts which artificially polarise distributed and concentrated leadership are unable to deal with this level of complexity, or evaluate whether exchanges between formal and 'ordinary' leaders open up or actually narrow down the space for distributed influence. The attention that Gronn (2009, 2016) and others (such as Collinson and Collinson, 2009) have given to configurations, blends and hybrids of leadership provides a realistic basis for beginning to address questions of this nature. Distributed influence is accepted as a legitimate focus for leadership research, albeit in combination with concentrated authority and the agency of those who occupy formal positions. An integrated conceptualisation of the different levels and dimensions of leader behaviour is essential for greater accuracy in studies of leadership practice, and for appropriate applied work that can make it more inclusive and less controversial.

Rethinking attributions of leadership

A short review of historical work on hidden (yet effective) leadership will help to develop this argument, and demonstrate the importance of connecting different levels and dynamics of leader behaviour. This involves stepping back from healthcare for a moment to think about the lessons that can be drawn from experiences with resistance leadership, specifically from a path-breaking re-examination of leadership roles in the American civil rights movement of the 1950s and 1960s.

In 1993, Bernice McNair Barnett delivered a compelling alternative history of leadership for social justice in American civil rights, magnifying relational interdependencies between ordinary and official leader behaviour. By contrast with traditional theories and popular attributions of leadership that essentially crudify the processes at work (in this context and beyond), she concentrates on how leaders interact, revealing some telling personal dilemmas and difficult experiences with leading, even when the collective impact is positive. Barnett (1993) challenges familiar impressions of civil rights leadership by giving serious attention to the crucial grass roots influence of southern Black women. Instead of following popular narratives about the great men of the movement, most obviously Martin Luther King Jr. (including Roberts et al., 2008), she fills out the detail of cross-boundary leadership behaviour, posing basic questions about why demonstrably important contributions could ever have been so widely neglected and regularly undervalued.

Barnett identifies a diverse range of women – including domestic workers, teachers, office secretaries, students and sharecroppers – who were de facto leaders on the front line of the civil rights struggles. Few of them moved into formal positions with the various rights organisations that were part of the overall movement, and all of them experienced tensions and difficulties as their initiatives and influence in galvanising cooperation encountered the contrasting and often competing agency of the recognised male leaders. Barnet attributes much of this to chauvinism within the movement, that itself reflected patriarchal traditions in the southern states of the country, and especially ministerial traditions in the Black Baptist Church. Subsequent writers have developed and reinforced this analysis, demonstrating that sexism affects how people differentiate between acknowledged leaders and others who actually perform such roles (West, 2008).

Barnett herself tackles prejudicial notions in earlier historical studies of the civil rights movement, most notably in a book chapter by Payne (1990) entitled 'Men led, but women organized'. Her reaction to this has wider relevance for rethinking attributions of leadership, questioning the distinction here and exposing the jaundiced impressions which lie behind it. For Barnett, organising is as important and elemental to leadership as the exercise of initiative and concern to apply fairly systematic influence, and provides insufficient grounds for classifying the contributions of the women as something less than, or secondary to, the input of men. Indeed, she demonstrates how her 'sisters in struggle' coupled the initiation and organisation of action with the formulation of tactics and the provision of resources to fulfil legitimate leadership roles, and satisfy any reasonable understanding of what leadership actually involves:

> The roles that they performed, whether at the grass roots level or behind the scenes, represent profiles in courage and suggest that they were *leaders* in their communities, *leaders* in the day-to-day fight against various forms of oppression, and *leaders* in the modern civil rights movement. (Barnett, 1993: 177, emphasis in original)

For Barnett, the frontline, informal, hidden and under-appreciated leadership of the women is comparable to the agency of the Black male leaders (1993: 163), amounting to more than complementary, enabling and supporting activities. By this interpretation, effective leadership was distributed throughout the movement and its various initiatives, meaning that successful outcomes are not attributable to leaders at any particular level. The typically recognised leaders were no more decisive in their influence than 'ordinary leaders'. Barnett documents the different levels of leadership in some of the most famous and effective protests of the time to demonstrate this, including the Montgomery Bus Boycott of 1955–56.

Although recognised figures such as Martin Luther King Jr. and Ralph Abernathy are often credited with directing this (since it raised their profile nationally and internationally), it was initiated and actively sustained by Black women who were devising effective fundraising and communication programmes to raise awareness and coordinate the activism, including transportation for the boycotters, for example. JoAnn Robinson and others in the Women's Political Council started the protest by creating flyers calling for the boycott the same day that Rosa Parks was arrested for refusing to give up her bus seat to a white passenger. Georgia Gilmore created the Club from Nowhere to raise money for the boycott by selling food while maintaining the anonymity of supporters, who were likely to experience hostile reactions if their donations were recognised by members of their family or community. Both Robinson and Gilmore paid a high price for their leadership activities, with the loss of employment, the former as an English professor and the latter as a cook. However, their influence and interventions continued to make a difference for the duration of the boycott, along with the contributions of other women. Their roles were not taken over by, nor did they slip in significance by comparison with, the leadership activities of the more prominent ministers, including King, Abernathy and their colleagues in the Montgomery Improvement Association.

Distributed influence remains important within social movements, even as a strategy for resistance leadership. While this book was in development, towards the end of 2019, distributed leadership emerged as an important feature of pro-democracy protests in Hong Kong. These were initially sparked by proposed legislation that would have allowed criminal suspects to be extradited for trial in mainland China. As the protests escalated, innovations were identified in patterns of leadership and organisation, especially when comparisons were drawn with the 'Umbrella Revolution' of 2014, an earlier uprising by democracy activists in Hong Kong. To avoid the difficulties faced by recognised leaders of that movement (who were targeted and jailed by the authorities), the 2019 protesters initiated street demonstrations and organised the occupation of buildings through the use of encrypted messaging applications on mobile phones. Their purpose was to frustrate surveillance technology and protest with greater anonymity, although this produced a fresh and distinctive approach. These protesters were organising their activities in safer and more distributed ways, in the absence of traditional and familiar patterns of concentrated and clearly structured leadership behaviour. As a BBC journalist explained on camera, from the front line of the activism:

> Hong Kong has seen months of protests. These have not been organised by individuals. They've been organised by lots of people online, and tens of thousands have taken to the streets. (Vincent, 2019)

Of course, it is impossible to understand the dynamics of this resistance movement, or to evaluate outcomes realistically, without appreciating the role of concentrated, hierarchical leadership, certainly on the side of officialdom and the Chinese state. Leadership may not be restricted to those in formal positions of authority, although their sense of the situation and decisions about appropriate interventions will undoubtedly have a major impact on the working out of this movement. Relational interdependencies are part of the leadership story, here as elsewhere, magnifying the connection between informed analysis and detailed scrutiny of struggles between leaders at different levels.

Leadership alignment

Gronn commended research on distributed leadership for 'visibilising' important work and piercing through the rhetoric of exceptionalism to expose real world phenomena (2003: 280). Barnett's study exemplifies this quality of grounded and penetrating analysis, providing a valuable corrective to conventional top-driven and frequently overblown accounts of heroic leadership by revealing the important agency of unsung heroes and hitherto neglected or marginalised leaders. She exposes the regular neglect of everyday de facto leadership contributions, demonstrating the positive impact of local leaders in protests that were also undoubtedly strengthened by input from the recognised male leaders.

Barnett's study adds weight to Gronn's investigations into leadership configurations, though reaches further into the analysis of tensions and struggles between formal and local leaders. In addition to documenting the leadership roles of Black women on the front line of the civil rights protests, she exposes the pressures that were often added to their work by the most prominent of formal leaders. Her evidence is very clear on this. These local leaders were making a difference despite the attitudes and behaviour of the men, in a sexist context that made it extremely difficult for them as women to sustain their leadership roles. The configurations of formal and distributed influence were not in tune or particularly well aligned in the civil rights case, although clearly the movement was fundamentally progressive and effective overall.

Available evidence within healthcare points to similar tensions beneath the surface of hybridised leadership contributions. The contextual challenges are highly significant here, with ideas about pre-eminent influence frequently complicating professional relations (Currie and Spyridonidis, 2018). Distributed and hierarchical leadership impulses co-exist, and these can be constructive in some moments and certain areas, while restrictive and even corrosive in others (Beirne, 2017). While empirical studies leave no doubt that frontline nurses and doctors are fulfilling leadership roles jointly and autonomously in a range of specialisms, ongoing pressures to contain this from within professional and organisational hierarchies are considerable (Martin et al., 2015). Studies of nurses' reactions to their experiences with distributed leadership echo Barnett's finding that the constraining effects of concentrated leadership are far more pronounced and obvious to local leaders than complementary tendencies (Beirne, 2017). Empirical evidence suggests that for nurses, like the women at the forefront of Barnett's investigation, ordinary leadership is difficult to sustain and repeatedly contested, as senior figures continue to assert their authority and prerogatives.

Some research on distributed leadership in the education sector concludes that senior figures have a decisive and generally negative impact, even when they express a principled commitment to distribution (Torrance, 2013; Woods, 2016). There is a serious concern that gatekeeping inclinations within established hierarchies will prove to be irresistible, and prompt repeated interventions that frustrate local leaders and curtail their contributions. While this may be a familiar and even typical outcome, inhibiting hybrids are far from inevitable, and are likely to encounter repeated and serious opposition over time. The relational understanding of leadership that is advocated here, and which is entirely consistent with Barnett's study and the industrial relations research noted earlier, denies that the self-empowering agency of local leaders is ever crushed or completely overwhelmed. Indeed, ordinary leaders are often very adept at deploying whatever influence they can muster. As the examples recounted in this chapter demonstrate, the independent pressures that are channelled through grass roots leadership are capable of challenging formal leaders and achieving beneficial outcomes that compensate for executive behaviour that is considered to be unreasonable or gratuitous.

Again, there are signs of this within health organisations. In a study of healthcare innovation, Currie and Spyridonidis (2018) show that nurses confronted difficulties with both senior managers and doctors, yet exercised a practical leadership influence with the diffusion of innovation that was possibly more significant than action taken by their formal leaders. Of course, a conducive alignment of formal and informal elements would be much easier to achieve if authority figures were more consistently supportive and seriously inclined to engage with distributed leadership, either on principle or in response to external influences and pressures from below. The situation facing ordinary leaders is obviously more favourable if such a positive commitment is forthcoming, with executives and senior professionals making a conscious effort to enable local leadership to thrive. So what action does this analysis require? What is to be done? What strategies and programmes can be anticipated to protect the space available for distributed leadership and harness more of the energy and initiative of ordinary leaders?

Promoting constructive configurations

One lingering weaknesses with the overall body of writing on distributed leadership is that applied work to encourage change is underdeveloped. With so much already invested in theory-building and investigative scholarship, there is now scope to follow through on the practicalities of designing viable development projects and instigating responsive action research initiatives. An obvious priority on this front is to devise constructive forms of engagement with current and aspiring positional leaders.

It will be clear from the comments above that formal leaders provide a legitimate target for developmental interventions that are capable of promoting a wider appreciation of distributed leadership. Two particular elements or distinctive lines of development seem appropriate for this, first claiming and then protecting space for ordinary leadership contributions. The former attends to the provision of educational processes for executives and senior professionals, to promote a healthy scepticism of leadership orthodoxy and counteract the propensity to import problematic theories via consultancy contracts and existing markets for business services. The second priority area considers the scope for cultivating conducive conditions and enabling arrangements to support ordinary leaders, and secure more constructive hybrids of positional and local leadership in practice.

Fortunately, research in the critical tradition of leadership studies already provides some guidance to begin filling out the detail of this, and to anticipate what is possible on each front. Studies of established leadership development programmes have exposed the limitations of mainstream approaches, and coupled this with forms of advocacy and means of loosening the grip of traditional assumptions (Carroll and Nicholson, 2014; Gagnon and Collinson, 2014). These reach beyond the basic arguments for more inclusive forms of leadership to anticipate viable ways forward for education and development. Since this alternative agenda has not yet been applied within health organisations, a sense of the potential benefits may be taken, once again, from projects involving resistance leadership.

Alvarez and Alvarez (2018) draw lessons from almost two decades of delivering and revising leader development programmes for trade unionists in the United States. Their reflections about this work reveal a strong commitment to diversity and involving many more women and younger people in union leadership. However, there is also a sense of frustration about the constraints imposed by traditional leadership thinking, within both the unions and the conventional logic of development that informed their early work with practitioners to encourage diversification. This extends to a candid admission that their initial attempts to design programmes in pursuit of equality, inclusion and innovation were inadequate, basically because they relied upon an orthodox competency-based approach to filling gaps in the leadership skills of participants: 'Looking back, we were clearly "training" leaders to be more skilful versions of current labour leaders' (Alvarez and Alvarez, 2018: 509).

These educators and researchers were initially accepting the status quo in leadership development, and reinforcing established preoccupations with positional influence and the orchestration of followers, instead of laying the foundations for change. There is also an admission from Alvarez and Alvarez (2018) that insufficient attention was given, at least at the outset, to shifting attitudes among women and young people, who were more obviously critical of existing hierarchies within trade unions and the directive inclinations of the officials they encountered. While participant resistance to the orthodox approach is not as prominent in this study as the agency of those involved with design and delivery, it provides detailed insights into programme revisions and practical interventions that were devised to nurture critical inclinations and encourage participants to challenge and change leadership practice within their unions. This involved a fundamental shift from the 'mastering' of taken-for-granted skills to experiential and collective learning initiatives that aimed to build confidence in critical thinking and channel this towards leadership reform through the sharing of experiences and strengthening of support networks. Participation was extended beyond union organisations themselves to include people in other organisations, largely from a recognition that quasi-independent group ties are needed to sustain momentum and reduce the danger of non-traditional leadership inclinations being marginalised or dissipated when new leaders return to their own organisations:

> The truly powerful aspect of the program was the space we had created for leaders from across the movement to sit together and learn about and from each other and share strategies . . . We tried to help the participants gauge their own level of leadership in their organisations and in their leadership practices, and differentiated *formal authority* from *influence.* (Alvarez and Alvarez, 2018: 509, 510; original emphasis)

There is significant potential to build on foundational projects such as this, although available reviews of alternative leader development initiatives still need more of a push towards distributed leadership. The interventions reviewed by Alvarez and Alvarez (2018) are clearly focused on developing the next generation of formal union leaders, prioritising matters of access and personal resilience so that well-prepared and innovative young people can deliver change from positions of authority. Ordinary leaders remain out of focus in this, although it is not difficult to imagine a role for them within the sort of extended leadership learning and development networks that are identified. There are regular calls for immersive and contextualised learning in this sort of critical development literature, to counteract the potential for concentrated work with executive peer groups to reinforce elitist tendencies and perceptions about aloofness, insularity or otherness that may exist (Gagnon and Collinson, 2014; Raelin, 2018). Extending the logic of shared or networked co-development to include ordinary leaders provides a potentially powerful means of sensitising senior figures to the consequences of constraining distribution and folly of treating workers as just recipients of leadership.

Carroll and Nicholson suggest that resistance can itself be an effective medium for 'learning *in* leadership as opposed to learning *about* leadership' (2014: 1428). Making leadership development a joint venture between appointed and de facto grass roots leaders could bring attitudes and assumptions that encourage resistance or reticence to the fore, providing opportunities to weaken entrenched views and boundary lines by channelling attention towards respective contributions and the practicalities of building complementary leadership configurations. They also underline the importance of balancing critical engagement with an ethic of care to support participants through development programmes that involve critical self-assessment and potentially challenging group encounters (Carroll and Nicholson, 2014: 1432).

This is a vital consideration, since a critical agenda that promotes distributed leadership may be unsettling and even fraught, especially for senior figures who feel that their core ideas are being undermined or that they have earned the right to be directive. There is also the possibility that ordinary leaders will feel hesitant or vulnerable under these conditions, sensing that they are straying over boundaries that were previously rigid or non-negotiable. Some action research would be valuable to extend the available stock of knowledge on participant reactions to co-development programmes, and also viable support structures that can help people to adjust to the learning process and distributed leadership itself. Separate sessions may be necessary to prepare the ground for joint learning and co-development, although bringing people from different levels of leadership together to experience distributed thinking and envisage constructive configurations (or at least to confront some of the challenges that will arise) is more likely to 'force the issue' and encourage progressive change.

Filling out the detail of the developmental approach anticipated here obviously requires further investigation, and more active engagement with wider groups of practitioners. The primary purpose here is to establish the importance of recognising and extending the reach of distributed leadership through new forms of development. The options identified above are offered to stimulate interest and provide a platform for further applied work that can pull the different strands of supportive scholarship together in a consistent fashion. As much of the writing in this collection demonstrates, distributed leadership is happening despite established leadership theories and development programmes. It could have much wider relevance for leadership learning and practice if executives and senior professionals can be persuaded to be more responsive and accommodate local leaders within formal support structures and decision-making arrangements.

Conclusion

Critical writing about leadership has expanded in recent years, much of it questioning conventional preoccupations with exceptional people, exclusive traits and hierarchical authority. The popular turn towards distributed thinking, in healthcare as elsewhere, demonstrates the importance of accommodating different levels of leadership contribution. It provides an antidote to the limiting preoccupations of conventional research and commentary, while speaking to everyday concerns about the costs and consequences of directive, top-down leaderism in both public and commercial organisations (O'Reilly and Reed, 2010; Francis, 2013; Keogh, 2013). Distributed leadership opens a door to fresh possibilities, exploring how distinctive hybrids of positional and local leadership are configured, and potentially reconfigured, through the agency of multiple leaders in specific situations under particular conditions.

Connecting the scholarship of Gronn and Barnett provides a powerful means of demonstrating the significance of these leadership alignment issues, 'visibilising' hidden contributions (Gronn, 2003), exposing tensions between different levels of leadership behaviour, and also struggles to address these. Leadership emerges from this as a more inclusive and fluid phenomenon, as something that is embedded in collective processes rather than linked tightly to position, status or formal recognition. It is distributed rather than concentrated, shifting instead of restricted to a special category of people who are best placed to occupy (or be cultivated to fulfil) official leadership roles. There are undoubtedly people who exude charisma or convey a sense of credibility that helps them to influence others, though not all the time or in predictable ways, and they are not always called leaders or consider themselves to be involved in exercising leadership.

Despite this injection of realism into discussions of leader behaviour, more constructive combinations of distributed and concentrated leadership are unlikely to emerge, or last, without an alternative developmental approach that is capable of de-stabilising the status quo. This means resisting the exceptionalism that permeates traditional thinking, at the same time cutting demand for established approaches to leadership development. Inequalities of influence need to be rebalanced so that ordinary leadership is taken seriously. The alignment of formal and grass roots leadership agency merits attention at the centre of leader development programmes, with a basic recognition and positional support agenda for current and aspiring leaders, alongside enabling arrangements that can help ordinary leaders to feel less vulnerable and more confident about this aspect of their practice. Despite the attention that distributed leadership has captured, it currently represents an undervalued and underdeveloped potential in practitioner education and leadership reform, certainly in healthcare. Pressure on the old orthodoxy will need to be sustained if this is to change, and leadership is really to be appreciated as something that wider populations of professional and other workers can demonstrate and collectively enhance.

Key concepts discussed

- This chapter established the value of leadership learning from non-traditional sources in social movements, rather than relying on lessons from work organisations, political institutions and commercial ventures. Changed in response to question from editorial services. Work organisations, political institutions and commercial ventures.

- Leadership can exist even where there is no official or easily identifiable authority figure.
- There are different types of leader: official, approved, ambitious, ideological, conservative; and also unofficial, informal, accidental, occasional, reluctant, reactionary (and more); and none of them have a monopoly on wisdom, insight, principled behaviour, innovation, constructive creativity, progressive practice or effectiveness.
- It is important to recognise hidden leadership and the influence of unsung heroes.
- It is impossible to understand the nature and appreciate the impact of leadership behaviour without accounting for the interdependent agency of leaders at different levels and with contrasting objectives.
- Local leaders can have a significant impact on organisational behaviour, whether positively or negatively, despite directive inclinations and restrictive tendencies within the formal realms of leadership.
- Concentrated positional leaders also have an important bearing upon the extent and conduct of distributed leadership via degrees of constraining or enabling influence.
- The alignment of distributed and formal leadership roles and relationships is a pressing concern for progressive work towards more effective forms of leader development.

Key readings

- Barnett, B. (1993) Invisible southern Black women leaders in the civil rights movement: The triple constraints of gender, race and class, *Gender and Society*, 7 (2): 162–182.
  This landmark historical study challenges taken-for-granted impressions and misconceptions of leadership, claiming space in dramatic fashion for a more inclusive understanding and revision of prevailing approaches to leader support and development.
- Currie, G. and Lockett, A. (2007) A critique of transformational leadership: Moral, professional and contingent dimensions of leadership within public service organisations, *Human Relations*, 60 (2): 341–370.
  This article provides a compelling account of the weaknesses with orthodox leadership thinking and a clear indication of the logic of critical leadership studies.
- Gronn, P. (2009) Leadership configurations, *Leadership*, 5 (3): 381–394.
  Gronn is one of the most influential and reflective commentators on distributed leadership. In this paper, he candidly reviews the development of scholarship in this area, modifying prominent lines of argument and setting out a broader agenda for developmental initiatives and contributions. He continues this work in 'Fit for purpose no more?' (2016), which is included in the references below.

Examples of applied research and developmental studies

- Alvarez, S. and Alvarez, J. (2018) Leadership development as a driver of equity and inclusion, *Work and Occupations*, 45 (4): 501–524.
- Carroll, B. and Nicholson, H. (2014) Resistance and struggle in leadership development, *Human Relations*, 67 (11): 1413–1436.
- Gagnon, S. and Collinson, D. (2014) Rethinking global leadership development programmes: The interrelated significance of power, context and identity, *Organization Studies*, 35 (5): 645–670.

Useful websites

- The King's Fund: https://www.kingsfund.org.uk/
  Provides a range of literature and advice sheets on leadership in healthcare, including advocacy on distributed leadership.
- NHS Leadership Academy: https://www.leadershipacademy.nhs.uk/
  A developmental agency, offering programmes and resources, including a Healthcare Leadership Model that aims to be inclusive and relevant, even for health workers who are not in formal leadership roles.
- The Leadership Conference on Civil and Human Rights: https://civilrights.org/about/history/
  With a history dating back to the American civil rights struggles of the 1950s, this coalition of activist interests and resources both reveals and reflects the challenges of leading progressive change.

References

Alvarez, S. and Alvarez, J. (2018) Leadership development as a driver of equity and inclusion, *Work and Occupations*, 45 (4): 501–524.

Alvesson, M. and Spicer, A. (2012) Critical leadership studies: The case for critical performativity, *Human Relations*, 65 (3): 367–390.

Anonson, J., Walker, M., Arries, E., Maposa, S., Telford, P. and Berry, L. (2014) Qualities of exemplary nurse leaders: Perspectives of frontline nurses, *Journal of Nursing Management*, 22 (1): 127–136.

Atzeni, M. (2009) Searching for injustice and finding solidarity? A contribution to the mobilisation theory debate, *Industrial Relations Journal*, 40 (1): 5–16.

Barnett, B. (1993) Invisible southern Black women leaders in the civil rights movement: The triple constraints of gender, race and class, *Gender and Society*, 7 (2): 162–182.

Beirne, M. (2017) The reforming appeal of distributed leadership: Recognising concerns and contradictory tendencies, *British Journal of Healthcare Management*, 23 (6): 262–270.

Beirne, M., Hurrell, S. and Wilson, F. (2019) Mobilising for equality? Understanding the impact of grass roots agency and third party representation, *Industrial Relations Journal*, 50 (1): 41–56.

Carroll, B. and Nicholson, H. (2014) Resistance and struggle in leadership development, *Human Relations*, 67 (11): 1413–1436.

Collinson, D. and Collinson, M. (2009) Blended leadership: Employee perspectives on effective leadership in the UK further education sector, *Leadership*, 5 (3): 365–380.

Currie, G. and Spyridonidis, D. (2018) Sharing leadership for diffusion of innovation in professionalized settings, *Human Relations*, 72 (7): 1209–1233.

Darlington, R. (2018) The leadership component of Kelly's mobilisation theory: Contributions, tensions, limitations and further development, *Economic and Industrial Democracy*, 39 (4): 617–638.

Francis, R. (2013) *Report of the Mid Staffordshire NHS Foundation Trust Public Enquiry: Executive Summary*, London: HMSO. Available at: https://www.gov.uk/government/publications/report-of-the-mid-staffordshire-nhs-foundation-trust-public-inquiry (accessed 14 October 2020).

Gagnon, S. and Collinson, D. (2014) Rethinking global leadership development programmes: The interrelated significance of power, context and identity, *Organization Studies*, 35 (5): 645–670.

Gronn, P. (2003) Leadership: Who needs it?, *School Leadership and Management*, 23 (3): 267–291.

Gronn, P. (2008) The future of distributed leadership, *Journal of Educational Administration*, 46 (2): 141–158.

Gronn, P. (2009) Leadership configurations, *Leadership*, 5 (3): 381–394.

Gronn, P. (2016) Fit for purpose no more?, *Management in Education*, 30 (4): 168–172.

Jones, S. (2014) Distributed leadership: A critical analysis, *Leadership*, 10 (2): 129–141.

Keogh, B. (2013) *Review into the Quality of Care and Treatment Provided by 14 Hospital Trusts in England: Overview Report*, London: HMSO.

Martin, G., Beech, N., MacIntosh, R. and Bushfield, S. (2015) Potential challenges facing distributed leadership in health care: Evidence from the UK National Health Service, *Sociology of Health and Illness*, 37 (1): 14–29.

McKee, L., Charles, K., Dixon-Woods, M., Willars, J. and Martin, G. (2013) 'New' and distributed leadership in quality and safety in health care, or 'old' and hierarchical? An interview study with strategic stakeholders, *Journal of Health Services Research and Policy*, 18 (suppl. 2): 11–19.

O'Reilly, D. and Reed, M. (2010) Leaderism: An evolution of managerialism in UK public service reforms, *Public Administration*, 88 (4): 960–978.

Payne, C. (1990) Men led, but women organized, in V. Crawford, J. Rouse and B. Woods (eds.) *Women in the Civil Rights Movement*, New York: Carlson, 1–12.

Raelin, J. (2018) What are you afraid of? Collective leadership and its learning implications, *Management Learning*, 49 (1): 59–66.

Roberts, D., Roberts, L., O'Neill, R. and Blake-Beard, S. (2008) The invisible work of managing visibility for social change: Insights from the leadership of Reverend Dr. Martin Luther King Jr, *Business and Society*, 47 (4): 425–456.

Torrance, D. (2013) The challenges of developing distributed leadership in Scottish primary schools: A catch 22, *Education*, 41 (3): 330–345.

Vincent, D. (2019) Click, *BBC News*, 15 September.

West, T. (2008) Gendered legacies of Martin Luther King Jr.'s leadership, *Theology Today*, 65 (1): 41–56.

Wing, T., Regan, S. and Spence Laschinger, H. (2015) The influence of empowerment and incivility on the mental health of new graduate nurses, *Journal of Nursing Management*, 23 (5): 632–643

Woods, P. (2016) Authority, power and distributed leadership, *Management in Education*, 30 (4): 155–160.

Zoller, H. and Fairhurst, G. (2007) Resistance leadership: The overlooked potential in critical organization and leadership studies, *Human Relations*, 60 (9): 1331–1360.

6 Theorising leadership development: From executive solutions to more active cultivation of contemporary roles and capabilities

Vivienne Byers

Chapter topics

- Developing the concept of distributed leadership in healthcare practice
- The logic of distributed leadership
- Distributed leadership development initiatives in terms of roles and capabilities
- Strategies for improving role distribution and leadership practices
- Benefits of distributed leadership development
- Problems associated with neglect of distributed leadership practice

Introduction

This unique book has set out the extant literature on distributed leadership in healthcare. This chapter builds upon this work by reframing leadership as a distributed concept from a practice perspective, involving those with particular skills and abilities across multiple institutional levels, rather than a traditional hierarchical 'concentrated' phenomenon. According to Martin et al. (2015), the arguments in favour of distributed leadership in healthcare are unequivocal, in improving quality and safety and for the wellbeing of patients, professionals and the health system itself. So much so, that distributed leadership has been adopted across systems, including as a key strand of policy in the UK National Health Service.

Researchers agree that there is no established definition of distributed leadership (Currie and Lockett, 2011). Thorpe et al. define distributed leadership 'as a variety of configurations which emerge from the exercise of influence that produces interdependent and conjoint action' (2011: 241). A framework is useful to review research on its enactment or practice within healthcare. Fitzgerald et al. (2013) advance an understanding of distributed leadership with three core components. This is based on the levels and roles of the potential actors within healthcare organisations and comprises: senior leaders with the capability and interest to support change, credible opinion leaders at middle levels, and individuals who are willing to engage in change efforts. Then, following Nzinga et al. (2018), to look at how these actors co-create a shared understanding of their interactions to examine distributed leadership. They describe in their study how the functions that are played can create a constellation, where each individual member plays distinct roles and all members work together. They use distributed leadership to frame the process of leadership as a co-construction of shared meaning and action to accomplish common objectives.

Although distributed leadership in healthcare delivers change and improvement, few studies have examined how it is enacted (Currie and Lockett, 2011). This chapter seeks to explore the how, who and where of practice to examine distributed leadership beyond a theoretical conceptualisation and to attend to required roles and capabilities. The logic of distributed leadership that underpins practice is addressed, and in particular its enactment in terms of the co-construction of shared meaning and action in context. The concluding section of this chapter comments on the consequences of neglecting distributed leadership in healthcare practice.

Developing the concept of distributed leadership in healthcare practice

The wider literature on distributed leadership looks at the practice of leadership differently from a work-based perspective by '*illuminating the possibilities for organisational transformation*' (Harris and Spillane, 2008: 33, emphasis added). The concept of distributed leadership in healthcare practice has continued to develop over the last decade (Bolden, 2011). Bolden's literature review considered the similarities and differences between distributed leadership and related leadership concepts, including 'shared', 'collective', 'collaborative', 'emergent', as well as 'co-' and 'democratic' leadership. Although, there is a common basis to these concepts, the usage and understanding of these terms varies across health systems, sectors and countries. Bolden notes that research in distributed leadership practice in healthcare is of proportionally more interest to researchers in the UK than in the US. He also notes that those in the UK or based in the education sector refer to it as distributed, whilst those in the US or in the healthcare sector often refer to it as shared or collective leadership.

Earlier work on distributed leadership in healthcare was carried out by Denis and colleagues in Canada (Denis et al., 1996, 2001). They emphasised that there is a significant influence from outside agencies, through externally imposed professional work arrangements and government policy, on the enactment and development of distributed leadership. They examined how this particular context frames the interactions of leadership actors or agents. Healthcare organisations face fragmented and often contradictory external and internal pressures that are more influential than the pressures faced by other types of organisations (Chreim et al., 2010). In Mintzberg's (1993) seminal typology, a healthcare organisation is classified as a professional bureaucracy characterised by many varied and competing groups. It relies on the skills and knowledge of health professionals to function and to produce services. Typical health professionals such as doctors, nurses and social workers are governed by professional bodies that subscribe to different views and have varying and often competing interests (Byers, 2019). In rationing of resources, these professionals exercise discretion and decision-making power, and in so doing are considered not only to have autonomy and leadership responsibilities, but to have policy-making powers too (Lipsky, 2010). In delivery of services, they also possess professional expertise that sets them apart, both from the patients they serve and the general managers who manage them. Rather than a concentrated view of authority, this type of segmentation in healthcare creates a 'pluralistic domain' of multiple agents, pursuing different objectives in changeable relationships (Denis et al., 2001: 809). Thus, being complex in nature healthcare organisations require that strategic leadership roles are shared, with each member of a leadership constellation playing a distinct role, and all members working together to drive change. It is a difficult task to manage internal as well as external stakeholders to agree a change agenda. Chreim et al. (2010) advise enacting distributed leadership where different constituencies can share in change agency roles.

Currie and Lockett (2011) review the influence of complex social, political and power relations in a healthcare context on the enactment of different conceptions of distributed leadership. A number of considerations are required to develop this distribution, which include autonomy in service delivery, self-regulation for the professional core of staff and changing a culture of hierarchy, which is paternalistic and can limit change beyond powerful professional groups. The external influence of the policy context with an emphasis upon performance management and accountability can also push leadership towards concentration rather than distribution.

West and Lyubovnikova (2013) argue that the concept of distributed leadership is particularly apposite in healthcare because the delivery of high-quality care is dependent on the effective collaboration and communication between individuals and groups, which is critical to team working. Healthcare delivery requires the coordination of contributions from a range of different disciplines at different levels as well as patients. According to Ezziane et al. (2012: 429), teamwork and the ability to both lead and follow within teams in healthcare is not optional, but the only way to deliver care that is person-centred. Cultivating teamwork leads to improved patient outcomes and patient satisfaction. Thus, distributed leadership can be seen as especially suitable for healthcare contexts (King's Fund, 2011, 2012).

However, while distributed leadership is regarded as important in healthcare, in terms of change and improvement there is limited consideration of how it is enacted on the ground (see, for example, Denis et al., 2001). Benington and Hartley (2010) argue that solving complex cross-cutting problems requires whole systems thinking, joined up policy-making and service delivery, as well as less concentrated patterns of leadership. Distributed leadership addresses the interconnections between issues, negotiates coalitions between different stakeholders, manages inter-organisational networks and partnerships, pulls together disparate resources to serve a common purpose and achieve positive measurable outcomes for citizens, communities and other stakeholders.

The logic of distributed leadership

The core logic of distributed leadership is compelling – it requires engaging multiple agents in a complex organisation in order to solve complex problems through 'concertive' action. Gronn (2002) identifies two dimensions by which distributed leadership can be distinguished from other forms of leadership: concertive action and conjoint agency. He argues that distributed leadership is 'the multiplicity or pattern of group functions' of leaders and to the many roles constituting leadership (Gronn, 2002: 429). In this sense of distribution, the behaviour which is the unit of analysis is concertive action, rather than the sum of individual acts. Essentially, it refers to institutionalised levels of collaboration and the sharing of leadership roles in work groups (Martin et al., 2015). This is achieved through collaborative modes of engagement, the intuitive understanding that develops as part of working relations among colleagues, and a variety of institutionalised arrangements, which approach regularising distributed action. These represent sequential stages in a process of institutionalisation. However, individuals constituting the membership of the units act conjointly. Conjoint agency means that agents synchronise their actions by having regard to their own plans, those of their peers, and their sense of unit membership. This concept relates to the nature and quality of interactions among individuals in work groups.

Currie and Lockett (2011) aver that researchers need to move beyond a reified concept of distributed leadership and ask how power is actually distributed, what it accomplishes and what is its rationale. Gosling et al. (2009) suggest that distributed leadership draws attention to the large number of actors involved in leadership, the importance of organisational processes in shaping that engagement, but that it has limited use as an analytical heuristic. Instead, it has a number of rhetorical functions that make a significant contribution to the way in which leadership is accomplished. Bolden (2011: 257, citing Bennett et al., 2003) identified three underlying premises of distributed leadership (which are not contested in the literature):

- Leadership is an emergent property of a group or network of interacting individuals.
- There is openness to the boundaries of leadership.
- Varieties of expertise are distributed across the many, not the few.

However, the logic of distributed leadership may not be that simple. A number of authors have questioned its underlying function. Martin and Learmonth (2012) cite a small but increasingly influential body of work termed critical leadership studies (see also Ford et al., 2008; Grint, 2010) which questions the rhetoric of the benefits of distributed leadership. They contest that it can be seen as a narrative to engage different professional groups in organisational reform such as modernisation and performance improvement. To conclude, Oborn et al. (2013) argue that distributed leadership, at its simplest, includes the ability to acknowledge the strengths of others and to identify where they are more suited or able to fulfil a role. To conclude this section, the logic of distributed leadership is as an intuitive approach and an emergent process. It evokes an aspiration for the way leadership is configured, and draws attention to iterative 'relations between leadership, followership and context' (Currie and Lockett, 2011: 286).

Why and how have governments promoted distributed leadership in the public sector?

Denis et al. (2007) outline the case for a more dispersed and collective leadership approach in public organisations. They argue that in order to achieve change and development in such organisations, there needs to be a recognition of the informal and complex dynamics as the basis for sustaining legitimacy. Answering 'why' governments have promoted distributed leadership in the public sector begins with the imperative of managing complex organisations with diffuse power structures, divergent objectives and burgeoning rules. One perspective taken by governments has been to facilitate an entrepreneurial approach in the public sector allowing creative and innovative professionals to respond to problems and service demands (e.g. Health Canada, 2015), as well as to limit the power or opportunistic behaviour of autonomous leaders (Denis et al., 2007). Distributed leadership has been adopted as a key strand of policy in the UK National Health Service (Martin et al., 2015). This political focus had been driven by a series of scandals, including the failings in the Mid Staffordshire NHS Foundation Trust. The two Francis inquiries reported these failings, highlighting serious deficiencies in the standard of patient care and raised questions about the leadership and culture of frontline services in the NHS (Francis, 2010, 2013). The underlying assumption of these distributed leadership initiatives is that perceived failings in the service and their solutions can be attributed to a leadership deficit, which needs to be remedied in organisations (Thorpe et al., 2011).

In terms of the 'how' of promoting distributed leadership in the public or health sector, a succession of distributed leadership initiatives in the UK have looked to improve organisational and clinical effectiveness through attending to the nature, role and attributes of leaders and leadership (Martin et al., 2015). These initiatives included the establishment of the NHS Leadership Academy, sponsorship of clinical leadership research and reports on leadership from the Academy of Medical Royal Colleges and the King's Fund (2011, 2012). The King's Fund has argued for leadership with partnership arrangements that devolve decision-making to doctors and nurses (King's Fund, 2011). They have developed competency frameworks in the NHS, outlining the nature of leadership roles in which doctors and other clinicians are expected to participate. These are based on distributed or shared leadership principles that have been defined by the NHS Leadership Academy as 'an activity that is shared or distributed among members of a team that will underpin this way of working' (2011: 7).

Distributed leadership: Leader development initiatives in terms of roles and capabilities

The question many health practitioners ask is, how is distributed leadership put in to practice, or as Harris and Spillane enquire, how is leadership '*distributed, by whom and with what effect*'? (2008: 32, emphasis added). Their work poses a number of key questions, such as how – and in what form – distributed leadership contributes to improvement and is there evidence to show that lateral, less hierarchical staff structures result in gains in organisational performance? These questions focus primarily on how leadership is distributed, and which patterns of distribution are the most effective or influential and provide a framework for analysing leadership practice. To tease out the learning from these initiatives in terms of roles and capabilities, one must be cognisant that distributed leadership is not something done by an individual to others, or a set of individual actions through which people contribute to their organisation – it needs to be explored both within an organisational context and as enacted by individuals. It is group action working through and within relationships, rather than individual action, that we must attend to in research and practice (Bolden, 2011). This group action includes building relationships, networking, trust, commitment within social and political contexts, and their influence on certain leadership styles and practices (Fulop, 2012). To be successful, distributed leadership needs to connect directly with the experiences and aspirations of leadership practitioners, within the context of organisational power and politics (Bolden, 2011). However, a limited number of relevant studies have explored how it is enacted in healthcare (Currie and Lockett, 2011; Marles, 2017). The following sections review some of these leader development initiatives in the literature to tease out leadership roles and to consider the capabilities required.

In reviewing practice-oriented papers, a number of different conceptions of distributed leadership are identified. Martin and colleagues' (2015) adaptation of Thorpe, Gold and Lawler's (2011) matrix illustrates different configurations of distributed leadership based on two dimensions. The first dimension is whether distributed leadership is a planned, top-down process used by management to create concertive action with more centralised influence, or whether it is emergent, as a consequence of bottom-up activities. The second dimension is whether distributed leadership practice is aligned or misaligned, whereby individuals across the organisation act with a common or differing purpose. Thus, the papers in this section can be grouped according to their approach: (1) emergence of roles and capabilities (bottom up); (2) management-driven and/or supported development of roles and capabilities (top down); as well as (3) a more focused approach to development of distributed roles and capabilities in the organisation.

Emergence of distributed leadership roles and capabilities

One group of development initiatives reported in the literature, examining the emergence of distributed leadership, make some observations about how roles and capabilities are revealed. In their qualitative study, Buchanan et al. (2007) reviewed service improvements in the treatment of prostate cancer at an acute hospital. They examined how change roles were distributed more widely and influenced by change goals, as well as by the organisational context through which services were delivered. They describe the emergence of distributed leadership from triggers in the organisational and wider environments, such as changes in government or organisational regulations and/or policies. The roles that the practitioners played were similar to those seen in an innovation process with players engaging and disengaging over time in different roles. They posit that the lesson for the practice of distributed leadership is that it is advantageous not to have a dedicated change agent, and thus to encourage fluid and migratory responsibilities by having 'nobody in charge' (Buchanan et al., 2007: 1086).

Another study tracking the emergence or evolution of distributed leadership over time is that of Chreim et al. (2010) in relation to primary care in Canada. Their study tracked the development and the evolution of the change agency roles of individuals and groups over two phases of a service integration change initiative over a four-year period. Change agency can best be described as change leaders who lead organisational change efforts and may design, direct, influence, facilitate or persuade others to accomplish activities in support of change initiatives (Burke, 2005). The first stage involved setting up the change project in terms of creating a coalition, visioning the plan and establishing supporting structures. The key practitioners involved at this stage included physicians, regional health authority (RHA) managers, the provincial government, the project coordinator and the integration team. At the second stage, where the programme was more fully developed and focused on change implementation, it also included RHA personnel across different levels in the organisations and nurse practitioners. The findings revealed that the leadership of change could not be attributed to any specific agent. The leaders identified in the project did not identify themselves as leaders; instead, distributed leadership occurred in action, which was more emergent and spread out both vertically and horizontally across the levels and organisations. As change progressed, individuals needed to adapt their roles. Similar to Buchanan and colleagues' (2007) case study, Chreim et al. detailed the fluid emergence of responsibilities and roles. They described the emergence of distributed leadership as requiring 'a movement from abstraction to concretization of the change and from adoption of a macro perspective to a local view' (Chreim et al., 2010: 198). Their attention to roles and capabilities focused on the role of the practitioner as a change agent situated in an organisational context and having influence, as well as the importance of the coalition of agents themselves. They suggest that the capabilities required of practitioners are collaborative skills and mindsets that transcend limited professional and organisational boundaries.

Management supporting development of distributed leadership roles and capabilities

A number of studies have addressed management support from higher up the hierarchy in enabling enactment of distributed leadership. In their case study of an initiative in healthcare, Boak et al. (2015) tracked the change from autonomous working to a team-based approach with greater distributed leadership. They noted a crucial part of the change was the granting of authority by management to those team members who were willing to engage in the change efforts. Teams were given responsibilities and resources to develop their own ways of working, including allotted time, IT system access and appropriate service delivery information to enable them to make decisions and give them an active leadership role with support from the wider organisation. However, the authors focused on the influence of context and the emergence of distributed leadership, rather than on roles and capabilities. Positive factors for change included the setting of a small department with a narrow clinical focus and a recognised problem that needed to be addressed. In terms of staff capabilities, they noted the importance of a positive attitude and willingness to engage.

Günzel-Jensen et al. (2018) looked at the role of formal leadership styles and organisational efficacy on the development of distributed leadership. Based on large-scale survey data from a study at a Scandinavian public hospital, the researchers found that all the leadership styles used by senior managers had a significant positive impact on employees' perceived agency in distributed leadership. They noted the importance of formal leaders in enhancing employee involvement in leadership functions. However, the researchers also noted that employees sought to participate in leadership functions when they perceived that the organisation was struggling to achieve its goals. Though a number of studies view management support and senior leadership as an important factor to inculcate distributed leadership in organisations, initiatives also emerged from bottom-up situations, where healthcare professionals deem there are organisational issues that remain unsolved (Byers, 2017).

Developing distributed leadership roles and capabilities

A number of other distributed leadership initiatives have taken a more focused look at roles and capabilities, include that of Chreim and MacNaughton (2016). They found that distributed leadership in healthcare teams results in leadership constellations or groups, where leadership role overlaps and gaps can arise creating ambiguity. The lessons from their review are that it is important to recognise areas of overlap and gaps in leadership roles and to provide clarity about role boundaries. These researchers suggest that role mapping exercises and open discussions need to be considered. Furthermore, spreading formal leadership responsibilities informally among individuals is not always a workable strategy for addressing team needs. Crucially, organisations need to examine the allocation of resources for leadership activities if they are to be successful. Another study looking at enactment of distributed leadership was conducted in Kenyan hospitals (Nzinga et al., 2018). The authors emphasised how context, power and inter-professional relationships moderated each individual's ability to bring about change. They found that using a distributed leadership lens revealed that, although medical and nursing leadership occurred in parallel, only doctors in leadership roles were able to directly influence behaviour among their own colleagues. The leadership roles played by individuals were influenced by local culture and accepted norms. Structures within healthcare organisations and medical professional dominance affected how leadership was practised, rather than any particular individual capabilities.

Fitzgerald et al. (2013) also focused on medical professional engagement. They referred to the influential leadership roles performed by medical hybrids in facilitating change in healthcare. They described these hybrids as medical professionals who move from their clinical role to take on managerial responsibilities. These healthcare professional/managerial hybrids can perform crucial lateral facilitation activities, adapting and extending their roles to suit their organisational context (see also Fulop, 2012; Burgess and Currie, 2013). Fitzgerald et al. (2013) found that senior management created a vision and enabled people to achieve it.

Then, general managers acted as change drivers, initiating and implementing collaborative change with external and internal stakeholders. This in turn facilitated the medical hybrids to adopt change leadership roles. The researchers reported that a definite plan of change and assigning responsibilities did not work and was not always practical. Instead, there was a need for flexibility and to respond to priorities as they evolved. The authors identified a number of capabilities that successful medical hybrids should possess, including knowledge of national standards and awareness of local needs, being able to work collaboratively and adapt services to fit circumstances, as well as to customise evidence-based medicine and policy standards. So although the above studies referred to role enactment they did not clarify their boundaries, and instead reviewed the influence of organisational context.

In contrast, Jønsson et al. (2016) set out to measure distributed leadership agency in a hospital context through the development and validation of an instrument that measures employees' active participation in tasks. Using a unidimensional questionnaire of seven items (derived from meta-categories of leadership behaviour) across sixteen different occupational groups, they found that distributed leadership agency was positively related to self-efficacy, job satisfaction and innovative behaviour. Chief physicians, permanent employees and employee representatives scored higher on the scale than the rest of their colleagues. The authors concluded that the field of distributed leadership lacks research that focuses on leadership from the viewpoint of the individual as an agent. Their contribution to assessing roles and capabilities in distributed leadership is that the questionnaire directly asks employees – not leaders – about their active participation in leadership tasks. They tapped into experiences of active involvement in different leadership tasks.

Improving role distribution and leadership practices

In light of the limited work focusing on developing role distribution and leadership practices, the question remains: how can organisations improve this development? Pearce (2004: 55) contends that organisations need to (1) ascertain when leadership is most appropriately distributed, (2) determine how distributed leadership is developed, and (3) attend to how both vertical and distributed leadership is utilised to leverage the capabilities of knowledge workers. In addressing the first point, Chreim et al. (2010) pointed to the importance of distributed leadership in certain contexts where there already is devolution of authority and where social capital is more prevalent through positive pre-existing relationships between management and professional groups. They suggest that building a winning coalition of individuals with complementary skills and resources allows distributed leadership to emerge. The implication for practice is the importance of time invested in finding common ground and building trust. Chreim et al. also advise that a key leader or champion is more successful in managing the change process than asking overburdened healthcare practitioners, because of possible dilution of focus and loss of momentum. The researchers noted that, as change progressed in their study, individuals needed to be able to adapt their roles.

This movement from visioning to implementation requires a development from abstraction to implementation of the change and moving from a macro perspective to a local view.

In addressing the second point, how distributed leadership is developed, Marles (2017) advises building capacity. Her research was completed in an aged care service in Australia, and employed a longer-term approach investing time in developing linkages required to create the conditions for staff to exercise distributed leadership. She provided a practical example of an evidence-based organisational development approach designed to introduce distributed leadership. The focus was on improving resident care and organisational efficiency. In terms of developing leadership practice, a 'sensemaking' approach was employed to make sense of the concept of distributed leadership as it applies to practice. This sensemaking process was facilitated through the use of action research. The important consideration was developing self-reflection within staff, and building in support from management. Interestingly, the study also identified that a dedicated change agent was required to maintain the impetus in developing distributed leadership.

Finally, addressing the third point, how to utilise both vertical and shared leadership to leverage the capabilities of knowledge workers, Oborn et al. (2013: 255) note that there is a poor understanding of 'how' and 'why' collaborative styles are enacted and he cites the approach taken in education, in how leadership should be 'stretched over' individuals, beyond the formal leader. He emphasises that it is useful to examine interactions as they unfold in relation to specific tasks (following Spillane et al., 2001) – in other words, addressing the end goal rather than the means. However, can this be applied in the healthcare context? (Currie and Lockett, 2011). There is a need to be cognisant of the importance of the social, political and power relations within healthcare organisations in order to improve both vertical and shared leadership and to leverage the capabilities of individuals (Gosling et al., 2009). McKee et al. (2013) suggest that in order for distributed leadership to operate effectively, individuals require infrastructural administrative support and/or positional power to influence and lead others. They note that having legitimacy and credibility with a range of local actors was important, but it needs to be supported by management. It is crucial that organisations allocate resources to these leadership activities.

Other authors have suggested using leadership coalitions or constellations to support, influence and maintain change (Denis et al., 2001; Golden, 2006). However, Chreim et al. (2010) did not show support for the use of a constellation, mainly because the leaders that were identified did not see themselves as leaders. They found instead that the development of distributed leadership in their study spread out emergently both vertically and horizontally across levels and the organisations and was less deliberate than a constellation.

Benefits of distributed leadership development

Researchers have identified patterns of distributed leadership linked to delivering improvements in both service and patient outcomes, as well as professional satisfaction and organisational and service innovation (Chreim et al., 2010;

Fitzgerald et al., 2013; Currie and Spyridonidis, 2019). Service improvement has been identified as a key benefit of distributed leadership in terms of healthcare delivery. This is defined by Fitzgerald et al. as a 'planned and targeted effort to improve patient-facing outcomes from a service, whether process outcomes, such as throughput, or final outcomes, such as treatment' (2013: 228). It can reduce costs and improve clinical outcomes through more effective decision-making (McKee et al., 2013). Many researchers have found that well-developed hybrid roles are associated with better patient outcomes through devolved responsibility and autonomy (Chreim et al., 2010; Fitzgerald et al., 2013; Currie and Spyridonidis, 2019)

Distributed leadership also benefits greater professional work satisfaction through collective endeavour, where knowledge, ideas and influence are shared and where all staff have responsibility for leading in service development (McKee et al., 2013). It is seen as significant in improving and maintaining the quality of services (Ezziane et al., 2012; West and Lyubovnikova, 2013). Martin and Learmonth (2012) note that distributed leadership is positively associated with both individual and group satisfaction, retention and performance. A number of studies of distributed leadership show a positive link between autonomy, working life quality and organisational performance (Cleary et al., 2011; Tomlinson, 2012), as well as supporting a collaborative leadership process for highly skilled health professionals to mitigate resistance to change (Oborn et al., 2013).

Distributed leadership has a supporting role in the diffusion and adoption of innovation. Senior managers are important in promoting and supporting innovation, but more powerful healthcare professionals (e.g. physicians) play a significant role in engaging their peers, influencing resource allocation and adapting innovation to local context. Currie and Spyridonidis's (2019) healthcare study focused on leadership configurations in the process of diffusion of innovation. They found practices of distributed leadership with interdependent working of hierarchical managerial or professional influence, which encouraged innovation diffusion. However, shaping this shared leadership requires contingencies such as organisational financial performance, whether nurses enact hybrid leadership roles and whether the organisation is hierarchical or collaborative.

Problems associated with neglect of distributed leadership in practice

Patterns of widely distributed leadership can be associated with greater service improvement, and with incomplete patterns being associated with limited progress (Fitzgerald et al., 2013). Healthcare organisations present particular challenges for distributed leadership because structural power is all-pervasive (Currie and Lockett, 2011). In this context, the ability to draw together a powerful coalition with both internal and external actors is crucial, otherwise the organisation can become fragmented through health professionals disconnecting and remaining in disciplinary silos (Martin et al., 2015). This in turn limits effective organisational communication. Distributed leadership initiatives were instigated as a means of reviving poorly performing public-service organisations in response to the failings in service delivery overseen by a concentrated hierarchical leadership (Thorpe et al., 2011). Some of the outcomes from this initiative were to increase organisational integration and effectiveness through communication and staff empowerment. A lack of distributed leadership may lead to poor organisational culture, a lack of wider engagement and organisational commitment, decreased autonomy and being unable to fully leverage the skills and knowledge of staff (Bartels, 2005). This lack of distributed leadership facilitates a culture of managerial control with a focus on ill-informed performance targets, which in turn undermine quality-driven, person-centred care delivery (Halligan, 2013).

Conclusion

A distributed leadership perspective recognises the inclusive and collaborative nature of the leadership process (Oborn et al., 2013). This is particularly apposite where frontline work is accomplished by highly trained and educated healthcare professionals. This chapter has reviewed the logic and practice of leadership development initiatives in healthcare and the neglect of distributed leadership and what this might involve. Field research on distributed leadership in healthcare is still at an early stage, but the papers reviewed in this chapter suggest that there are positive outcomes from implementing distributed leadership. This approach has received support from healthcare professionals (Cleary et al., 2011; Currie and Spyridonidis, 2019). Byers (2017) concurs that health professionals are interested in a democratic governance model since this allows them to lead from the front line and participate in practice-driven change with colleagues, within a strong supportive environment with multi-stakeholder participation.

Finally, Chreim and colleagues' (2010) findings indicate the concept of distributed leadership is too important to ignore in managing complex healthcare organisations. McKee et al. (2013) suggest that distributed leadership may be most effective when blended with conventional concentrated leadership for healthcare quality and safety. However, Harris (2008) explains that this blending from a distributed perspective should mean that leadership is grounded in activity, rather than a position or role, and in practical terms requires facilitation from higher up the hierarchy through the creation of internal conditions for it to thrive. The authors suggest that academic research would benefit more from the experience of those who work in organisations that have traditional structures and power relationships.

Key concepts discussed

- Academics and practitioners outline the concept of distributed leadership distinguishing between traditional hierarchical 'concentrated' leadership associated with particular positions, and distributed leadership involving those with particular skills and abilities across multiple institutional levels.
- Researchers identify a pattern of distributed change leadership linked to delivering improvements in service and patient outcomes.
- Professional/managerial hybrids perform crucial lateral facilitation activities, adapting and extending their roles in response to their organisational context.

- Practitioners and managers need to consider areas of overlap and gaps in leadership roles and to provide clarity about role boundaries to avoid ambiguity.
- A foundation of good pre-existing staff relationships underpins the capacity of distributed leadership to implement service improvements.
- Organisations need to examine critically the allocation of resources and support to leadership activities.

Key readings

- Chreim, S. and MacNaughton, K. (2016) Distributed leadership in health care teams: Constellation role distribution and leadership practices, *Health Care Management Review*, 41 (3): 200–212.
  This paper outlines how distributed leadership in healthcare results in leadership constellations that cause leadership role overlaps and gaps creating ambiguity within teams. The authors provide guidance on how to distribute authority through role-mapping exercises and open discussions.
- Chreim, S., Williams, B.B., Janz, L. and Dastmalchian, A. (2010) Change agency in a primary health care context: The case of distributed leadership, *Health Care Management Review*, 35 (2): 187–199.
  This paper provides examples of studies in distributed leadership undertaken in primary care settings
- Currie, G. and Lockett, A. (2011) Distributing leadership in health and social care: Concertive, conjoint or collective?, *International Journal of Management Reviews*, 13 (3): 286–300.
  This paper examines different conceptualisations of distributed leadership, and analyses the influence of a health and social care context on attempts to enact distributed leadership.

Examples of studies

- Fitzgerald, L., Lilley, C., Ferlie, E., Addicott, R., McGivern, G. and Buchanan, D. (2006) *Managing Change and Role Enactment in the Professionalised Organisation*, London: NCCSDO.
- Fitzgerald, L., Ferlie, E., McGivern, G. and Buchanan, D. (2013) Distributed leadership patterns and service improvement: Evidence and argument from English healthcare, *Leadership Quarterly*, 24 (1): 227–239.
- Martin, G., Beech, N., MacIntosh, R. and Bushfield, S. (2015) Potential challenges facing distributed leadership in health care: Evidence from the UK National Health Service, *Sociology of Health and Illness*, 37 (1): 14–29.

Useful websites

- The King's Fund: https://www.kingsfund.org.uk/projects/review-leadership-nhs
  Provides reviews and information on studies in Leadership in healthcare
- NHS Leadership Academy: http://www.leadershipacademy.nhs.uk/resources/

References

Bartels, J.E. (2005) Educating nurses for the 21st century, *Nursing and Health Sciences*, 7 (4): 221–225.

Benington, J. and Hartley, J. (2010) Knowledge and capabilities for leadership across the whole public service system, in S. Brookes and K. Grint (eds.) *The New Public Leadership Challenge*, London: Palgrave Macmillan.

Bennett, N., Wise, C., Woods, P.A. and Harvey, J.A. (2003) Distributed Leadership: A Review of Literature. *National College for School Leadership*: London. Available at http://oro.open.ac.uk/8534/ (accessed 9 July 2020)

Boak, G., Dickens, V., Newson, A. and Brown, L. (2015) Distributed leadership, team working and service improvement in healthcare, *Leadership in Health Services*, 28 (4): 332–344.

Bolden, R. (2011) Distributed leadership in organizations: A review of theory and research, *International Journal of Management Reviews*, 13 (3): 251–269.

Buchanan, D.A., Addicott, R., Fitzgerald, L., Ferlie, E. and Baeza, J.I. (2007) Nobody in charge: Distributed change agency in healthcare, *Human Relations*, 60 (7): 1065–1090.

Burgess, N. and Currie, G. (2013) The knowledge brokering role of the hybrid middle level manager: The case of healthcare, *British Journal of Management*, 24 (suppl. 1): S132–S142.

Burke, W.W. (2005) Implementation and continuing the change effort, in W.J. Rothwell and R.L. Sullivan (eds.) *Practicing Organization Development: A Guide for Consultants*, San Francisco, CA: Pfeiffer.

Byers, V. (2017) The challenges of leading change in health-care delivery from the front-line, *Journal of Nursing Management*, 25 (6): 449–456.

Byers, V. (2019) Across the borders of scholarly communities, in P.L. Hupe (ed.) *Research Handbook on Street-Level Bureaucracy: The Ground Floor of Government in Context*. Cheltenham: Edward Elgar.

Chreim, S. and MacNaughton, K. (2016) Distributed leadership in health care teams: Constellation role distribution and leadership practices, *Health Care Management Review*, 41 (3): 200–212.

Chreim, S., Williams, B.B., Janz, L. and Dastmalchian, A. (2010) Change agency in a primary health care context: The case of distributed leadership, *Health Care Management Review*, 35 (2): 187–199.

Cleary, M., Horsfall, J., Deacon, M. and Jackson, D. (2011) Leadership and mental health nursing, *Issues in Mental Health Nursing*, 32 (10): 632–639.

Currie, G. and Lockett, A. (2011) Distributing leadership in health and social care: Concertive, conjoint or collective?, *International Journal of Management Reviews*, 13 (3): 286–300.

Currie, G. and Spyridonidis, D. (2019) Sharing leadership for diffusion of innovation in professionalized settings, *Human Relations*, 72 (7): 1209–1233.

Denis, J.-L., Langley, A. and Cazale, L. (1996) Leadership and strategic change under ambiguity, *Organization Studies*, 17 (4): 673–699.

Denis, J.-L., Lamothe, L. and Langley, A. (2001) The dynamics of collective leadership and strategic change in pluralistic organizations, *Academy of Management Journal*, 44 (4): 809–837.

Denis, J.-L., Langley, A. and Rouleau, L. (2007) Rethinking leadership in public organizations, in E. Ferlie, L. Lynn and C. Pollitt (eds.) *The Oxford Handbook of Public Management*, Oxford: Oxford University Press.

Ezziane, Z., Maruthappu, M., Gawn, L., Thompson, E.A., Athanasiou, T. and Warren, O.J. (2012) Building effective clinical teams in healthcare, *Journal of Health Organization and Management*, 26 (4): 428–436.

Fitzgerald, L., Ferlie, E., McGivern, G. and Buchanan, D. (2013) Distributed leadership patterns and service improvement: Evidence and argument from English healthcare, *Leadership Quarterly*, 24 (1): 227–239.

Ford, J., Harding, N. and Learmonth, M. (2008) *Leadership as Identity*, Basingstoke: Palgrave Macmillan.

Francis, R. (2010) *Independent Inquiry into Care Provided by Mid Staffordshire NHS Foundation Trust, January 2005–March 2009 (The Francis Report)*. London: The Stationery Office. Available at: https://www.gov.uk/government/publications/independent-inquiry-into-care-provided-by-mid-staffordshire-nhs-foundation-trust-january-2001-to-march-2009 (accessed 19 October 2020).

Francis, R. (2013) *Report of the Mid Staffordshire NHS Foundation Trust Public Enquiry: Executive Summary*, London: HMSO. Available at: https://www.gov.uk/government/publications/report-of-the-mid-staffordshire-nhs-foundation-trust-public-inquiry (accessed 19 October 2020).

Fulop, L. (2012) Leadership, clinician managers and a thing called 'hybridity', *Journal of Health Organization and Management*, 26 (5): 578–604.

Golden, B. (2006) Transforming healthcare organizations, *Healthcare Quarterly*, 10 (special issue): 10–19.

Gosling, J., Bolden, R. and Petrov, G. (2009) Distributed leadership in higher education: What does it accomplish?, *Leadership*, 5 (3): 299–310.

Grint, K. (2010) The sacred in leadership: Separation, sacrifice and silence, *Organization Studies*, 31 (1): 89–107.

Gronn, P. (2002) Distributed leadership as a unit of analysis, *Leadership Quarterly*, 13 (4): 423–451.

Günzel-Jensen, F., Jain, A.K. and Kjeldsen, A.M. (2018) Distributed leadership in health care: The role of formal leadership styles and organizational efficacy, *Leadership*, 14 (1): 110–133.

Halligan, A. (2013) The Francis report: What you permit, you promote, *Journal of the Royal Society of Medicine*, 106 (4): 116–117.

Harris, A. (2008) Distributed leadership: According to the evidence, *Journal of Educational Administration*, 46 (2): 172–188.

Harris, A. and Spillane, J. (2008) Distributed leadership through the looking glass, *Management in Education*, 22 (1): 31–34.

Health Canada (2015) *Unleashing Innovation: Excellent Healthcare for Canada. Report of the Advisory Panel on Healthcare Innovation*, Ottawa: Health Canada. Available at: http://www.healthycanadians.gc.ca/publications/health-system-systeme-sante/report-healthcare-innovation-rapport-soins/alt/report-healthcare-innovation-rapport-soins-eng.pdf (accessed 9 January 2020).

Jònsson, T., Unterrainer, C., Jeppesen, H.J. and Jain, A.K. (2016) Measuring distributed leadership agency in a hospital context: Development and validation of a new scale, *Journal of Health Organization and Management*, 30 (6): 908–926.

King's Fund (2011) *The Future of Leadership and Management in the NHS: No More Heroes*, London: The King's Fund.

King's Fund (2012) *Leadership and Engagement for Improvement in the NHS*. Available at: http://www.kingsfund.org.uk/publications/leadership-engagement-for-improvement-nhs (accessed 31 March 2020).

Lipsky, M. (2010) *Street-Level Bureaucracy: Dilemmas of the Individual in Public Services*, 30th anniversary expanded edition, New York: Russell Sage.

Marles, K. (2017) *Distributed leadership: Building capacity to maximise collaborative practice in a new teaching research aged care service*, Doctor of Business Administration thesis, Fremantle: University of Notre Dame Australia. Available at: https://researchonline.nd.edu.au/theses/157/ (accessed 26 February 2020).

Martin, G. and Learmonth, M. (2012) A critical account of the rise and spread of 'leadership': The case of UK healthcare, *Social Science and Medicine*, 74 (3): 281–288.

Martin, G., Beech, N., MacIntosh, R. and Bushfield, S. (2015) Potential challenges facing distributed leadership in health care: Evidence from the UK National Health Service, *Sociology of Health and Illness*, 37 (1): 14–29.

McKee, L., Charles, K., Dixon-Woods, M., Willars, J. and Martin, G. (2013) 'New' and distributed leadership in quality and safety in health care, or 'old' and hierarchical? An interview study with strategic stakeholders, *Journal of Health Services Research and Policy*, 18 (2 suppl.): 11–19.

Mintzberg, H. (1993) *Structure in Fives: Designing Effective Organizations*, Englewood Cliffs, NJ: Prentice-Hall.

National Health Service (NHS) Leadership Academy (2011) *The Leadership Framework*, Warwick: NHS Institute for Innovation and Improvement. Available at: http://www.leadershipacademy.nhs.uk/wp-content/uploads/2012/11/NHSLeadership-Leadership-Framework-Clinical-Leadership Competency-Framework-CLCF.pdf (accessed 31 March 2020).

Nzinga, J., McGivern, G. and English, M. (2018) Examining clinical leadership in Kenyan public hospitals through the distributed leadership lens, *Health Policy and Planning*, 33 (suppl. 2): ii27–ii34.

Oborn, E., Barrett, M. and Dawson, S. (2013) Distributed leadership in policy formulation: A sociomaterial perspective, *Organization Studies*, 34 (2): 253–276.

Pearce, C.L. (2004) The future of leadership: Combining vertical and shared leadership to transform knowledge work, *Academy of Management Perspectives*, 18 (1): 47–57.

Spillane, J.P., Halverson, R. and Diamond, J.B. (2001) Investigating school leadership practice: A distributed perspective, *Educational Researcher*, 30 (3): 23–28.

Thorpe, R., Gold, J. and Lawler, J. (2011) Locating distributed leadership, *International Journal of Management Reviews*, 13 (3): 239–250.

Tomlinson, J. (2012) Exploration of transformational and distributed leadership, *Nursing Management*, 19 (4): 30–34.

West, M.A. and Lyubovnikova, J. (2013) Illusions of team working in health care, *Journal of Health Organization and Management*, 27 (1): 134–142.

7 General nursing practice through the lens of distributed leadership: A case study

Phil Halligan and Catherine Clune Mulvaney

Chapter topics

- Concept of distributed leadership in practice
- Types of distributed leadership appropriate to general nursing
- The context of general nursing practice

Introduction

This chapter uses a case study to illustrate how distributed leadership (DL) can be effectively utilised by general nurses in the acute healthcare environment. Hospitals are busy, complex organisations, where professionals with a diverse range of skills and expertise make life and death decisions as part of their roles. Healthcare professionals collaborate across specialities, disciplines, departments and healthcare organisations both internally and externally. Furthermore, healthcare settings are an intricate network of communications and relationships. Kotter (2003) argues that as the healthcare industry becomes more competitive and unpredictable with ever-changing regulatory guidelines, leadership will become the mainstay for setting future direction, aligning and motivating people, and inspiring change. It is argued however that leadership in acute healthcare environments is different from that found in other jurisdictions due to the myriad of entrenched professional bureaucracies (Burns et al., 2011).

The importance of leadership in professional nursing practice is well recognised with modules on leadership firmly embedded across all programmes at undergraduate and graduate levels. Nurses at every level are expected to exercise leadership (Institute of Medicine, 2011). Given that nurses and midwives account for nearly 50% of the healthcare workforce globally (WHO, 2020a), they are ideally positioned to lead on initiatives promoting enhanced care delivery, contribute to the quality improvement agenda and the delivery of safe, interprofessional care.

The chapter will highlight how many of the key components within Gronn's (2002) and Spillane's (2006) models of DL (see Table 7.1) can be effectively employed as a leadership framework by nurses in clinical practice, particularly in

Table 7.1 Key components of Gronn's (2002) and Spillane's (2006) models of distributed leadership

Gronn (2002)	Spillane (2006)
Fusion between 'hierarchical and heterarchical' elements	Practice focused
Individual leaders are equally significant and co-exist with collective forms of leadership	Leader, follower and situation
Numerical-concertive actions – formal and informal leaders, may take up leadership individually or jointly	Multiple individuals function as leaders – the leader-plus aspect and leadership is generated from interactions in practice
No fixed pattern – distributed leadership evolves over time and differs from one context to the next	Four patterns: collaborative, collective, coordinated and parallel

the development and implementation of quality improvement initiatives. We suggest that this approach can be potentially transferred across all professional groups. The chapter views leadership from the perspective of a collective notion, rather than the traits and behaviours of an individual, with consideration of the activities in an organisation related to improving patient outcomes.

But first, we provide a brief overview of general nursing practice in an Irish context.

General nursing practice

Nursing is a human endeavour in which nurses seek to make a difference in people's lives and person-centred care is a key principle guiding nurses in their role (Peate, 2019). During their career, nurses work with colleagues from many disciplines who are part of a wider team supporting the care of patients. Nursing encompasses autonomous and collaborative care of individuals of all ages, families, groups and communities, sick or well and in all settings. Advocacy, the promotion of a safe environment, research, helping shape health policy, contributing to patient and health systems management, and education are also key nursing roles (International Council of Nurses, 2010). Before registering as a general nurse, each student must demonstrate the competencies for critical analysis, problem-solving, decision-making, collaborative team working, leadership, professional scholarship, effective interpersonal communication and reflection that are essential to the art and science of nursing (NMBI, 2020).

In the past decade, healthcare in Ireland has attracted much attention in the media, partially due to the increase in costs and concerns over the overall quality of care delivery. The number of health inquiries and the profusion of healthcare errors have prompted many questions into the functioning of organisations and the actions required to ensure effective care delivery. Effective leadership is crucial to implementing the necessary changes and shaping the environment into a safe and quality-driven one (Department of Health and Children, 2008). Nurses are uniquely positioned to address this as they provide hands-on care, twenty-four hours a day, seven days a week and have a duty of care to safeguard people in their care under their code of professional conduct and ethics (NMBI, 2014).

When people are hospitalised, they are at their most vulnerable (Burns et al., 2011). The first healthcare professionals they are likely to encounter and spend the greatest amount of time with are nurses; together with other healthcare providers, patients depend on nurses for their recovery (Institute of Medicine, 2011). However, challenges with nursing staff recruitment and retention have been shown to impact on the quality of care delivery, with suboptimal care and patient safety to the forefront of health policy agendas internationally (WHO, 2020b). Whitby (2018) posits that the behaviour of frontline nurses is a major determinant of patients' healthcare experience and their perception of the quality of care they receive. Frontline leaders in healthcare settings are professionals with the strongest and most immediate influence on staff behaviour and patient outcomes. Therefore, registered general nurses are well placed to improve care if they have appropriate leadership behaviours that embody teamwork and shared decision-making, while simultaneously being supported with training and an empowering culture. The nurse's ability to make independent clinical decisions, enact change and work within their expanded scope of practice concerning patients in their care (Kramer and Schmalenberg, 2003) requires an appropriate style of leadership. However, many reports to date have emphasised that the system is too complex for leadership to be entrusted to one individual with recommendations promoting the distribution to all employees (Institute of Medicine, 2004). The notion of concentrated leadership in the hands of a single person (for example, Clinical Nurse Manager or Director of Nursing) may be obsolete in today's healthcare environment (Gronn, 2000; Spillane, 2006). The inclusion of nurses in decision-making has benefits for all:

- Since nurses work closely with patients and families, they have better information and expertise as to 'what works' and 'what does not work' for the patient,
- Nurse participation in decision-making leads to a greater sense of efficacy and job satisfaction.
- Greater commitment or 'buy-in' to decisions will ultimately support any innovation and change.
- The more people involved in decision-making, the better chance of making the best possible decision.

Distributed leadership in healthcare

Historically, research and theory development have focused predominantly on leader-centric leadership that conforms to a list of characteristics, behaviours and outcomes of the work of a single individual. The traditional perspective of a single leader suggests that the leadership function is a specialised role that cannot be shared without jeopardising group effectiveness. This view represents most hierarchical leadership in which the leader directs all activities (Ensley et al., 2003). However, the dominance of individualised conceptions of leadership has been increasingly challenged, resulting in a movement towards re-defining leadership in more collective terms. In these approaches, leadership occurs with actions, stretching across different agents, all of whom can exert influence on the situation (Ross et al., 2005). Those who view leadership as a shared process argue that 'important decisions about what to do and how to do it are made through the use of an interactive process that involves many different people who influence each other, not by a single person' (Yukl, 1998: 3).

Distributed leadership is not a new area of research and much of the research to date has taken place in the educational sector and schools in particular. Recently, the conceptual models of Spillane et al. (2004) and Gronn (2000, 2002) have received a lot of attention in the literature. Within these models of DL, leadership is conceptualised as an important aspect of daily tasks and interactions between employees (Günzel-Jensen et al., 2018). Distributed leadership emerged as a result of the development of flatter structures and vertical organisations requiring greater interdependence and coordination (Gronn, 2002).

Distributed leadership, as a term, is closely related to a family of terms that includes participative leadership, delegated leadership, democratic leadership, dispersed leadership and shared leadership. Despite these terms invoking similar interpretations, Harris (2007) asserts that in contrast to shared leadership, distributed leadership is essentially about practice, not people. Many definitions of DL have been offered in the literature. Bennett and colleagues' (2003) review of definitions pointed out that the primary challenge in the research was the absence of an explicit and commonly accepted definition of the concept. In its early conceptualisation, DL was mainly perceived as an analytical lens to observe the interactions among people when they enacted leadership work (Bennett et al., 2003). Definitions often adopted a structural view to examine 'the distribution of resources and responsibilities, cultural ideas and values, as well as social relations' (Woods et al., 2004: 450). In contrast, studies of agency examined the actions and interactions of people in taking initiatives, making choices and participating in leadership work. Woods et al. (2004) explicitly pointed out that distributed leadership had both structural and agential dimensions and that in practice these two dimensions would often work together. Distributed leadership focused on examining various kinds of social interactions in schools. It perceived leadership as an emergent characteristic created by social interactions. Thus, traditional leadership theories that related positional leaders and organisational effectiveness were openly challenged. Gronn (2003), Spillane et al. (2004) and Spillane (2006) have stated that any school member and even artefacts can exert leadership influence on activities, not just the 'official' leader. Thus, researchers aimed to capture key tasks, actors, actions and interactions of distributed leadership.

From a distributed perspective, leadership takes shape in the interactions of people and their situation, rather than the actions of an individual leader. Essentially, it is about practice rather than leaders, leadership roles or leadership functions, and leadership practice is at its core. Leadership practice is not equivalent to the actions of one appointed person or some other leader and the critical issue from a distributed perspective is not that leadership is distributed, but *how* it is distributed across leaders, followers and their situation.

The extent to which leadership is shared or dispersed is likely to take one of the two following forms: *aggregated* or *holistic* (Gronn, 2002). An *aggregated* pattern of DL is one in which many individuals, on different occasions, as part of different activities, for varying periods, and a variety of reasons, are believed by their colleagues to exercise leadership. Within this pattern, leadership is taken to mean influencing others to do what they might not otherwise have done, i.e. agents are willing to be influenced. They are, so to speak, free agents who are not constrained in their decision-making. The individuals to whom influence is attributed include all members of the organisation not just managers in a position of authority (Gronn, 2002). In contrast, a *holistic* pattern is taken to mean that, when the parts are combined to form a whole, the result is a functioning unit with a unique structural integrity that acts back on the parts themselves. It is the relationship which determines how they think and act as individual persons – for example, the partnership between a director of nursing and a Clinical Nurse Manager, or between Clinical Nurse Managers at different levels can be viewed as working together in synergy. Two other types of distribution are also identified – *coordinated* and *collective* distribution. In a *coordinated* distribution situation, leaders work separately or together on different leadership tasks that are arranged sequentially. In a *collective* distribution situation, leadership is stretched over the practice of two or more leaders who work separately but interdependently. The actions of two or more leaders working separately generate leadership practice.

While a paucity of research has been published regarding distributed leadership in healthcare (Chreim et al., 2010; Fitzgerald et al., 2013; Günzel-Jensen et al., 2018), nursing as a profession shares many similarities with teachers in educational settings, as both professions are service-orientated practice disciplines, utilising significant 'people skills' to interact with a cross-section of professionals and the population. Also, both professions are predominately female and anyone seeking a career in either profession is required to be educated to degree level 8. Thus, DL practices potentially can align effortlessly with disciplines within healthcare and the professional practice environment given that DL is considered a more sustainable approach in the contemporary complex and fast-changing world (Hargreaves and Fink, 2000). Its associated characteristics of (1) *collaboration* rather than a hierarchical structure; (2) *a shared purpose*; (3) *shared accountability and responsibility*; (4) and the *building of leadership capacity amongst the members of a group or organisation* (West-Burnham, 2004; Marshall, 2006) will also be familiar to, and sit comfortably with, the working practices of healthcare professionals. The recognition of leadership irrespective of role or position within an organisation provides opportunities for nurses and other healthcare professionals – with the appropriate expertise – to initiate quality improvement initiatives and enhance the delivery of patient-centred healthcare. Such activities foster the building of trust, the creation of a learning culture, and the sharing and dissemination of information (Brown and Littrich, 2008), all of which are key characteristics of both DL and the continuous quality improvement environment of healthcare. Interdependence and coordination have also been identified by Gronn (2003) as key features of DL, which, unsurprisingly, are key characteristics in interdisciplinary working arrangements in healthcare.

We now present a case study and undertake an analysis of DL practices through the prism of Spillane's (2006) and elements of Gronn's (2002) model of DL identified previously in Table 7.1. In addition, elements of DL as identified by Woods et al. (2004) will be used to illuminate the various but important practices within the case study.

Case study

The case study was completed by a registered nurse working in an interventional radiology department of a large, tertiary, urban, academic, acute hospital in Ireland. The initiative was undertaken in the context of a quality improvement project and further details can be accessed in the literature (Farrell and Halligan, 2017).

Background: Interventional radiology (IR) is a rapidly expanding specialty within medicine. Patients, who are often frail and elderly, are discharged from an IR department with a drainage device in situ (for example, gastrostomy, cholecystostomy, abscess, nephrostomy, biliary) to primary care (community home but frequently to their residence). Currently, there is a shift away from conventional open surgery using general anaesthesia, to safer percutaneous approaches in IR using local anaesthetic and conscious sedation, in most cases allowing same-day patient discharge. Thus, patients are fast-tracked and treated as a day case and discharged with drainage devices in situ for either curative or preventative purposes. As a result, a new cohort of patients has emerged requiring nursing care from nurses (Public Health Nurses and Community Nurses) working in the primary care setting that would not have been encountered before.

Initiation: A problem was identified relating to the patient discharge care – mainly fragmentation in care. The IR department was receiving numerous phone calls from patients, family members and nurses in the community with queries or concerns regarding the drains. Adverse events often saw patients returning to the IR department or being readmitted via the emergency department, increasing patient discomfort, staff workload and costs. Problems have arisen with the drains as they have the potential to become displaced, blocked, break or fall out, or the surrounding skin can become inflamed or excoriated if not cared for appropriately. A registered nurse who was directly involved in the care of patients in the radiology department took the 'extraordinary' step of assembling a team whose members were directly involved in the care of the patient in the department and the primary care setting. The goal was to resolve the issue and enhance the patient's care journey as they transition from an IR department to the community and to improve the quality of nursing care delivered to patients with IR drains in both the acute and community care settings. Over three months, the registered nurse assembled a team to include: one Clinical Nurse Manager 1 and Clinical Nurse Manager 2, and representatives from the nursing staff, the medical staff, Public Health Nurses and Community Nurses. This process aimed to explore and possibly develop a way forward to alleviate the issues emerging from patient discharges and to develop a clear plan to enhance the patients' transitioning experiences to the community.

Implementation: To begin, an audit was undertaken over the three months of the number of queries via the telephone from the community regarding the IR drains, resulting in an average of five calls per week, totalling approximately sixty phone calls in that short period. A workshop was held in the department and in the community to elicit the problems from each of the stakeholders' viewpoints. Workshops were audio-recorded, and field notes were taken by an observer present. Participants were also invited to submit feedback via Google forms on how they had found the experience of receiving patients with a drainage device in situ. Six nurses from the IR department and community (Public Health and Community Nurses) were interviewed to elicit their views on the discharge process.

Overall the problems identified were as follows:

- There was a gap in their knowledge of IR due to the new and expanding specialty, an inability to provide appropriate patient support, lack of knowledge-sharing among community nurses and family members about IR drains.
- Transfer of care: there were inadequate discharge summaries, a lack of communication and information on patient transfer, a lack of standardised patient-specific information, a lack of a written policy and online information, and a lack of a Public Health Liaison Nurse.
- Education and training was required for patient and family in some format, education of community nurses about the theory and skills of managing IR drains and how to troubleshoot any problems.

Outcomes achieved: As a result of participating in this collaborative project, feedback from the service providers and service users reported a greater awareness and understanding of each other's needs and expertise and greater willingness to cooperate with each other in the future. Queries were reduced and as hospital and community services had not previously worked together, this initiative resulted in improved working relationships and a deeper understanding of each other's service needs was reported. Outcomes included a formal training and awareness workshop, a written hospital policy, patient-specific discharge summaries in the form of a patient 'passport', improved patient and family education leaflets, the introduction of IR into education programmes/modules and a clinical rotation in the IR department.

Application of distributed leadership models

As a collective agency, it incorporated activities of many internal and external individuals who worked collaboratively in a process of change whereby positive outcomes of care emerged. Spillane and colleagues' (2004) framework considers leaders as individuals who work together to improve care. Followers are the individuals who are influenced by the leaders to improve the process of discharge planning. However, they are not fixed but dynamic and fluid whereby a leader is leading on one task and a follower on another activity. Thus, in this case, leadership is extended to all service providers other than the Clinical Nurse Managers. As well as the leaders which Spillane refers to as 'the leader-plus aspect', the role of followers is vital in shaping the interaction that occurred. The leader influences the followers and vice versa enhancing their knowledge, expertise and shaping their practice. Spillane also includes the situation as another important element of distributed leadership and shifts the focus from

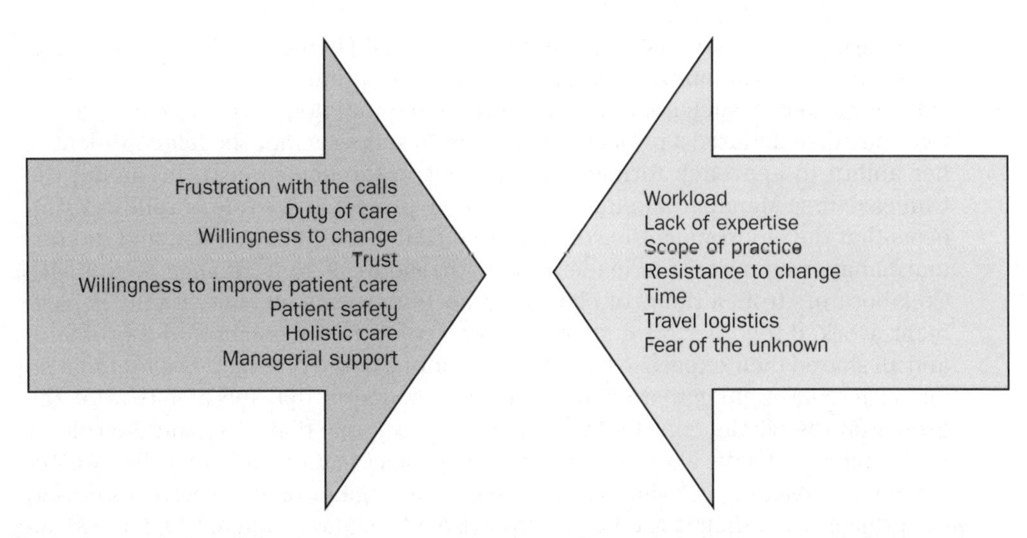

Figure 7.1 Push and pull factors

positional leaders to a web or network of leaders, followers and their situations that give rise to leadership practices. The situation encompasses organisational tools, routines and structures, and in this case study the environment of care. Situation and practice are intertwined closely in DL and often the situation will enhance or inhibit the development of the leaders' actions, motivation and ability. Spillane and Diamond (2007) warn of the need to identify the aspects of the situation that may interfere with the practices. In this case study, many were noted (see Figure 7.1).

The social elements of the interrelationships were also noted. Teams of service providers bring an array of capabilities and experiences that shape the environment and complement the leadership practices and assist in securing the quality improvement initiative. Furthermore, it facilitated the engagement of multiple groups and the establishment of a shared vision for patient care. Spillane (2006) identified three categories of leadership practice distribution: collaborative, collective and coordinated. This case study meets the criteria of coordinated distribution and elements of the other two – collaborative and collective distribution – are evident. Coordinated distribution is where leadership practices are formed by tasks completed sequentially and this can be completed independently or together for the tasks to be performed. In this case, elements of leadership practices were completed by some hospital nurses and others by the community nurses. Collaborative distribution is where two or more leaders work together in the same place to accomplish the same leadership practice; this element was achieved by conducting the audit in the hospital where the queries originated. Finally, collective distribution involves leaders working towards a shared leadership separately but their actions are interdependent; this is illustrated by all of the members (hospital and community) working separately but interdependently on the hospital policy for patients being discharged to the community.

Many of the characteristics mentioned previously in the chapter are evident in the case study. The nurse who initiated the quality improvement project was a staff nurse and as such not a formal leader in the radiology department. The fact that the nurse initiated a project independently suggests that she felt confident in her ability to approach formal management in the department. Involving the Clinical Nurse Manager and Radiologist in the project in the role of follower suggests that the environment is collaborative rather than hierarchical and the formal manager supported the 'leader-plus' with resources (time, finance, personnel). Collaborators from a range of clinical areas, both within and outwith the department, worked together for a shared vision (i.e. to find a solution to a problem) and all shared their expertise to identify solutions to the problem. The fact that so many outcomes emanated from this project suggests that the members of the group, on the whole, contributed constructively to the dialogue, and the role of leader-plus may have alternated among the project team members as the project developed, resulting in 'followers' taking on the member-plus role at times during the project when they shared their expertise, ideas and insights. Given the scale of the research, the duration and the success of the project, it is reasonable to suggest that the majority of the stakeholders shared a strong sense of accountability and responsibility in keeping with their professional code of conduct. The inclusion of a patient representative could have strengthened and enhanced the overall project outcomes and contributed to the public-engagement and involvement agenda.

The literature on DL also highlights many important dimensions. In a systematic review of distributed leadership, Woods et al. (2004) identified key variables about distributed leadership: they include openness to boundaries, emergent property, and leadership and expertise. A brief discussion of these dimensions will now be provided as they further highlight the practices of DL within this case study.

Openness to boundaries

Openness to boundaries of leadership (Woods et al., 2004) is a key feature in DL. In this case study, the staff nurse was able to orchestrate ways to include all key stakeholders (Clinical Nurse Managers, Public Health Nurses, Radiologists) in the resolution of the problem. Using organisational routines (meetings) and tools (audit), the staff nurse was able to establish direct links between key leadership activities (discharge planning) and community care. Spillane and Diamond (2007) refer to these routines and tools as boundary practices and boundary objects and are a key component of leadership practice.

In general, the lead nurse (leader-plus) made every effort to include everyone in the development process. The extension of decision-making to nurses beyond the acute hospital was more limited and this may be as a result of resources (time, logistics of travelling). Involving the staff in primary care and the radiology department created many opportunities to widen the net of leaders. The boundaries can however be as wide as necessary. Collaborative meetings with the staff allowed for the boundaries of leadership to expand beyond the immediate area and allow for collaboration. Furthermore, the boundary was more of an interface where key information and issues were exchanged between the practice and the community.

Although one staff member took the lead, everyone played a significant leadership role and made an important contribution by having a voice in the change. The individual grew into the position of leadership as she was not appointed to it. There was no hierarchy and accountability was to the community as a whole not to any individual in particular. Authority was specific to the project and ended when the project closed. In this case, leadership was shared and stretched across two main domains of healthcare. This also served to widen the scope of the leadership team to include members of the wider community. The result of this interaction between the leaders, followers and their situation created interdependence of thinking and actions, facilitating better care and contributing to a culture of trust, change and quality improvement.

Emergent property

Distributed leadership sees leadership as an emergent property of a group or network of interacting individuals (Woods et al., 2004). It is shaped by the evolving interactions of various leaders at different times and in different situations. There is a need for 'give and take' between leaders and followers. Leadership, as in this case study, was more organic and less hierarchical than traditional approaches, what Gronn (2002) refers to as 'conjoint activity' or 'concertive action'. The need for nursing practice to build leadership capacity is always warranted. Clinical Nurse Managers are overburdened with many responsibilities. Expanding the scope of their work to everyone within the unit is welcomed.

Within this case study, leadership emerged at a local level. A staff nurse had the opportunity to enact change and bring about an improvement in practice and was interested in providing leadership in the area of practice improvement. The aggregated effect or 'conjoint activity' of several individual contributions to service improvement and expertise was manifested in different ways. Working in this way allowed for the pooling of expertise which is more productive than any individual actions. The practice of distributed leadership can lead to a change in culture by facilitating the development of trust, commitment and transparency within the team. Furthermore, it serves to reinforce and encourage professionals, working within their scope of practice to feel confident in the expertise they contribute to the achievement of the organisation's goals.

Leadership and expertise

General nursing by its very nature requires all nurses to be competent and each nurse is responsible for identifying concerns about their competence under the Nurses and Midwives Act 2011 (Government of Ireland, 2011, Part II 87(1)). In this case study, the leadership function was stretched over the work of a number of individuals (internal and external), and the task was accomplished through interaction and collective action. In addition, community nurses were proactive in seeking the expertise of their colleagues concerning the management of indwelling drainage devices. This in effect calls for the expertise of other colleagues at various times. It also allowed for the anchoring of leadership practices as the expertise was spread across a range of individuals. The result of the synergy is that initiatives are often generated by people who have the relevant skills within an empowering and trusting culture resulting in improved patient outcomes. In this case, the expertise of the nurses in interventional radiology was shared and transferred to others through leadership practices.

Nurses and midwives are required to be proactive in identifying areas where an expansion in their scope of practice would lead to improvements in patient outcomes and the quality and range of available services. Distributed leadership entails that diverse levels of expertise are distributed across many areas (Woods et al., 2004). The collaborative nature of DL, with its associated group responsibility, supports the development of leadership capacity across a department or institution rather than placing reliance on a single leader, thereby equipping that department or institution to cope with change, succession planning and capacity-building. Collaborative quality improvement initiatives also engender a learning culture resulting in environments capable of: 'building trust; redesigning jobs; changing organisational structures; and creating a learning culture' (West-Burnham, 2004: 2 cited in Lefoe et al., 2007: 2). However, the degree of control and autonomy is a major variable in DL (Woods et al., 2004). Frequently, this depends on the extent to which the organisation enables or constrains initiatives, as many are required from the top to meet certain key performance indicators to be supported or maintain funding.

Conclusion

This chapter summarises our understanding of DL through the analysis of a single case study to determine how distributed leadership is practised and executed at the front line of clinical nursing practice. It provides an overview of the context in which general nurses practise and the evolution of DL in the educational sector. A case study from a real clinical practice setting, focused on the management and discharge care in an interventional radiology department, was examined through the lens of DL. The analysis of the case study provided invaluable insights into how aspects of DL are enacted in general nursing practice.

The analysis of the case study also suggests that through the use of distributive leadership practices several positive outcomes occurred. It assisted the nurse involved in completing the project and, at the same time, opened possibilities for collaboration both at an institutional and community level. On reflection, the process illustrates a high level of alignment between the principles of distributive leadership and the case study. It provided great clarity around the conditions that may be developed or modified to promote the distribution of leadership practices at the front line of healthcare. The interdisciplinary nature of healthcare and the goal of delivering patient-centred, quality care requires professionals to work collaboratively, with shared accountability and responsibility.

Distributed leadership, with its focus on how leadership takes shape in the interactions between leader, follower and the situation offers a clear framework for busy practitioners to conceptualise, understand, collaborate and articulate their leadership practice. The authors contend that DL aligns effortlessly with the values of professional disciplinary practice across the healthcare arena. Furthermore, we suggest that the principles of distributive leadership can successfully be used as a framework for evaluating quality improvement initiatives in the clinical and other milieus. Clinically based quality improvement projects require the involvement and participation of multiple stakeholders, and this framework can also provide insights into how collaborative projects can be planned, implemented and evaluated.

To conclude, the rise of distributed leadership in professional nursing practice represents an important shift in the perspective on leadership in healthcare. It acknowledges that leaders at the top are not the sole owners of change and DL can be considered in other settings outside of acute care where people work interdependently, take joint responsibility for their performance, and have a considerable degree of autonomy over how their work is carried out.

Key concepts discussed

- Distributed leadership practice is an appropriate framework to shape quality improvements in the context of general nursing practice.
- As similarities were identified between nurses in practice and teachers in education, more robust research is required in the context of healthcare.
- The core principles of nursing are aligned to distributed leadership practice: collaboration with others, trust and quality of practice.
- It is important to recognise the importance of social interaction and the expertise of colleagues when planning initiatives in professional nursing practice.

Key readings

- Chreim, S., Williams, B.B., Janz, L. and Dastmalchian, A. (2010) Change agency in a primary health care context: The case of distributed leadership, *Health Care Management Review*, 35 (2): 187–199.
- Fitzgerald, L., Ferlie, E., McGivern, G. and Buchanan, D. (2013) Distributed leadership patterns and service improvement: Evidence and argument from English healthcare, *Leadership Quarterly*, 24 (1): 227–239.
- Günzel-Jensen, F., Jain, A.K. and Kjeldsen, A.M. (2018) Distributed leadership in health care: The role of formal leadership styles and organizational efficacy, *Leadership*, 14 (1): 110–133.

Examples of studies about distributed leadership in healthcare

- McKee, L., Charles, K., Dixon-Woods, M., Willars, J. and Martin, G. (2013) 'New' and distributed leadership in quality and safety in health care, or 'old' and hierarchical? An interview study with strategic stakeholders, *Journal of Health Services Research and Policy*, 18 (2 suppl.): 11–19.
- Nzinga, J., McGivern, G. and English, M. (2018) Examining clinical leadership in Kenyan public hospitals through the distributed leadership lens, *Health Policy and Planning*, 33 (suppl. 2): ii27–ii34.

Useful websites

- Nursing and Midwifery Board of Ireland: http://www.nmbi.ie
  NMBI is the independent, statutory organisation which regulates the nursing and midwifery professions in Ireland. They work with nurses and midwives, the public and key stakeholders to enhance patient safety and patient care.
- Nursing and Midwifery Council: http://www.nmc.co.uk
  The NMC is the regulator for nursing and midwifery professions in the UK. They maintain a register of all nurses, midwives and specialist community public health nurses and nursing associates eligible to practise within the UK.
- Royal College of Nursing: https://www.rcn.org.uk/
  The RCN is a membership organisation of more than 450,000 registered nurses, midwives, nursing support workers and nursing students. They are both a professional body, carrying out work on nursing standards, education and practice, and a trade union. They promote and engage in nursing research, recognising that high-quality nursing research has the power to transform patient care.
- International Council of Nurses: https://www.icn.ch/nursing-policy/nursing-definitions
  The ICN advances nursing, nurses and health through its policies, partnerships, advocacy, leadership development, networks, congresses and special projects.
- World Health Organization: https://www.who.int/
  WHO works worldwide to promote health, keep the world safe and serve the vulnerable. Its goal is to ensure that a billion more people have universal health coverage, to protect a billion more people from health emergencies, and provide a further billion people with better health and wellbeing.

References

Bennett, N., Wise, C., Woods, P. and Harvey, J. (2003) *Distributed Leadership: Full Report*, Nottingham: National College for School Leadership.

Brown, N. and Littrich, J. (2008) Using a cross-institutional collaborative model to deliver a national roundtable conference on assessment: A case study, *Journal of University Teaching and Learning Practice*, 5 (1). Available at: http://ro.uow.edu.au/jutlp/vol5/iss1/2 (accessed 21 April 2020).

Burns, L., Bradley, E. and Weiner, B. (2011) *Shortell and Kaluzny's Healthcare Management: Organization Design and Behavior*, 6th edition, Boston, MA: Cengage Learning.

Chreim, S., Williams, B.B., Janz, L. and Dastmalchian, A. (2010) Change agency in a primary health care context: The case of distributed leadership, *Health Care Management Review*, 35 (2): 187–199.

Department of Health and Children (2008) *Building a Culture of Patient Safety – Report of the Commission on Patient Safety and Quality Assurance*, Dublin: The Stationery Office. Available at: https://www.gov.ie/en/publication/5d9570-building-a-culture-of-patient-safety-report-of-the-commission-on-pat/?referrer=/blog/publications/building-a-culture-of-patient-safety-report-of-the-commission-on-patient-safety-and-quality-assurance/ (accessed 30 April 2020).

Ensley, M.D., Pearson, A. and Pearce, C.L. (2003) Top management team process, shared leadership, and new venture performance: A theoretical model and research agenda, *Human Resource Management Review*, 13 (2): 329–346.

Farrell, R. and Halligan, P. (2017) Nurses' experience of caring for patients in the community after discharge with an interventional radiology drain in Ireland: A qualitative study, *Journal of Radiology Nursing*, 36 (4): 228–235.

Fitzgerald, L., Ferlie, E., McGivern, G. and Buchanan, D. (2013) Distributed leadership patterns and service improvement: Evidence and argument from English healthcare, *Leadership Quarterly*, 24 (1): 227–239.

Gronn, P. (2000) Distributed properties: A new architecture for leadership, *Educational Management Administration*, 28 (3): 317–338.

Gronn, P. (2002) Distributed leadership, in K. Leithwood and P. Hallinger (eds.) *Second International Handbook of Educational Leadership and Administration*, Dordrecht: Kluwer, 653–696.

Gronn, P. (2003) Leadership: Who needs it?, *School Leadership and Management*, 23 (3): 267–290.

Government of Ireland (2011) *Nurses and Midwives Act, 2011*. Available at: http://www.irishstatutebook.ie/eli/2011/act/41/enacted/en/print (accessed 30 April 2020).

Günzel-Jensen, F., Jain, A.K. and Kjeldsen, A.M. (2018) Distributed leadership in health care: The role of formal leadership styles and organizational efficacy, *Leadership*, 14 (1): 110–133.

Hargreaves, A. and Fink, D. (2000) The three dimensions of reform, *Educational Leadership*, 57 (7): 30–34.

Harris, A. (2007) Distributed leadership: Conceptual confusion and empirical reticence, *International Journal of Leadership in Education*, 10 (3): 315–325.

Institute of Medicine (2004) *Keeping Patients Safe: Transforming the Work Environment of Nurses*, ed. A. Page, Committee on the Work Environment for Nurses and Patient Safety. Washington, DC: National Academies Press.

Institute of Medicine (2011) *The Future of Nursing: Leading Change, Advancing Health*. Washington, DC: National Academies Press. Available at: https://www.ncbi.nlm.nih.gov/books/NBK209891/?report=reader (accessed 21 April 2020).

International Council of Nurses (2010) *Nursing Definitions*. Available at: https://www.icn.ch/nursing-policy/nursing-definitions (accessed 21 April 2020).

Kotter, J. (2003) What leaders really do, in J.M. Kouzes and B.Z. Posner (eds.) *Business Leadership*, San Francisco, CA: Jossey-Bass, 29–43.

Kramer, M. and Schmalenberg, C. (2003) Magnet hospital nurses describe control over nursing practice, *Western Journal of Nursing Research*, 25 (4): 434–452.

Lefoe, G.E., Smigiel, H. and Parrish, D. (2007) Enhancing higher education through leadership capacity development: Progressing the faculty scholars' model, in *Proceedings of the 30th HERDSA Annual Conference: Enhancing Higher Education, Theory and Scholarship*, Milperra, NSW: HERDSA, 304–309. Available at: http://ro.uow.edu.au/edupapers/97 (accessed 21 April 2020).

Marshall, S.J. (2006) *Issues in the development of leadership for learning and teaching in higher education*, Occasional Paper, Canberra, ACT: Carrick Institute for Learning and Teaching in Higher Education. Available at: https://ltr.edu.au/resources/grants_leadership_occasionalpaper_stephenmarshall_nov06.pdf.

Nursing and Midwifery Board of Ireland (NMBI) (2014) *Code of Professional Conduct and Ethics*, Dublin: NMBI. Available at: https://www.nmbi.ie/Standards-Guidance/Code (accessed April 28 2020).

Nursing and Midwifery Board of Ireland (NMBI) (2020) *Pre-Registration Honours Degree Programmes 2020, Nursing/Midwifery: A career for you*, Dublin: NMBI. Available at: https://www.nmbi.ie/NMBI/media/NMBI/WebversionNMACFY2020.pdf?ext=.pdf (accessed 21 April 2020).

Peate, I. (2019) *Alexander's Nursing Practice: Hospital and Home*, 5th edition, London: Elsevier.

Ross, L., Rix, M. and Gold, J. (2005) Learning distributed leadership, Part 1, *Industrial and Commercial Training*, 37 (3): 130–137.

Spillane, J.P. (2006) *Distributed Leadership*, San Francisco, CA: Jossey-Bass.

Spillane, J.P. and Diamond, J.B. (2007) *Distributed Leadership in Practice*, New York: Teachers College Press.

Spillane, J.P., Halverson, R. and Diamond, J.B. (2004) Towards a theory of leadership practice: A distributed perspective, *Journal of Curriculum Studies*, 36 (1): 3–34.

West-Burnham, J. (2004) Think Piece: Building leadership capacity – helping leaders learn, in J. Creasy, P. Smith, J. West-Burnham and I. Barnes, *Meeting the Challenge: Growing Tomorrow's School Leaders – A practical guide for school leaders*, Nottingham: National College for School Leadership. Available at: https://www.rtuni.org/uploads/docs/meeting-the-challenge-growing-tomorrows-school-leaders.pdf (accessed 21 April 2020).

Whitby, P. (2018) Role of front-line nurse leadership in improving care, *Nursing Standard*, 33 (8): 30–34.

Woods, P.A., Bennett, N., Harvey, J.A. and Wise, C. (2004) Variabilities and dualities in distributed leadership: Findings from a systematic literature review, *Educational Management Administration and Leadership*, 32 (4): 439–457.

World Health Organization (WHO) (2020a) *Nursing and Midwifery: Key Facts*. Available at: https://www.who.int/news-room/fact-sheets/detail/nursing-and-midwifery (accessed 21 April 2020).

World Health Organization (WHO) (2020b) *State of the World's Nursing 2020: Investing in Education, Jobs and Leadership*, Geneva: WHO. Available at: https://www.who.int/publications/i/item/9789240003279 (accessed 19 October 2020).

Yukl, G. (1989) *Leadership in Organisations*, Englewood Cliffs, NJ: Prentice Hall.

8 Distributed leadership practices and interventions in intellectual disability services

Fintan Sheerin

Chapter topics

- Distributed leadership applied to intellectual disability service provision
- Person-centred approaches and personal service models
- Voice as an important aspect of distributed leadership
- Supporting voice in people with intellectual disability
- Challenges to achieving person-centred distributed leadership
- Strategies for supporting people with intellectual disability to become leaders in their own lives

Introduction

The history of intellectual disability service provision has been largely modelled around a societal response to perceived deviance and disorder (Sheerin, 2011). This is an important issue to note as that response led to the congregation, confinement and management of large numbers of people in institutional settings with hierarchical management systems controlling the way that their lives were conducted. It is arguable that such a scenario is anathema to the concepts underpinning modern leadership and that such *leadership* was closely allied to the hierarchical management structures, manifested in leadership teams. They are not, however, in any way, contiguous with those ensconced in distributed leadership.

Recent developments have seen significant change in how services are configured for people with intellectual disability and, whilst some smaller congregated units remain either on campuses or in close proximity to a central hub, there has been a general movement away from institutional, congregated models toward a situation whereby smaller numbers of people live in normative housing, located within the general community. Furthermore, attempts to ground such services in person-centredness has greatly challenged the concept of leadership within a central management structure, and has promoted the idea that a person can be a leader in their life and in the configuring of services to support that life. This is achieved, however, by bringing together the 'knowledge, abilities, and skills of several people' (Curtis, 2019: 55). This chapter explores emerging leadership models in the light of intellectual disability service changes and suggests that distributed leadership may be manifested in truly person-centred approaches to configuring service for people with intellectual disability.

A model bereft of leadership

A quick perusal of historical and social literature uncovers the fact that diversity has been a key characteristic of humankind (United Nations, 2006; Hristova et al., 2016). This diversity has been manifested in, for example, people's appearance, behaviour, culture, language and ways of understanding their surrounding realities. Some such variances have been considered to be acceptable deviations from a norm, whereas others have not. In particular, physical, mental and emotional impairments were responded to in very different ways, depending on the prevalent culture, with marginalisation, confinement and, in some cases, infanticide being acceptable solutions. The *Great Confinement* is the term afforded by Foucault (2006) to the advent of the institutions which predated those that were preponderant in the nineteenth and twentieth centuries. These were initially places of incarceration, where those displaying moral disorder could be kept and controlled – out of sight and mind of others in society. Similar places of confinements grew out of the Poor Law structures which became focal points for those who could not participate in the new affluence of the post-industrialisation years. It was in this context that intellectual disability became more obvious, as industrialisation led to formal schooling with the revelation that there were some who did not advance well in mainstream approaches to education and training. With time, the amassing of large numbers of people with intellectual and mental impairments led to such institutions coming under the ambit of medicine and healthcare, with management structures replicating those seen in Victorian hospitals; this will be revisited later.

These were, essentially, 'total institutions' (Goffman, 1991), where all aspects of the patients' lives were controlled. They were characterised by strict routines and daily patterns with little or no choice. Sheerin (2019) has argued that they were oppressive entities, the nature of whose regimes echoed those seen in imperial colonies (Memmi, 1990; Freire, 1996), with people denied voice and power; indeed, the only voice that directed many people's lives was the internalised voice of the oppressor (Freire, 1996). It is interesting to note that Carey (2016), in her grounded theory study into how formerly institutionalised people with intellectual disability enacted choice, found that, many years after moving to community settings, they still led their lives according to the voice of the institution. Nearly half a century ago, Wolfensberger (1972) produced his seminal work *The Principle of Normalization in Human Services*, which examined disability services through the developing lens of normalization. The use of the term 'human services' was important as it highlighted the fact that institutionalisation had produced a model which was focused on tasks rather than on the people whose lives those tasks served. Thus, industrialised 'top-down models of bureaucratic managerial control dominated' (Northway, 2019: 43). Such an approach is not bereft of leadership. Northouse (2016: 6) defines leadership as 'a process whereby an individual influences a group of individuals to achieve a common goal'; it is clear that hierarchical bureaucratic approaches can result in staff moving towards common goals. A question arises as to whether those goals are centred on achieving outcomes for the service recipients (person-driven) or for the organisation (task-driven). In the latter case, it is likely that objectification of the service recipients will result, and this was clearly evident in the service failures at Áras Attracta in Ireland (Áras Attracta Swinford Review Group, 2016) and Winterbourne View in the UK (Department of Health, 2012). These have been characterised as failures of leadership (Sheerin, 2019) and it is worrying that further similar failures continue to be exposed in the media.

Whilst such failures of leadership (and care) have occurred, many intellectual disability services have strived to move away from congregated models towards more individualised approaches located in normative community settings. The central driver for such approaches is *person-centredness* and this is discussed in the next section.

Person-centred approaches

In health and social care, person-centredness has become a key concept in the provision of human services. Often, it is understood as referring to an individualised approach which views the person rather than the group, and which attempts to offer options that are better attuned to that person's desires. It is, therefore, a process of discovery and action in respect of what is important for the person, seeking to design and deliver services and supports based on their wishes, preferences and aspirations (Department of Health, 2001). Part of this process involves the identification of those priorities, setting of goals and choosing of means to achieve them (Dew et al., 2019). Whilst there is limited evidence to support an assertion that person-centred approaches lead to *measurable* outcomes for people with intellectual disabilities, they have been shown to have positive effects in the domains of happiness, self-esteem, confidence (Wigham et al., 2008), social integration and choice (Robertson et al., 2005).

Prior to this, many intellectual disability services addressed provision as a care package that focused on meeting the person's needs and desires by drawing on the service's particular inventories. Therefore, programmes with limited options were created, which service users were required to engage in. These were described as individual programme plans (IPPs) but were often not really individualised. They were severely limited by staffing models, which meant that people had to undertake the available programmes in groups and with little real choice. Typically, these programmes were offered through campus-based day activity centres, occupational (sheltered) workshops and sports facilities. Such an approach focused on what a person could and could not do, with activities directed towards training and rehabilitation to address the limitations. In reality, Mansell and Beadle-Brown (2005) contend that they probably served to maintain people in services rather than promote independence.

When considered in its totality, though, person-centredness should be a game-changer and should lead to a re-imagining of the intellectual disability service as being only one of a number of possible contributors to the life of a person with intellectual disability – and not necessarily the main one! Furthermore, it should move the focus to the person him or herself and put them at the centre of all planning. The real challenge, however, is being able to offer an array of options, similar to those on offer to people in mainstream society, and thus allow an individualised service configuration to be realised. Unfortunately, congregated responses were maintained by a financial model that located funding centrally in services, with this being used to provide the varied service-based inventory of activities. This made real individually determined programmes almost impossible and, as Stainton (2007) suggests, created conflicts of interest whereby those assessing individuals, those providing activities and those managing funds were all part of the same organisation.

Whereas the congregated funding approach usually results in a service-determined set of options that may (or may not) meet the desires of service recipients as a group, an alternative approach of *personalised funding*, or individualised funding packages (Dew et al., 2019), offers the potential for individuals' monies to be used to pay for their eclectic set of possibilities, with them being able to *pick and choose* the configuration of their service: education may be obtained from a community adult education provider; personal assistance can be purchased based on who is the right care provider for the person in question; recreational and other endeavours can be chosen in keeping with their desires and interests. This is where person-centredness can significantly alter the role of service in the lives of people with intellectual disabilities, as it puts them at the centre of all planning. Whereas other models did not view the person as having an active and valid *leadership* role, person-centredness demands that the emergence of voice is supported and that, through this voice, the person contributes key expertise and knowledge to the imagining, creation and realisation of a service configuration that responds to their needs and desires.

Developing leadership in one's life: The role of voice

Leadership in one's own life presumes that the person has some capacity for self-determination, a quality that Wehmeyer and Abery define as 'the product of both the person and the environment – of the person using the skills, knowledge, and beliefs at his/her disposal to act on the environment with the goal of obtaining valued and desired outcomes' (2013: 2). It is important to note, however, that for most people, the skills, knowledge, beliefs and expertise required to make *and manage* decisions of self-determination are usually learned through life experience during one's formative years and require successful development and integration of higher cognitive functions. Such capacities may be more challenging for many people with intellectual disabilities and may compromise their ability to lead their own lives. This is where distributed leadership and person-centredness can provide a solution.

The directing of one's own life may not normally be considered to be grounded in leadership, but it is arguable that the person-centred model of life planning

(Sanderson et al., 2006) achieves this by bringing together key people with skills and values that are specifically relevant to the life goal of the person with an intellectual disability. This group, the *circle of support*, is the main mechanism for driving the formulation of ideas, development of solutions, planning of actions and management of resources/supports required for the achievement of this goal (National Disability Authority, 2006). The membership of this group has been seen to be crucial (Wigham et al., 2008), as it facilitates the provision of capacities, skills, perspectives and expertise and integrates these, compensating for what might otherwise have been absent. Along with the *focus person*, whose life plan is the goal, the interplay (*interaction*) of these individuals, planning and acting together (*practice*) in an integrated and person-focused way (*situation*) describes something that is akin to distributed leadership (Spillane, 2006). By exploring life planning in the context of enacted leadership, it could be proposed that distributed leadership offers a platform for supporting person-centred approaches.

It may seem repetitive, but it is vital to re-state that the person remains at the centre in person-centred approaches! It is their voice that provides the concepts upon which goals and actions are based and there must be surety that this voice is heard, despite the communication challenges which may present (National Disability Authority, 2006). It is clear, from Sanderson (2000), that person-centeredness must be grounded in true human engagement for it is this which facilitates the development of a trusting relationship that is free from the power imbalances of traditional service-based relationships. Person-centredness is about listening and hearing. It is about equalising the relationship between service user and service provider, which requires an offloading of those role-related behaviours and symbols, such as the wearing of uniforms, that have denoted positions of power and disempowerment. Thus, those who come together in the leadership process do so in a sense of equity and participation, all working towards the same goal and recognising the knowledge, expertise and potential in each other. Those who have been socialised in alternative leadership and managerial approaches may find this threatening, as it can lead to perceived vulnerability; this is necessary, though, if there is to be any possibility of person-centredness succeeding (Sheerin, 2018).

Leadership does not have to be objectifying, nor does it have to depend on the existence of an individual or management team which influences (and controls) the behaviour of others. Shalock and Verdugo (2012) focus on the inspirational and transactional aspects of leadership but again, this brings an expectation that others (followers) will be inspirationally influenced and, in the context of intellectual disability service, it does not necessarily result in the person with intellectual disability having equal voice in their own service. Voice has become an important concept in the normalisation movement and in attempts to produce person-centred service responses to the needs and desires of people with intellectual disabilities. By facilitating the emergence of the person's true voice, there is a potential for this to become a means of them enacting self-agency in their lives. Moreover, the person may be supported to become an actor in their own life, contributing, along with others, to the development and leadership of their own life and supports.

The ability of *person-centred life planning* processes to transfer to other situations where self-determination and self-direction may need to be supported, is an important point to note and, as such, approaches have also been used to effect organisational change by bringing together all stakeholders in a joint activity of leadership, with each contributing to the vision, plan and enactment, drawing on their respective expertise (Hughes et al., 2019). The requirement for engagement remains, though, and strategies for supporting such engagement with people with intellectual disability are explored in the following section.

Developing leadership through person-centred approaches

The process of supporting people with intellectual disabilities to develop leadership skills needs to be a developmental one, which takes account of each person's capabilities and desires, providing the opportunity for positive growth and confidence building (Wigham et al., 2008). There must also be a recognition that the emergence of voice can take some time and that various approaches may be needed, depending on the person's communication style and cognitive development. This is a necessary step if the person is to be able to be a real, active, leader in their own life, as otherwise, they would just be a passive recipient.

Two case studies will now be presented describing initiatives where person-centredness was employed to promote the voices of people with intellectual disabilities. One recounts a social action in which a group of people with intellectual disabilities became active leaders in a human rights project. The other was directed towards the recognition of voice, using creative interventions.

Case study: *IDRights* – Building leadership through participation

The problem: In 2010, I was approached by a number of individuals who felt that many people with intellectual disabilities were voiceless in their own lives and that, because of this, their rights were not being realised.

The action: It was in response to this problem that we set up *IDRights*, a participatory-action initiative. It quickly became apparent that the initial iteration of the project was over-laden with health and social care professionals and included too few people with intellectual disabilities. With no clear models to draw on, it was decided that a streamlined team would be set up to guide the project development and that each member would invite a person with intellectual disability to partner them on the team. Thus, each position on the team was populated by two people: a person with intellectual disability and another person.

Furthermore, a number of roles were identified, including chair, secretary and treasurer, and each of these was similarly filled by two individuals. The plan was that, by working as part of a dyad, the person with intellectual disability would gradually develop the skills and confidence to contribute to and, eventually, assume the responsibilities of that role. We also hoped that they would start to find their own voice. One further process was the development of reflective discussions between team members which allowed us all to critically explore our engagements in the dyads, to ensure that we were facilitating emergence of voice and not supporting passivity. Whilst not explicitly identified at the time, it has since become clear that the principles underpinning *IDRights* were those of distributed leadership, as they were grounded in developing participants' competence in the practice of leadership through dialogic interactions focused on exploring their life situations (Spillane, 2006).

IDRights organised a number of national events between 2010 and 2013, including three Rights Days, during which people with intellectual disability were encouraged to explore their rights and to express their opinions through facilitated activities. The most successful event was the *Our Say, Our Rights* quilt, which brought together images created by 147 people, each of which represented an important right in the artist's life. The quilt was launched at an event in Dublin, attended by 120 people with intellectual disabilities, and each person expressed what their image meant to them, either using voice or other means. Details of the quilt itself are available elsewhere (Keating and Sheerin, 2012, 2013), and it is the effect of the activity on individual members that I would like to focus on here.

The outcomes: The effect of the dyadic relationships and the normalised dialogic approach to the interactions (the participants, in this context, were not interacting as recipients of a service) were particularly marked in one young woman who had hitherto been quite passive in her life. She was receiving day service from an agency and was living at home with her parents. During her time on the team, she moved from being initially quiet and passive to becoming increasingly engaged in discussions and planning. In particular, she saw the team as a 'non-service' situation which placed different expectations on her. Thus, the internalised expectation that she should act in childish (infantilised) ways did not work in the team. Furthermore, the use of socially inappropriate behaviours (tantrums, for example), which are essentially secondary disabilities, did not elicit the responses that they received elsewhere. Over the months, as her confidence increased, she demonstrated her knowledge and expertise regarding the reality of what it was like to live with intellectual disability and she started to critically explore that reality. The clearest example of this was when she expressed an interest in speaking with support, at an international conference on intellectual disability, about her emergence from passivity; she had never spoken in front of an audience before. The team worked alongside her, each bringing their knowledge, experience and skills, to ensure that her presentation would express what she wanted to say. This is an example of person-centredness in action, but it is also a clear manifestation of distributed leadership. The manifestation of its success was in the first line of her presentation in which she said: 'In my life I have always been treated as a child. I am not a child! I am a woman, and I want to be treated as a woman'.

Case study: Maintaining mental health through self-sustainability

The problem: The second case study is an ongoing project, entitled SOOTHE, which has brought together partners from Ireland, Spain and the Netherlands* in an activity, supported by the European Institute of Innovation and Technology (EIT Health). The aim of the work is to assist adults with intellectual disability to co-create ways of maximising and regulating mental health and wellbeing in their lives.

The project seeks to address the reality whereby many people with intellectual disabilities experience poorer mental health than those in the mainstream population, with anxiety and depression being particularly prevalent (Sheerin et al., 2017). Furthermore, it has been shown that these issues present throughout the life span, with limited mental health support provided (Sheerin et al., 2019). In keeping with the recovery approach that has become popular in mainstream mental health settings, and which moves the locus of control from professional to the person themself, SOOTHE is developing interventions and solutions for maximising positive mental health that can be employed by people with intellectual disabilities. This is cognisant of the fact that many of these people have been passive recipients of healthcare and have not had an opportunity to develop autonomy or have a voice in their own healthcare.

The action: The initial work of the project has been centred on reaching personal and shared definitions of what *mental health* actually is. These discussions are still taking place but it is interesting to note that, when this project was discussed with another health professional, I was asked why I would be interested in hearing about how people with intellectual disability define mental health, as these definitions have already been produced in the likes of the International Classification of Diseases (WHO, 2018). It is arguable that such definitions cannot be considered to be complete, though, without the input of knowledge and experience from those who are living with such health issues; these people bring an expertise that can be used to expand our understanding. This is a key focus of the SOOTHE project and we see the potential for these adults to become leaders in the development of preventative and interventional strategies for the self-maintenance of good mental health and wellbeing. As with the participants in *IDRights*, the people in this project have been largely passive recipients of service for much of their lives, and their ability to enact real change for themselves has been stifled by the difficulty in finding and expressing their own voices. This has, arguably, been compounded by the presence of mental health challenges.

The outcomes: As the research team moves forward with this work, they will be engaging with people with intellectual disabilities using discursive innovation-focused working groups in which they will move from being service users, to learners and finally active participants. Throughout the process, this group will develop into a community of practice, sharing knowledge and skills, and networking with others in their communities, supporting them to become more active in their own health and wellbeing. This will incorporate dialogic interaction and listening, with participants being encouraged to find their own voice in contributing to the shared definition of mental health. They will also identify solutions that they have enacted to maintain good mental health or, if they have not yet achieved this, they will be supported to explore potential solutions. In a similar way to those person-centred approaches that were previously described, an innovation-based circle of support will be provided for each person to enact these solutions in their lives. The bringing together of leadership skills, the supported development of such skills in the participants, and the shared goals are, again, evidence of the role that distributed leadership can play in achieving person-centred outcomes in the lives of people with intellectual disabilities (Curtis, 2019). It had been anticipated that the project which this case study is based on would have been further progressed by the time of publication. Alas, the onset of the 2020 Covid-19 pandemic has delayed progress by some months.

*Trinity College Dublin and Daughters of Charity Health and Social Services for People with Disabilities (Ireland), Parc Sanitari Sant Joan de Déu (Spain), University Medical Centre Groningen and Hanze University of Applied Sciences (Netherlands).

Conclusion

This chapter has sought to explore how distributed leadership manifests in person-centred care, supporting people with intellectual disabilities to take control in their own lives. It has been suggested that person-centredness and distributed leadership can work in tandem, facilitating the person to become a leader in respect of the life that they choose and the services that they need to make that possible. In order for this to be realised, however, there is a need for people with intellectual disabilities to be supported to find and express their own voice (that is, their desires and needs), and not the internalised voices of others that usually direct their choices. This requires painstaking work, providing opportunities for them to explore different possibilities and to experience others' valuing of their opinions and perspectives. It is in these that the skills, knowledge and experience will be expressed, and which will form the basis for them taking on leadership roles alongside others. The two case studies provided insight into ways that this might be achieved.

Key concepts discussed

- Leadership approaches in intellectual disability service provision have been grounded in management of the congregated group rather than developing leadership around and with the individual person.
- Person-centred approaches to service provision, whereby the person, working with others, co-creates their own service, present a platform for distributed leadership.

- Innovative, inclusive approaches to supporting the *voice* of people with intellectual disability facilitate the possibility of them becoming recognised as knowledgeable experts of their own lives.

Key readings

- Cambridge, P. and Carnaby, S. (eds.) (2005) *Person Centred Planning and Care Management for People with Learning Disabilities*, London: Jessica Kingsley.
- Curtis, E.A. (2019) Distributed leadership: An alternative approach for intellectual disability, in F. Sheerin and E. Curtis (eds.) *Leadership for Intellectual Disability Service: Motivating Change and Improvement*, Abingdon: Routledge, 48–84.
- Mansell, J. and Beadle-Brown, J. (2012) *Active Support: Enabling and Empowering People with Intellectual Disabilities*, London: Jessica Kingsley.

Examples of studies involving people with intellectual disability

- Inclusive Research Network (2015) *Our Homes: Home and Independence Project*, Dublin: School of Social Work and Social Policy, Trinity College Dublin; Limerick: Department of Clinical Therapies, University of Limerick; Galway: National Federation of Voluntary Bodies.
- Inclusive Research Network (2019) *Doctors and Us: What It Is Like for People with Learning Disabilities to Go to the Doctor in Ireland*, Limerick: School of Allied Health, University of Limerick; Dublin: School of Social Work and Social Policy, Trinity College Dublin; Galway: National Federation of Voluntary Service Providers; Cork: Certificate in Contemporary Living/School of Applied Social Studies, University College Cork.
- McCarron, M., Haigh, M. and McCallion, P. (eds.) (2017) *Health, Wellbeing and Social Inclusion: Ageing with an Intellectual Disability in Ireland: Wave 3 IDS-TILDA*, Dublin: Trinity College Dublin.
- Sheerin, F. et al. (2020) *First Response to Mental Health Concerns in Adults with Intellectual Disability (SOOTHE)*. Ongoing research: www.sootheid.eu

Useful websites

- National Federation of Voluntary Service Providers Inclusive Research Network: http://www.fedvol.ie/Inclusive_Research_Network_IRN/Default.241.html
- The Tizard Centre, University of Kent, UK: https://research.kent.ac.uk/tizard/
- Trinity Centre for Ageing and Intellectual Disabilities, Trinity College Dublin, Ireland: https://www.tcd.ie/tcaid/

References

Áras Attracta Swinford Review Group (2016) *What Matters Most*, Dublin: Health Service Executive. Available at: https://static.rasset.ie/documents/news/aasrgwhatmattersmost.pdf (accessed 19 October 2020).

Carey, E. (2016) *Aligning with the flow of control: A classic grounded theory of choice in the lives of people with intellectual disabilities*, unpublished PhD thesis, Trinity College Dublin.

Curtis, E.A. (2019) Distributed leadership: An alternative approach for intellectual disability, in F. Sheerin and E. Curtis (eds.) *Leadership for Intellectual Disability Service: Motivating Change and Improvement*, Abingdon: Routledge, 48–84.

Department of Health (2001) *Valuing People: A New Strategy for Learning Disability in the 21st Century*, London: Department of Health.

Department of Health (2012) *Transforming Care: A National Response to Winterbourne View Hospital*, London: Department of Health.

Dew, A., Collings, S., Savage, I., Gentle, E. and Dowse, L. (2019) 'Living the life I want': A framework for planning engagement with people with intellectual disability and complex support needs, *Journal of Applied Research in Intellectual Disabilities*, 32 (2): 401–412.

Foucault, M. (2006) *Madness and Civilization: A History of Insanity in the Age of Reason*, Abingdon: Routledge.

Freire, P. (1996) *Pedagogy of the Oppressed*, London: Penguin Books.

Goffman, E. (1991) *Asylums*, London: Penguin Books.

Hristova, D., Williams, M., Musolesi, M., Panzarasa, P. and Mascolo, C. (2016) Measuring urban social diversity using interconnected geo-social networks, in *Proceedings of the 25th International Conference on World Wide Web*, Montréal, Quebec, 21–30. Available at: http://dx.doi.org/10.1145/2872427.2883065 (accessed 6 May 2020).

Hughes, C., Maclean, G. and Stringer, P. (2019) How person-centred planning can contribute to organisational change in a school, *Educational Psychology in Practice*, 35 (2): 229–238.

Keating, L. and Sheerin, F. (2012) *The Our Say, Our Rights Quilt*. Available at: https://issuu.com/frontline-ireland.net/docs/quilt_book (accessed 13 May 2020).

Keating, L. and Sheerin, F. (2013) The 'Our Say, Our Rights' quilt, *British Journal of Learning Disabilities*, 41 (3): 197–198.

Mansell, J. and Beadle-Brown, J. (2005) Person centred planning and person-centred action: A critical perspective, in P. Cambridge and S. Carnaby (eds.) *Person Centred Planning and Care Management for People with Learning Disabilities*, London: Jessica Kingsley, 19–33.

Memmi, A. (1990) *The Colonizer and the Colonized*, London: Taylor & Francis.

National Disability Authority (NDA) (2006) *Guidelines on Person Centred Planning in the Provision of Services for People with Disabilities in Ireland*, Dublin: NDA.

Northouse, P. (2016) *Leadership: Theory and Practice*, 7th edition, Thousand Oaks, CA: Sage.

Northway, R. (2019) Moving models: Leading through change, in F. Sheerin and E. Curtis (eds.) *Leadership for Intellectual Disability Service: Motivating Change and Improvement*, Abingdon: Routledge, 21–43.

Robertson, J., Emerson, E., Hatton, C., Elliott, J., McIntosh, B., Swift, P. et al. (2005) *The Impact of Person Centred Planning*, Hull: The University of Hull.

Sanderson, H. (2000) *Person Centred Planning: Key Features and Approaches*, Edinburgh: Joseph Rowntree Foundation.

Sanderson, H., Thompson, J. and Kilbane, J. (2006) The emergence of person-centred planning as evidence-based practice, *Journal of Integrated Care*, 14 (2): 18–25.

Shalock, R. and Verdugo, M. (2012) *A Leadership Guide for Today's Disabilities Organizations: Overcoming Challenges and Making Change Happen*, Baltimore, MD: Brookes Publishing.

Sheerin, F. (2011) The nurse's role as specialist practitioner and social activist, *Learning Disability Practice*, 14 (10): 31–37.

Sheerin, F. (2018) The cloaked self: Professional decloaking and its implications for human engagement in nursing, *International Journal of Nursing Knowledge*, 30 (2): 99–105.

Sheerin, F. (2019) Leadership and intellectual disability services., in F. Sheerin and E. Curtis (eds.) *Leadership for Intellectual Disability Service: Motivating Change and Improvement*, Abingdon: Routledge, 3–22.

Sheerin, F., Carroll, R., Mulryan, N., McCallion, P. and McCarron, M. (2017) Mental health, well-being, vitality and life events, in M. McCarron, M. Haigh and P. McCallion (eds.) *Health, Wellbeing and Social Inclusion: Ageing with an Intellectual Disability in Ireland: Wave 3 IDS-TILDA*, Dublin: Trinity College Dublin, 89–100.

Sheerin, F., Fleming, S., Burke, E., Byrne, K., Cleary, M., Doyle, C. et al. (2019) Exploring mental health issues in people with an intellectual disability, *Learning Disability Practice*, 22 (6): 36–44.

Spillane, J.P. (2006) *Distributed Leadership*, San Francisco, CA: Jossey-Bass.

Stainton, T. (2007) Case management in a rights-based environment: Structure, context and roles, in C. Bigby, C. Fyffe and E. Ozanne (eds.) *Planning and Support for People with Intellectual Disabilities*, London: Jessica Kingsley, 90–107.

United Nations (2006) *Convention on the Rights of Persons with Disabilities*, New York: United Nations. Available at: https://www.un.org/development/desa/disabilities/convention-on-the-rights-of-persons-with-disabilities.html (accessed 19 October 2020).

Wehmeyer, M. and Abery, B. (2013) Self-determination and choice, *Intellectual and Developmental Disabilities*, 51 (5): 399–411.

Wigham, S., Robertson, J., Emerson, E., Hatton, C., Elliott, J., McIntosh, B. et al. (2008) Reported goal setting and benefits of person centred planning for people with intellectual disabilities, *Journal of Intellectual Disabilities*, 12 (2): 143–152.

Wolfensberger, W. (1972) *The Principle of Normalization in Human Services*, Toronto: National Institute on Mental Retardation.

World Health Organization (WHO) (2018) *International Classification of Diseases (ICD-11)*, Geneva: WHO.

9 Distributed leadership interventions at advanced clinical practitioner level

Catherine Comiskey

Chapter topics

- The development of advanced practice roles
- Definitions of advanced practice
- Distributed leadership and advanced practice
- Cases studies of distributed leadership in advanced practice
- Challenges implementing distributed leadership in practice settings
- Opportunities for advanced practice and the nursing profession

Introduction

In 2020 the world was struck by a global pandemic the likes of which was unprecedented, unexpected and unseen for over 100 years. The lack of nations' preparedness combined with the global shortage of healthcare professionals experienced and trained with leadership skills was never more evident. The World Health Organization, at the forefront of the fight against this pandemic of Covid-19 in collaboration with the International Council of Nurses (ICN) and Nursing Now (WHO, 2020a), have stated that nursing professionals constitute the largest component of the health workforce. Yet their findings identified important gaps in the nursing workforce and priority areas for investment included nursing education, jobs and leadership. Addressing these gaps they believe will strengthen nursing around the world and improve health for all. Nurses account for more than half of all the world's health workers, providing vital services throughout the health system during the Covid-19 crisis. Between 2013 and 2018, nursing numbers increased by 4.7 million. But this still leaves a global shortfall of 5.9 million, with the greatest gaps found in countries with possibly the greatest challenges in terms of healthcare in Africa, South East Asia and the WHO Eastern Mediterranean region as well as some parts of Latin America (WHO, 2020b).

The recognition of the international need for increasing numbers of nursing professionals with leadership skills has been highlighted previously. Comiskey et al. (2015) drew attention to this need in South Africa and they also cite Thompson and Hyrkas (2014) who have commented on the demands on nursing, in particular nursing leadership at a global level. In their editorial to a special issue of the *Journal of*

Nursing Management on global nursing leadership, Thompson and Hyrkas (2014) provide a summary of work from over thirteen contributions from more than ten countries from Canada to Australia and New Zealand, from North and South America to Europe, from Finland to Israel and beyond. The authors state that the biggest demand facing nursing in the twenty-first century is the transformation within nursing. They believe that nurse leadership needs to be active not only in practice, but also in education, research and the policy and political arenas.

Defining advanced practice roles

The global shortage of nursing professionals educated at baccalaureate level and beyond has been highlighted (Comiskey et al., 2015). Countries are addressing these shortages by developing advanced nurse roles which require a master's degree at a minimum. According to Comiskey et al. (2014), specialist and advanced practice posts within nursing and midwifery were developed first over forty years ago in Canada (Bryant-Lukosius et al., 2004) and the United States (Kleinpell et al., 2012) and were introduced in the last two decades in Europe. The purpose of the posts is to improve the quality of clinical care and to provide leadership, audit and research activity in the nursing and midwifery professions (Pulcini et al., 2010). Although such specialist posts have been developed across the globe, they take many different titles (Bryant-Lukosius et al., 2004), with a resulting lack of role clarity described in New Zealand (Roberts et al., 2011), Australia (Lowe et al., 2012), Canada (Donald et al., 2010) and the United Kingdom (Jones, 2005; Brook and Rushforth, 2011).

According to the Canadian Nursing Association (2019), two advanced practice nursing roles are recognised within Canada. These are the clinical nurse specialist (CNS) and the nurse practitioner. *Clinical nurse specialists* are registered nurses with advanced nursing knowledge and skills in making complex decisions and who hold a master's or doctoral degree in nursing with expertise in a clinical nursing specialty. They are agents of change who bring value to clients, practice settings and organizations to improve safety, promote positive health outcomes and reduce costs. *Nurse practitioners* are registered nurses with additional educational preparation and experience who possess and demonstrate the competencies to autonomously diagnose, order and interpret diagnostic tests, prescribe pharmaceuticals and perform specific procedures within their legislated scope of practice. Both roles require leadership.

In Australia, the Nursing and Midwifery Board has defined advanced practice nursing (APN) as a level of nursing practice that uses comprehensive skills, experience and knowledge in nursing care (NMBA, 2016). They state that APN is the application of advanced levels of knowledge, skill and experience by the nurse to the nurse–patient/client relationship in order to achieve optimal outcomes through critical analysis, problem-solving and accurate decision-making. The Board supports the view that nurses practising at this level are educationally prepared at master's level and may work in a specialist or generalist capacity.

In Ireland, advanced nurse or midwife practitioner (ANP/AMP) roles have been developed in a systematic fashion according to the guidelines published by the National Council for the Professional Development of Nursing and Midwifery (NCNM,

2008). The role of the ANP/AMP is not only to promote wellness but to utilise advanced clinical nursing/midwifery knowledge and critical thinking skills to independently provide optimum care through caseload management. While the role is grounded in theory, it incorporates research, leadership and management skills in order to encourage a multidisciplinary approach to quality patient and service user care.

Distributed leadership and advanced practice

Leadership in healthcare according to Sheerin and Curtis (2019) has generated considerable interest because our lives are affected by it. The topic is of importance because it can inform us not only about who we are as individuals but perhaps more importantly who we are as a member of a group within and beyond the work setting. Furthermore, Hughes et al. (2006) tell us that leadership is the business and responsibility not of the individual but of the collective. According to Curtis et al. (Chapter 18, this volume), distributed leadership has emerged as an innovative alternative to the traditional top-down leadership structure. Effective leaders within an organisation may not necessarily be in a position of authority while those in authority may not necessarily be effective leaders. Curtis et al. also state that distributed leadership enables the action and influence of people at all levels within an organisation, and supports interventions from wider communities of health professionals.

While definitions of advanced practice may differ slightly across national nursing and midwifery boards, a key common component is leadership and a high standard of education. This is reiterated and recognised by the World Health Organization (2020b) in their report on the nursing profession worldwide, where they state that a high standard of nursing education is essential for the active involvement of nurses in leadership, health policy, system improvement, research and evidence-informed practice. Below we present two case studies which illustrate examples of distributed leadership in the context of advanced nursing practice. Advanced practice and distributed leadership in system improvement, education, research and evidence-informed practice is exemplified in the first case study. The second case study highlights health policy, system improvement and evidence-informed practice. Having presented the case studies we will then explore through these cases studies some of the enablers and barriers to implementing distributed leadership within advanced practice contexts.

Case study: Distributed leadership and enabling practice-driven research within an acute hospital setting

A university school of nursing and midwifery and its allied hospitals had a long history of working together to improve clinical practice and research. A newly established Centre for Practice and Healthcare Innovation merged expertise in these areas by bringing together the staff and practices of the hospital and the academic strength of the university in a symbiotic partnership of equals, with leadership and responsibility for the initiative distributed over a team of five experienced staff, two within the university and three within the hospital. The team met monthly in the hospital. The aims of the research initiative were as follows:

- to encourage and support collaborative innovations in research, education, practice and implementation
- to develop an extensive national network of practice innovation units that worked together to share ideas and resources for mutual benefit and for the common good.

Following preliminary consultation with the team, a needs analysis was conducted. This identified a need for research question development, data entry of existing nurse–patient data sets, data analysis and write up, assistance with access to relevant literature, assistance with obtaining funding, and finally assistance with dissemination to the wider professions in posters, talks or papers. The team decided that a quantitative researcher/research fellow would be required to assist advanced nurse practitioners and others in the hospital in realising their research outputs and taking advantage of the data they had generated as part of their ongoing practices. Together the team applied for and obtained research facilitation funding distributed across the various hospital departments. The funding enabled access to research support seminars at the School of Nursing and Midwifery and collaborative on-site education and training that addressed the needs of the advanced practice nursing staff.

Within the first year of operation the distributed leadership model of the coordinating team of advanced nurse practitioners, a director of nursing and academics produced twelve collaborative research teams with each team responsible for its own leadership and outputs. The tripartite research teams consisted of a practitioner, an academic and the research fellow, each leading in their area of expertise on the project. The research fellow worked across all teams. The practitioners were nurses with a research role, including advanced nurse practitioners and clinical nurse specialists. Practice-generated research questions were addressed. The projects were not for academic qualifications. The academics from the School of Nursing and Midwifery had discipline-specific knowledge and methodological and publishing experience. The research fellow had quantitative expertise, data management and analysis skills, and acted as the central contact point for the initiative. The fellow managed the operational elements of the joint initiative and also contributed to literature reviews and writing. Authorship for the outputs were distributed across the team members and order of authorship was decided at the start of the project and writing tasks allocated across the team. The research fellow was included on all publications where they had an input.

The model was evaluated by McKee et al. (2017). The evaluation utilised a mixed-methods design and an implementation science framework. The main method of evaluation was through focus groups. Output was analysed using thematic analysis. In addition, a short survey questionnaire was circulated to all participants to ascertain their self-reported research skills before and after the intervention. An inventory of research outputs was also collated.

In the first year, twelve new clinical nurse-led research projects were conducted and reported in six peer-reviewed papers, two non-peer-reviewed papers and twenty conference presentations. The main strengths of the intervention were its promptness to complete research, to publish and to showcase clinical innovations. The main barriers identified were time, appropriate support from academics and from peers. The majority of participants had increased experience at scientific writing and data analysis. The evaluation concluded that the initiative, which distributed research leadership across the clinical and academic domains, increased research outputs and capacity of clinically based nurses. Furthermore, it highlighted that interventions to enhance nursing research and their evaluation are crucial if we are to address the deficit of nurse-led patient-centred research in the literature.

Case study: Developing a nurse-led recovery model across a city's community addiction services

According to the International Nurses Society for Addiction (IntNSA, 2020), addiction 'knows no boundaries [of] gender, race, age, religion, socio-economic status, or country'. Substance use may present in any setting, be it primary care, emergency care, intensive care, community care including care homes, retirement homes, forensic settings such as prison/jail, and schools. By virtue of the known prevalence of drugs and alcohol misuse, nurses, wherever they are practising, will be confronted by addiction or problematic drug or alcohol use.

Nurses working specifically for the addiction services reflect the diversity of the challenge of addiction and have a wide range of professional experience and qualifications. Their clinical role is varied and encompasses a varied range of responsibilities and functions. This has evolved to meet the similarly diverse and complex health needs of clients attending the addiction services. These needs include addiction, mental health problems, blood-borne viruses, chronic and acute illnesses, pre- and post-natal care of a pregnant client with substance use issues, health promotion, and assistance with dealing with judicial systems, child and family agencies, and probation services. These personal and health system issues are often exacerbated by poverty, poor housing and social conditions (Comiskey et al., 2019).

In terms of workload, currently all clients admitted into centralised addiction treatment services or so-called local or 'satellite' clinics have been regarded as part of the nursing caseload. Within one such region, the nursing leadership team acknowledged that this position required a review in order to streamline care and workload, as well as providing the most appropriate care to match the discipline-specific skills and competencies of the nursing team. Furthermore, in an effort to maintain safe nursing practice, it was recognised that there was a need to evaluate the current systems of caseload management and delivery of quality care.

To address this need, local nursing leadership collaborated with people who used their services and with a local university to identify client needs, to review nursing models of practice, and to devise an implementation plan to pilot and evaluate a proposed new addiction nursing model. The region's nursing leadership team consisted of an experienced assistant director of nursing who worked alongside four senior nurses of varying disciplines from infectious diseases to community care and varying positions from advanced nurse practitioner to clinical nurse specialist. Decisions were made collectively at monthly meetings and each member of the nursing team decided to review a nursing model and report back to the wider team on the suitability of that model for addiction nursing. The local university led on obtaining client views of their nursing service and measuring their needs. Responsibility for the delivery and success of the project was distributed across the team and all results were fed back and reviewed by the nursing team where final decisions were made collectively. The result of this distributed leadership process, whereby each team member contributed and led on one aspect of the wider project, was the development of the evidence-informed, 'Healthy Addiction Treatment' (HAT) recovery model for addiction nursing (Comiskey et al., 2019). The findings on client needs emphasised the need to address clients' mental health within a range of settings. The model prioritised each client's individual need in a dedicated one-on-one session with their addiction nurse. The team decided they would provide six one-on-one sessions with a volunteering client and work with them in their setting, be it anxiety due to a pending court appearance or fears in relation to a new pregnancy. The first challenge had been addressed and the second challenge of wider implementation remained.

Within the implementation stage, distributed leadership again contributed to successful implementation. At each monthly meeting the implementation of the HAT model was a standing agenda item. Each team member brought their implementation challenge and their proposed solution to the meeting. The implementation framework of Van Dyke (2013), which identifies four stages of implementation from exploration, installation, initial implementation to full implementation was used to evaluate the roll out of the model (Figure 9.1).

During roll out and implementation of the model it was clear from the nursing and client feedback that the model did not always work in practice. We know from the Van Dyke (2013) model that stage 3 of implementation involves managing change, deploying data systems and initiating improvement cycles. The notion of improvement cycles is well documented in the area of change management

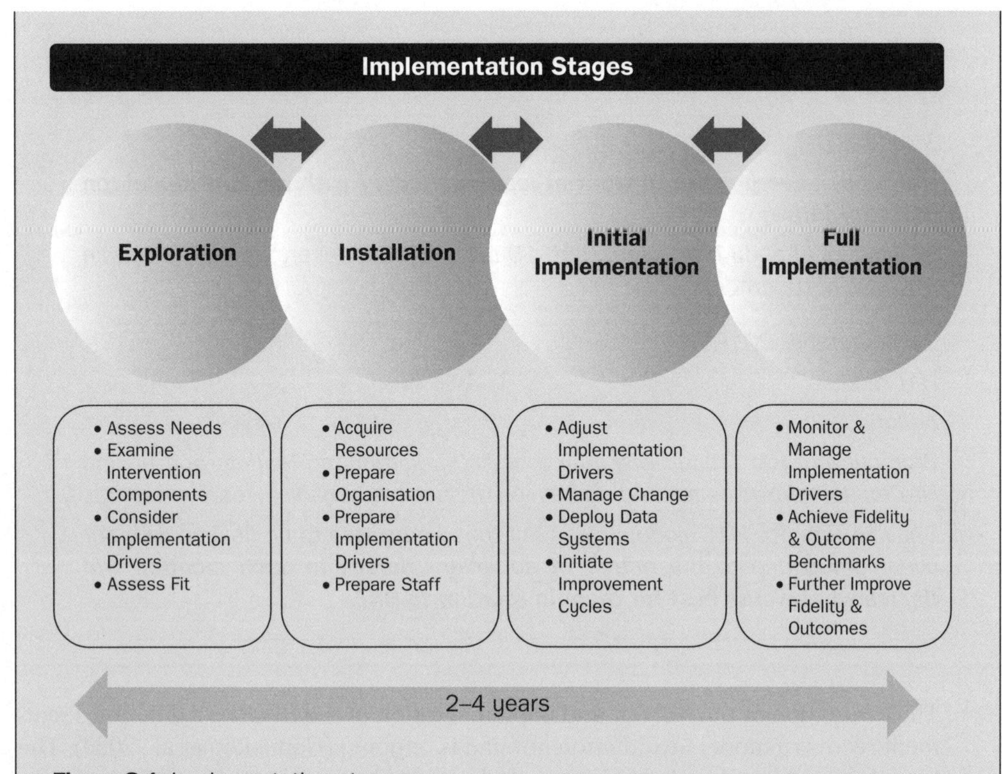

Figure 9.1 Implementation stages

within health services. Figure 9.2 summarises one such cycle known as a 'Plan, Do, Study, Act' (PDSA) cycle.

Working together the nursing teams initiated a series of PDSA cycles and together they refined the operationalisation of the HAT model. An extract from the team

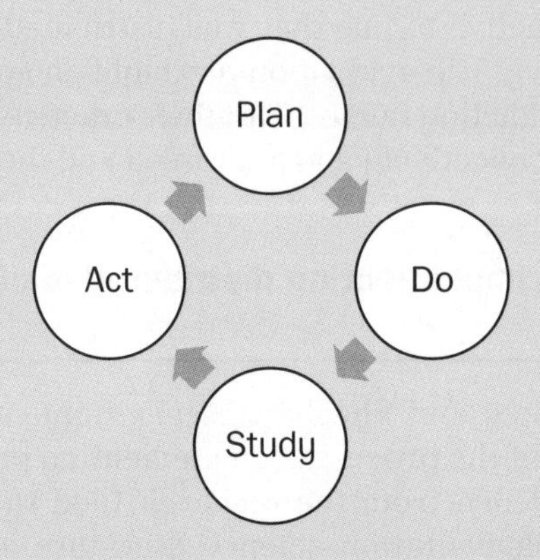

Figure 9.2 A model for improvement – the Plan, Do, Study, Act (PDSA) cycle

meeting minutes below illustrates this process of change distributed across the team (Comiskey et al., 2020).

1 June 2019

HAT Model: ***Every nurse to treat at least one client with the HAT model (on nurse initiative)****.*

HAT model already discussed. Core 10 to be done on every new client within 4 weeks of treatment.

11 September 2019

HAT model

Action Plan

Promotion of Hat Model: Displaying posters, distributing leaflets and having HAT model referral as a standing item on the agenda of clinical team meetings.

Specific Time for HAT Model: It was felt that we needed to be flexible with our client group due to the nature of addiction. ***Nurses in each location will decide what works best for them in relation to HAT****.*

The evaluation of the roll out and implementation of the Healthy Addiction Treatment recovery model in addiction nursing is ongoing (Comiskey et al., 2020). The team have returned to their original study clients to reassess their ongoing needs. The distribution of leadership is ongoing and work is underway to share the learning with other addiction teams. A Massive Open Online Course or MOOC in Addiction Nursing is also planned so that other nurses and other professions can learn from the experiences of the Irish nursing team. Nursing caseloads are no longer considered to be the full client registration list of the treatment centre, rather caseloads are defined as the group of current clients in receipt of the HAT model of care. Nurses in the services have changed their practice from one that was outdated and reactive to one that was distributed leadership driven, client-centred and innovative. The evaluation has highlighted the improved ownership and satisfaction of addiction nurses with their practice. Challenges, barriers and enablers were faced collectively and addressed and these we highlight below.

Enablers and barriers to implementing distributed leadership in advanced practice

According to Comiskey and Sheehan (2017), implementation science can be defined as the study of the process of implementing programmes and practices that have some evidence from the research field to suggest they are worth replicating. The implementation science literature as summarised by Burke et al. (2012) emphasises that implementation is a process rather than an event and that there are distinct phases or stages of implementation: (1) exploration,

(2) installation, (3) initial implementation and (4) full implementation. These phases and the enablers and barriers associated with them also apply to the implementation of advanced practice-based initiatives and we shall see within the case studies how distributed leadership assisted with this process.

Metz et al. (2015) propose three core implementation enablers that are important throughout all stages of implementation, which provides useful guidance for healthcare leaders in steering change efforts. These three elements are:

1. Building and using implementation teams to lead implementation efforts in an active manner
2. Using data to inform decision-making and continuous practice improvement
3. Developing sustainable implementation infrastructure.

Within the first case study on developing research capacity in a busy acute hospital setting, we saw that the project, while steered by an overall team of five members from the university and the hospital, when operationalised was founded on sets of core teams consisting of the nurse practitioner, nurse academic and the research fellow. Within the hospital all nursing staff in advanced nursing roles ($n = 72$) were invited to take part in the intervention. These invitations asked those with a clinically based research topic of interest they wished to develop or like support with, to volunteer to be part of the intervention. A total of seventeen advanced nurses met the eligibility criteria in that they were in an advanced nursing role and had a clinically based research topic they wished to develop. In the first year twelve clinical nurse researchers participated in the intervention. These nurses were all at an advanced level and therefore had qualifications up to master's level. Each member within a team led on an aspect of the project and took responsibility for their unique contribution. The output of a poster or paper or practice guideline could not be achieved without the input of each team member. With regards to the second enabler, the five-member steering group devised the model based on the data on nurse practitioner needs, monitored and evaluated the initiative after its first year of operation and addressed challenges. The research capacity-building inputs of research workshops on writing and publishing and applying for research grants enabled the sustainability of the research initiative and this initiative continues today within the Trinity Centre for Practice and Healthcare Innovation (see https://www.tcd.ie/tcphi/research-collaboration/). The second aim of establishing a network of research innovation units across a range of hospitals has been achieved with the current inclusion of ten national hospitals/services ranging in expertise and diversity from the National Children Hospital to St. Patrick's Mental Health Services, and from the regional hospital group to the Dublin Midlands Hospital Group.

Within the second case study, the key to success was the distribution of leadership across the core or base implementation team and beyond to each nurse working in an addiction service in the region. The base team consisted of the assistant director of nursing for the addiction services in the region, the key nursing personnel from infection disease nursing, community nursing and the methadone treatment centre, and three university academics with addiction research backgrounds and varying levels of experience. Each member within the team assumed a responsibility for leading on interviewing clients, leading on nursing model reviews, and leading on resource and time allocation for the initiative. This distribution can be seen in the quote below from one team member,

> And the team are very much part of this – they were involved in designing everything. They were designing posters. I mean a few of them designed the care plan. So they are very much part of the whole thing. And the communication is very very good. (Comiskey et al., 2020: 35)

With regard to data systems, evidence of the importance of data systems and capturing data on clients who participated in the model can be found in the comment below from the evaluation:

> And we have a shared folder. So all the tools (data collection instruments) are in that and if anything is changed, an email goes out to tell them. And obviously their comments are invited. (Comiskey et al., 2020: 35)

The importance of sharing the responsibility for the data management among the practitioners can also be seen. Data systems have also been deployed throughout the organisation to facilitate effective implementation. These have included online shared central folders, excel sheets, manuals, updated care plans, and posters and leaflets. This can be seen in the quote below:

> And it's all about setting up systems that work for yourself. I find the shared folder brilliant. Email is brilliant. All those systems of communication. Having you know, a system where staff are not afraid to ring you up, I mean the staff here would ring me up and X and Y all the time with different queries all the time in relation to the HAT (Healthy Addiction Treatment) model and any of us will answer the question. So they are probably the key things. And be a leader, not a dictator. (Comiskey et al., 2020: 43)

It is also interesting to note the use of the pronoun 'we' in this extract, again illustrating the idea of the collective leadership. Within the HAT implementation team the nursing care plan was also redesigned incorporating national metrics for mental health. Thus, monthly metrics on the HAT model were being captured, as can be seen form the quote below:

> The other thing that we have done is we had to redesign our care plan. So we designed the care plan and we used the care plan from the Mental Health Commission and we also incorporated the national metrics for mental health as well. So now they are both part of our care plan. So it means now that when we are doing metrics every month on the HAT model, all the information is in the care plan. So it doesn't mean that we are extracting it differently each day or each year and it makes it much easier for us and the nurses that could forget stuff once the care plan is built in. (Comiskey et al., 2020: 43)

The development of these systems and processes also addressed enabler 3 above, which says that a sustainable implementation infrastructure needs to be in place to ensure ongoing implementation.

According to Burke et al. (2012), barriers to implementation are grouped under three headings, namely, the external environment, vested interests and resistance to change. All three were present to a greater or lesser extent within the implementation of distributed leadership across the two case studies. McKee et al. (2017) in their evaluation of the first case study initiative, highlight in their findings the threats to the process. These were directly related to the three overall barriers and included a lack of time due to the busy hospital environment, dealing with competing interests from other work demands, and the resistance of some colleagues to change. These are summarised in the following quotes,

> Put under pressure, when no protected time at work.
> Colleagues felt I was removed, spent a lot of time on it (research).
> Seen not to be pulling your weight in practice if doing research. (McKee et al., 2017: 9–10)

The survey results also highlighted some of these barriers indirectly.

Similarly within the second case study barriers were encountered. Perhaps the greatest challenge was recognition of the model implementation beyond the nursing leadership. This was illustrated in the following quote,

> It was brought up at our meeting within the XXX about the lack of buy-in from our senior managers. It was noted. The information that came from that and other follow on meetings from conferences, was actually fed back to our senior managers. And a meeting was requested. During that meeting I met with my manager and explained the difficulty about buy-in. She did ask if there was anything she could do to help, so we are keeping it on the agenda. (Comiskey et al., 2020: 33)

According to the report the meeting has since taken place and the difficulties explained in relation to the buy-in documented along with an offer of help to address it. The item remains on the agenda until a solution is reached. The buy-in from senior managers remains an ongoing issue with this initiative and illustrates how difficult it can be to address these barriers.

Conclusion

In their conclusion to the evaluation of their initiative, McKee et al. (2017) look at the context of advanced nurse practice in Ireland and internationally. They state that the social context of advanced nursing in Ireland and internationally dictated a change in research involvement for newly created and growing advanced nursing roles. However, within the local context, the fact that a research culture was not embedded in the hospital site did cause issues in the implementation. The intervention was put in place to address some of these issues by developing a supportive nurse-led research intervention. This intervention however proved successful in increasing research capacity and research output of clinical nurses with a research competency attributed to their role.

Similarly, based on the evaluation findings of the wider pilot implementation of the Healthy Addiction Treatment (HAT) model in the second case study, it was evident that a highly motivated team of stakeholders from nurses to clients to leadership were involved but further development in the key area of data systems and fidelity to the model was required to ensure the ongoing successful scale up and roll out to other regions. The priority recommendation from the evaluation was that a brief time of review, reflection and capture is required to finalise and document the considerable work and learning from the Plan, Do, Study, Act improvement cycles and that this learning and leadership be shared across other nursing regions.

We have seen from Curtis et al. (Chapter 18, this volume) that effective leaders within an organisation may not necessarily be in a position of authority and that distributed leadership enables the action and influence of people at all levels within an organisation. Implementing distributed leadership and letting go of the recognition and security of the established hierarchy takes courage and confidence. This courage is required not only from the hierarchy but from the collective. Assuming a measure of leadership at every level of an organisation shifts not only the authority but also the responsibility and accountability to the collective. The implementation of any new practice across a healthcare organisation is in itself a science. This need for collective distributive and courageous leadership was never more evident than in the World Health Organization's approach to tackling the Covid-19 virus pandemic in 2020. The recognition of the work of the global collective was noted in the words of Irishman Dr Michael J. Ryan, head of the WHO Emergencies Program and the WHO response to the pandemic, when he noted,

> . . . the ability of international health agencies to respond has greatly improved. There is greater international collaboration, improved supply chains, more involvement with private-sector supplies and improved scientific capacity. (Ryan, 2020)

Perhaps out of this pandemic and given the work by local advanced nursing practitioners, the seeds of distributed leadership and their benefits are sown for the benefit of all.

Key concepts discussed

- There is a global shortage of nurses and nursing leadership at a time when leadership was never more important.
- Across several continents the leadership role of advanced nurse practitioners has emerged and developed with varying but similar definitions.
- Advanced nurse practitioners can make use of the distributed leadership model to enhance nursing and nursing education, research, service and patient outcomes.
- Implementing distributed leadership within an acute hospital or community nursing service is supported by known key enablers and hindered by barriers.
- Implementing distributed leadership and letting go of the recognition and security of the established hierarchy takes courage and confidence. This courage is required not only from the hierarchy but from the collective.
- This need for collective distributive and courageous leadership was never more important than now as nurses engage with the Covid-19 virus pandemic.

Key readings

- Burke, K., Morris, K. and McGarrigle, L. (2012) *An Introductory Guide to Implementation*, Dublin: Centre for Effective Services. Available at: https://www.effectiveservices.org/assets/Guide_to_implementation_concepts_and_frameworks_Final.pdf (accessed 21 October 2020).
  This is a free downloadable guide that provides an overview and a summary of key readings in implementation science.
- McKee, G., Codd, M., Dempsey, O., Gallagher, P. and Comiskey, C. (2017) Describing the implementation of an innovative intervention and evaluating its effectiveness in increasing research capacity of advanced clinical nurses: Using the consolidated framework for implementation research, *BMC Nursing*, 16 (1): 21. Available at: https://bmcnurs.biomedcentral.com/articles/10.1186/s12912-017-0214-6 (accessed 21 October 2020).
  This article provides a practical example of distributed leadership implemented in an acute hospital setting.

Examples of studies

- Comiskey, C.M. and Sheehan, A. (2017) Using implementation science to guide leadership and determine readiness for change in healthcare, in E. Curtis and J. Cullen (eds.) *Leadership and Change for the Health Professional*, London: Open University Press, 238–253.
- Comiskey, C., Coyne, I., Lalor, J. and Begley, C. (2014) A national cross-sectional study measuring predictors for improved service user outcomes across clinical nurse or midwife specialist, advanced nurse practitioner and control sites, *Journal of Advanced Nursing*, 70 (5): 1128–1137.

Useful websites

- Centre for Effective Services: https://www.effectiveservices.org/
  The Centre for Effective Services has an excellent section on implementation and provides access to a range of free downloadable resources.
- The National Implementation Research Network: https://nirn.fpg.unc.edu/national-implementation-research-network
  This online network uses the science and practice of implementation to solve real-world problems.
- The International Nurses Society on Addictions: https://www.intnsa.org/
  This is a global society of nurses with an interest in addiction nursing.

References

Brook, S. and Rushforth, H. (2011) Why is the regulation of advanced practice essential?, *British Journal of Nursing*, 20 (16): 996, 998–1000.

Bryant-Lukosius, D., DiCenso, A., Browne, G. and Pinelli, J. (2004) Advanced practice nursing roles: Development, implementation and evaluation, *Journal of Advanced Nursing*, 48 (5): 519–529.

Burke, K., Morris, K. and McGarrigle, L. (2012) *An Introductory Guide to Implementation*, Dublin: Centre for Effective Services. Available at: https://www.effectiveservices.org/assets/Guide_to_implementation_concepts_and_frameworks_Final.pdf (accessed 7 May 2020).

Canadian Nurses Association (CNA) (2019) *Advanced Practice Nursing: A Pan-Canadian Framework*, Ottawa: CNA. Available at: https://www.cna-aiic.ca/-/media/cna/page-content/pdf-en/advanced-practice-nursing-framework-en.pdf?la=en&hash=76A98ADEE62E655E158026DEB45326C8C9528B1B (accessed 7 May 2020).

Comiskey, C.M. and Sheehan, A. (2017) Using implementation science to guide leadership and determine readiness for change in healthcare, in E. Curtis and J. Cullen (eds.) *Leadership and Change for the Health Professional*, London: Open University Press, 238–253.

Comiskey, C., Coyne, I., Lalor, J. and Begley, C. (2014) A national cross-sectional study measuring predictors for improved service user outcomes across clinical nurse or midwife specialist, advanced nurse practitioner and control sites, *Journal of Advanced Nursing*, 70 (5): 1128–1137.

Comiskey, C.M., Mathews, A., Williamson, C., Bruce, J., Mulaudzi, M. and Klopper, H. (2015) Scaling up nurse education: An evaluation of a national PhD capacity development programme in South Africa, in the context of the global shortage of nursing graduates, *Nurse Education Today*, 35 (5): 647–652.

Comiskey, C.M., Galligan, K., Flanagan, J., Deegan, J., Farnham, J. and Hall, A. (2019) Clients' views on the importance of a nurse-led approach and nurse prescribing in the development of the Healthy Addiction Treatment Recovery Model, *Journal of Addictions Nursing*, 30 (3): 169–176.

Comiskey, C., Galligan, K. and McDonagh, D. (2020) *Report on the roll out and implementation of the Healthy Addiction Treatment Recovery Model in Addiction Nursing Services*, Report for the Health Service Executive and the Nursing and Midwifery Planning and Development Unit, Ireland.

Donald, F., Bryant-Lukosius, D., Martin-Misener, R., Kaasalainen, S., Kilpatrick, K., Carter, N. et al. (2010) Clinical nurse specialists and nurse practitioners: Title confusion and lack of role clarity, *Nursing Leadership*, 23 (spec. issue): 189–201.

Hughes, R.L., Ginnett, R.C. and Curphy, G.J. (2006) *Leadership: Enhancing the Lessons of Experience*, 5th edition, New York: McGraw-Hill/Irwin.

International Nurses Society for the Addictions (IntNSA) (2020) https://www.intnsa.org/our-community/

Jones, M.L. (2005) Role development and effective practice in specialist and advanced practice roles in acute hospital settings: Systematic review and meta-synthesis, *Journal of Advanced Nursing*, 49 (2): 191–209.

Kleinpell, R.M., Hudspeth, R., Scordo, K.A. and Magdic, K. (2012) Defining NP scope of practice and associated regulations: Focus on acute care, *Journal of the American Academy of Nurse Practitioners*, 24 (1): 11–18.

Lowe, G., Plummer, V., O'Brien, A.P. and Boyd, L. (2012) Time to clarify – the value of advanced practice nursing roles in health care, *Journal of Advanced Nursing*, 68 (3): 677–685.

McKee, G., Codd, M., Dempsey, O., Gallagher, P. and Comiskey, C. (2017) Describing the implementation of an innovative intervention and evaluating its effectiveness in increasing research capacity of advanced clinical nurses: Using the consolidated framework for implementation research, *BMC Nursing*, 16 (1): 21. Available at: https://bmcnurs.biomedcentral.com/articles/10.1186/s12912-017-0214-6 (accessed 20 October 2020).

Metz, A., Naoom, S.F., Halle, T. and Bartley, L. (2015) *An Integrated Stage-Based Framework for Implementation of Early Childhood Programs and Systems*, Research Brief OPRE 2015-48, Washington, DC: Office of Planning, Research and Evaluation, Administration for Children and Families, US Department of Health and Human Services. Available at: http://www.acf.hhs.gov/sites/default/files/opre/es_cceepra_stage_based_framework_brief_508.pdf (accessed 7 May 2020).

National Council for the Professional Development of Nursing and Midwifery (NCNM) (2008) *Framework for Establishment of Clinical Nurse/Midwife Specialist Posts*, 4th edition, Dublin: NCNM. Available at: https://www.pna.ie/images/ncnm/CNS%20doc%204ed%20nov08.pdf (accessed 21 September 2020).

Nursing and Midwifery Board of Australia (NMBA) (2016) *Guidelines: For nurses applying for endorsement as a nurse practitioner*, Melbourne: NMBA. Available at: https://www.nursingmidwiferyboard.gov.au/Codes-Guidelines-Statements/Codes-Guidelines/Guidelines-on-endorsement-as-a-nurse-practitioner.aspx (accessed 5 June 2020).

Pulcini, J., Jelic, M., Gul, R. and Yuen Loke, A. (2010) An international survey on advanced practice nursing education, practice, and regulation, *Journal of Nursing Scholarship*, 42 (1): 31–39.

Roberts, J., Floyd, S. and Thompson, S. (2011) The clinical nurse specialist in New Zealand: How is the role defined?, *Nursing Praxis New Zealand*, 27 (2): 24–35.

Ryan, M. (2020) Irishman leading WHO response to coronavirus outbreak optimistic, *The Irish Times*, 2 February. Available at: https://www.irishtimes.com/news/health/irishman-leading-who-response-to-coronavirus-outbreak-optimistic-1.4159547 (accessed 7 May 2020).

Sheerin, F. and Curtis, E. (eds.) (2019) *Leadership for Intellectual Disability Service: Motivating Change and Improvement*, New York: Routledge.

Thompson, P. and Hyrkas, K. (2014) Global nursing leadership, *Journal of Nursing Management*, 22 (1): 1–3.

Van Dyke, M. (2013) *The Science and Practice of implementing science into practice*, presentation at the 2013 Global Implementation Conference. Available at: https://www.effectiveservices.org/resources/the-science-and-practice-of-integrating-science-into-practice (accessed 21 September 2020).

World Health Organization (WHO) (2020a) *WHO and partners call for urgent investment in nursing*, News release, 7 April, Geneva: WHO. Available at: https://www.who.int/news-room/detail/07-04-2020-who-and-partners-call-for-urgent-investment-in-nurses (accessed 5 June 2020).

World Health Organization (WHO) (2020b) *State of the World's Nursing: Investing in Education, Jobs and Leadership*, Geneva: WHO. Available at: https://www.who.int/publications-detail/nursing-report-2020 (accessed 4 May 2020).

Further reading

Comiskey, C. (2020) *Addiction Debates: Hot Topics from Policy to Practice*, Swift Series, London: Sage.

Curtis, E. and O'Connell, R. (2011) Essential leadership skills for motivating and developing staff, *Nursing Management*, 8 (5): 32–35.

Curtis, E.A., de Vries, J. and Sheerin, F.K. (2011) Developing leadership in nursing: Exploring core factors, *British Journal of Nursing*, 20 (5): 306–309.

10 Enacting distributed leadership in midwifery practice

Rhona O'Connell

Chapter topics

- A lack of effective leadership has been identified in reports on adverse maternity care.
- For effective working of multidisciplinary teams, shared leadership is required in the management of maternity emergencies.
- New leadership roles for midwives are emerging and models of distributed leadership should be considered for midwives at all levels of practice.

Introduction

Do midwives see themselves in leadership roles and if not, why not? Midwives enter their profession for a variety of reasons but when asked, they generally share a vision for what midwifery is – the satisfaction of accompanying women and their partners through a special time in their lives. Midwives share the joy of supporting women through pregnancy and birth, yet they also encounter traumatic events when birth may not be as expected. Midwives are required to balance supporting normality and routine care for healthy women, providing care for those with more complex needs, constantly assessing risk and a possible need to escalate care including dealing with emergency situations. Midwives who work in hospital or community settings recognise how routine care can change rapidly where the mother or baby's life may be at risk.

The absence of effective leadership is mentioned as a key factor in reports on adverse maternity care (HIQA, 2013; Kirkup, 2015; MBRRACE-UK, 2016), and management structures have been held to account with midwifery leads identified as part of the solution (Holohan, 2014; Divall, 2015; Read, 2019). While traditionally leadership was considered the role of managers of an organisation, there is greater awareness for leadership to be valued at all levels of practice (Turnbull James, 2011; NHS England, 2016; Deery and Fisher, 2017). As will be explored in this chapter, leadership is a key element in maternity strategies, and all midwives have a role not just in ensuring quality maternity care, but also in ensuring that the values of woman-centred care are enacted (Byrom and Kay, 2011; Deery and Fisher, 2017). While not being risk-averse, midwives can support normality in pregnancy and childbirth while also addressing the needs of women with diverse or complex care needs. Most midwives work collaboratively in the delivery of maternity care and contribute to multidisciplinary teams as required, particularly in emergency situations. This chapter will also explore recent discussions on midwifery leadership and where the leadership contributions of staff are valued, to see where a distributed model of leadership may provide solutions to the contemporary challenges in maternity care. This may require midwives to dismantle assumptions about leadership based on a hierarchical structure (Turnbull James, 2011) and be open to new approaches where the contributions of all are valued.

Leadership and maternity policies

Midwifery involvement in leadership, management and governance has been identified as a key factor to ensure effective provision of maternal, newborn and child health (Campbell et al., 2016; Bannon et al., 2017; WHO, 2018). In contrast, several reports, including that of MBRRACE-UK (2016), identified a lack of leadership in regard to care for women with multiple or complex care needs.

The maternity strategies of various nations see leadership as a key factor for leading on improvements of the maternity services, but how each body addresses this varies. To take a broad overview, a number of maternity strategies were reviewed to see how leadership was reflected in national strategies (this was restricted to published maternity strategies in the English language). The maternity strategies of Australia (Commonwealth of Australia, 2009), Ireland (Department of Health, 2016) and various UK strategies (Department of Health, Social Services and Public Policy, 2012; NHS England, 2016; Scottish Government, 2017; Welsh Government, 2019) were accessed.

In Australia, the national maternity strategy highlighted that leadership was required by the Australian Government to collaborate with states and territories to deliver on improvements required in maternity care (Commonwealth of Australia, 2009).

In the first national maternity strategy for Ireland (Department of Health, 2016), effective clinical leadership was repeatedly highlighted. While this was not explored in depth, this was the first report where midwives were identified as having a leadership role in the delivery of maternity care. In Ireland, obstetricians take the lead in all aspects of maternity care and the strategy provided a model of care which midwives can lead and deliver care to low-risk women. This was to provide choice for women and continuity of care, within a multidisciplinary framework of care. Effective leadership, management and governance arrangements, delivered by a skilled and competent workforce, in partnership with women, were put forward as key elements to the delivery of the strategy.

In a review of maternity services in Northern Ireland (Department of Health, Social Services and Public Policy, 2012), leadership was presented as a key driver for change in maternity care. The review identified the need for senior clinical leaders to take responsibility for changing the culture towards birth to one with a focus on keeping childbirth normal with safe, high-quality evidence-based care. Good clinical leadership and communication were portrayed as fundamental to support women, their partners and family. Consultant midwives were seen as pivotal in having a leadership role in the promotion of midwifery skills for normalising birth, with a potential to reduce intervention rates, and advance midwifery models of care, including midwife-led units and home births. Clinical leadership was presented as essential for quality improvement and innovation in maternity care. Senior midwives were required to be experts in the field, as well as being competent clinical leaders and team members, and must know and understand the responsibilities of other members of the team.

Similarly, the Scottish Government (2017) maternity strategy recognised that leadership was not just a governmental and organisational issue, but rather that collective leadership was important to the development of a positive work environment and that senior staff, across all disciplines, had a role to play. Strong and collective leadership was presented as important to the development of a positive work environment, with senior staff having a key role, including demonstrating positive behaviours and tackling poor behaviours when they arose. The strategy noted that governance, accountability and leadership are required at national, regional and local levels and, reflecting findings from the MBRRACE-UK report (2016), all maternity units should have high-performing, multi-professional teams in place. A key area of consensus was that maternity care should be multidisciplinary and involve a collaborative, team-based approach.

The maternity service five-year plan for Wales (Welsh Government, 2019) presented a vision of high-performing multi-professional teams delivering family-centred maternity care. The report acknowledged that this would require strong leadership, and while a particular model of leadership was not identified, it stated that leadership should be within a culture of research, development, continuous learning, best practice and innovation. Multi-professional leadership was required along with a need to embed leadership into practice areas, both to ensure safe, high-quality services and also for succession planning for future leaders. One recommendation was that structured multi-professional leadership programmes should be developed.

The *Better Births* report (NHS England, 2016) was a comprehensive review of maternity services in England with many recommendations for service development. This report highlighted the importance of leadership at all levels for the implementation and delivery of improvements in maternity services. As in other reports, there was a focus on the activities of multidisciplinary teams, with a need for shared training, common practices and respectful input from all professionals. Clear protocols for dealing with emergencies were required with effective leadership according to the situation that should not be dominated by one individual.

While the term distributed leadership is not mentioned, collective leadership is recognised throughout the *Better Births* report (NHS England, 2016). The report maintains that collective leadership is vital to creating a multi-professional learning culture with leadership roles for both midwifery and obstetric professionals and that leadership is a key determinant of the organisational culture in which multidisciplinary teams operate. In addition, it recommends that leaders from the top of an organisation should encourage, support and monitor the culture and leadership within their organisations. Midwives and obstetricians must work together as part of a single team focused on the needs of the women and babies in their care. This was considered vital for ensuring organisational cultures were continually improving, providing compassionate care for women and their families, with clear goals and objectives at every level. The provision of accurate data on performance against objectives is considered important so that teams can work to improve the quality of care.

Leadership in practice: Multidisciplinary teams

In all strategies reviewed, the working of the multidisciplinary team was considered key to the delivery of safe high-quality maternity care. This was also a recommendation contained within the last MBRRACE-UK report (2016), which highlighted the need to have high performing, multi-professional teams in place in all maternity units. The fluid nature of dealing with an emergent, potentially critical situation requires various clinicians to undertake a variety of roles as part of a multidisciplinary team. There are many situations where distributed leadership is a factor in the delivery of safe and effective care. An example of this is in the working of multidisciplinary teams as identified in the following case study.

Case study: Response to a potential maternity emergency

Problem: With a degree of autonomy, midwives provide care to childbearing women yet are aware that they may have to respond rapidly to an emergency as part of a multidisciplinary team.

Issue: A message is received that a pregnant woman with a significant antepartum haemorrhage (APH) is arriving by ambulance to a maternity unit. The woman is 34 weeks pregnant. Multidisciplinary teamwork is required for safe and effective care and to ensure optimum outcomes. Midwives, doctors and ancillary staff are involved.

The midwife who receives this call will identify key factors and inform the senior midwife and the other members of the team including obstetric doctors, an anaesthetist, other midwives and the neonatal team. Preparations will be made for the arrival of the woman and, following rapid assessment by the midwife and obstetric doctor, a plan of care will be determined which may involve an emergency caesarean birth. Theatre preparation and neonatal clinicians will be involved.

Various members of the multidisciplinary team share responsibilities and take leadership roles in the activities required to undertake care for this woman, her baby and her partner who may accompany her. How this scenario is managed may depend on the individuals on duty at the time of the event. If a consultant obstetrician is required, is it always the non-consultant hospital doctor (NCHD) who makes the decision or does a midwife identify when greater expertise is required? If there is a delay or potential error, does someone identify this quickly and seek solutions? Does it matter if this is a senior or junior member of the team, a midwife or a doctor?

Outcomes achieved: Midwives are in a strong position to provide leadership in maternity emergencies. The admission of the woman will require rapid assessment of her wellbeing and that of the baby. If, on arrival, the woman's blood loss is not excessive and if she and her baby are not compromised, the situation can stand down to the more routine aspects of care. If there are concerns about the wellbeing of mother or baby, the multidisciplinary team will be mobilised quickly to ensure optimal care is provided. Leadership is required at many levels to deliver safe and effective care.

Experienced midwives respond to potential emergency situations and are aware of the requirements to work as part of a multidisciplinary team. Midwives rely on obstetric doctors to lead, yet some obstetric staff (trainees or consultants) have less clinical experience or leadership expertise than the midwives themselves (Dekker et al., 2013). Midwives will have experience of this and know to escalate their concerns to a more senior clinician if greater expertise is required. While senior clinicians are required to take the lead for obstetric emergencies, even with skilled and experienced staff, the management of the situation requires not one leader, but many taking responsibility for various aspects of care (Rydenfält et al., 2015).

One study that explored the leadership functions of the members of a multidisciplinary team in maternity emergencies, used video analysis of simulated emergency scenarios (Janssens et al., 2019). It was noted that a midwife undertook dominant leadership roles in four out of the sixteen scenarios. Overall, obstetricians were more likely to take a leadership role related to clinical issues, while the leadership of midwives was more often reflected in their coordination of care, communication skills and supportive roles. The study concluded that midwives working within a hospital setting are in a strong position to provide leadership in maternity emergencies, in particular to perform non-clinical leadership functions. Janssens et al. (2019) described this as a model of shared interdisciplinary leadership but a similar paper in a theatre setting used this as an example of distributed leadership at work (Rydenfält et al., 2015).

Rydenfält et al. (2015) identified the following leadership criteria enacted by members of the theatre team:

1. Initiative and decision-making regarding the work, such as medical decisions and the initiation of practical actions
2. Maintaining routines and the formal procedures required
3. Physical arrangements such as transporting the patient
4. Personnel issues, such as ensuring sufficient personnel were available when needed
5. Equipment issues, including organising, checking and placing the equipment
6. Asking for advice or help and responding to questions
7. Providing supervision or suggestions, without explicitly being requested to do so

8. Information retrieval necessary for work
9. Handing over important information regarding work, such as communicating changes in the patient's condition, warning or alerting co-workers of something, and speaking up if they see something that is going wrong.

All these were carried out by a variety of personnel with various clinicians taking leadership roles related to the activity. For Rydenfält et al. (2015), a form of distributed leadership takes place.

Situational awareness: A key leadership role

It is increasingly recognised that when involved in managing an emergency situation, senior midwives or doctors are expected to provide leadership including maintaining situational awareness (Winter et al., 2017). This can be difficult where often the most senior member of the medical team is engaged in specific tasks such as performing a Category 1 caesarean birth or resuscitating a newborn baby. Senior midwives may be required to manage resources and other midwives may also be involved in tasks such monitoring vital signs, managing medication or assisting with fluid requirements. Where there are several clinicians participating in care and an awareness that additional leadership responsibilities may be required, any member of the team can observe and articulate what needs to be done. Leadership in this situation may involve responding and taking initiative in a changing situation, providing information where an escalation of care may be required, asking questions or anticipating the next aspect of care. The quick action and busyness of individuals undertaking tasks rapidly can lead to a lack of awareness of broader issues. Situational awareness and leadership are important aspects in emergency scenarios; comments and suggestions, by even a junior member of the team, should be clear and loud enough to be heard, and most importantly valued by the team, particularly if errors are to be avoided. This can occur where there is a recognition that leadership is distributed among the team, there is a culture of safety and trust within a unit and where each member of the team is valued.

In all emergency situations, there is a need to maintain situational awareness and a willingness to speak up and highlight concerns, such as recognising changing clinical parameters or anticipating the next aspect of care. Where there is an awareness that leadership is not invested in just one individual but can move around according to need, errors are less likely to occur. Situational awareness – being sensitive to important cues, thinking ahead, anticipating problems and sharing concerns with the team – is a key factor in the Practical Obstetric Multi-Professional Training (PROMPT) programme (Winter et al., 2017).

Leadership and effective communication are essential parts in the delivery of the PROMPT programme which requires a team leader to both direct the team and to ensure safety. This may involve the team leader becoming involved in managing care or standing back to delegate tasks. Good team leaders should be willing to listen, open to criticism and constructive feedback, and respect the expertise of each member of the team (Winter et al., 2017). Debriefing after an event should adopt a 'no blame' culture, inviting feedback from each member of the team with an acknowledgement of what went well, what could have been done better and an openness to learning from the event.

Training of multidisciplinary team members together has been shown to improve team relationships and break down barriers between midwives and obstetricians (Kirkup, 2015; NHS England, 2016). This is endorsed by the PROMPT programme which has a focus on shared learning (Winter et al., 2017). This approach has led to improvements in communication, multidisciplinary team performance in emergency situations and clinical outcomes (Siassakos et al., 2010; Shoushtarian et al., 2014; Kumar et al., 2018).

Leadership in midwifery

Traditionally, leadership in maternity care has been viewed as bureaucratic and hierarchical (Byrom and Kay, 2011). In recent years, leadership has moved away from focusing on individual leaders with a set of static skills to more holistic approaches (Divall, 2015) with increasing recognition of the interdependence of workers at all levels of an organisation (Turnbull James, 2011). In practice settings, not just in the management of emergencies, tasks can be distributed among core staff. This can be a form of distributed leadership if staff are willing to take on additional roles, with a move from focusing solely on daily activities and routines to sharing a vision, with an openness to ideas and a willingness to introduce change.

It has long been recognised that clear leadership is required to effect change but it is also widely recognised that there are barriers to enacting change (Martin et al., 2015; Zwedberg et al., 2015; Madeley et al., 2019) and that hierarchical leadership models exist in healthcare which can impede innovation (Sandall et al., 2009; Pollard, 2011). This is why increasingly, distributed leadership, where leadership is valued at all levels in an organisation, is recommended as an appropriate model for midwives to consider in both practice and the delivery of care (Fitzgerald et al., 2013; Deery and Fisher, 2017). An example of this can be seen in the following case study, which demonstrates the leadership skills required to implement a practice change.

Case study: Leadership for change

Problem: Skin-to-skin care is recommended by the WHO (2018) for all newborn babies as it enhances mother–infant bonding, provides thermal-stabilisation and promotes breastfeeding. The barriers to introducing skin-to-skin care in theatre include concerns about safety, staffing levels and a lack of policies to support this practice (Balatero et al., 2019).

Issue: An audit of optimal skin-to-skin care for all newborn babies was undertaken by a midwife and while the prevalence of this was high for women who had vaginal births, women having caesarean births did not have this experience as this was not practice in the unit at the time and a previous attempt to introduce it had not been successful.

Following the audit, the midwife undertook an action research (Coghlan and Brannick, 2014) study to see if skin-to-skin care could be implemented for women experiencing a caesarean birth. Discussions with key stakeholders revealed a willingness to introduce this but that a policy would have to be developed and approved to ensure safe implementation of this practice change. The policy was developed in consultation with key personnel that included, medical, midwifery and nursing staff. Education was provided to the theatre staff, including the need to re-position ECG leads on the woman's back, and front-opening theatre gowns were obtained. The baby would also have to be monitored by a staff member and the practice of skin-to-skin care documented.

Outcomes achieved: Skin-to-skin care was introduced and subsequent audits revealed that this had become routine practice for caesarean births. A survey of women revealed satisfaction that this could be provided for caesarean births and this contributed positively to women's birth experience (Campbell and O'Connell, 2020).

This change in practice was introduced due to the desire of the midwife to improve the care of women experiencing a caesarean birth. Leadership skills were required to follow through and to implement the change. This required providing the evidence to endorse the need for change, sourcing the support of senior clinicians, developing the policy with the quality improvement office, and providing education and support for the midwives and nurses who would be required to implement the change. A key element for the staff was the positive response from the women and the awareness that this change would improve the birth experience for women having a caesarean birth.

A similar approach was reported by Sheard et al. (2017) who found that when implementing change, the personal determination of the individual was important. Equally important was their ability to connect with disparate teams, use evidence to influence others and utilise the organisational culture. Gathering robust data to demonstrate that their innovation had a positive impact was seen as essential to its progression. While the participants did not see themselves as leaders, to change established practice a model of distributed leadership was evident in all successful innovations (Sheard et al., 2017).

Leadership roles

To advance the challenges in healthcare and provide clinical leadership, many countries have introduced clinical roles such as clinical midwifery specialists (Australia/Ireland/UK), advanced midwife practitioners (Belgium/Ireland/UK), consultant midwives (UK) and certified nurse-midwives (USA). These midwives work with greater autonomy in practice settings and take on various amounts of responsibility for quality and safety, with leadership and inter-professional collaboration a key element in their role (Gaskell and Beaton, 2015; Fealy et al., 2018;

Casey et al., 2019). The following categories of leadership outcomes were identified for advanced practice roles: (i) capacity- and capability-building of the multidisciplinary team, including training and mentoring across the team and motivating staff development; (ii) measures of esteem, including satisfaction of the multidisciplinary team; (iii) new initiatives for clinical practice and healthcare delivery; and (iv) clinical practice based on evidence (Elliott et al., 2014). In Belgium, Van Hecke et al. (2019) found that leadership roles for advanced practitioners were mainly directed towards change management and innovation and included guideline development, but few nurses or midwives in advanced practice roles contributed to policy development at hospital or department level. For advanced practice midwives in England, their work focused on clinical practice, leadership and collaborative practice, and improving quality and developing service, while developing competency in self and others was seen to be key to their role (Gaskell and Beaton, 2015). Their leadership role was largely self-directed, focused on service developments and facilitated by close interdisciplinary collaboration.

Without leadership roles to support a broad approach to quality in the delivery of maternity care, midwives in management roles can find that their role is driven by staffing, budgetary constraints, quality measures and risk assessments. Divall (2015) highlighted the challenges for midwifery leads who are expected to remain clinically active. With additional responsibilities, the midwives found it difficult to maintain a clinical role and remain clinically credible. A challenge for midwives undertaking these roles is to seek a balance between clinical and non-clinical work and to resolve conflicts between their professional values and corporate responsibilities (Divall, 2015).

According to Byrom and Downe (2010), the attributes of good midwifery leadership include the ability to act knowledgeably, safely and competently with a capacity to lead by example and to empower others. Valued aspects of good leaders included approachability, empathy, supportiveness, good communication and negotiation skills, and the ability to motivate others rather than exercise power. For Byrom and Downe (2010), this equates to transformational leadership theory and good midwifery leadership. Similarly, Hewitt et al. (2019) explored the attributes of good leaders for midwifery group practices and found what was important for the midwives in the group was someone who stands up for midwives and women, can remain clinically credible and can juggle the management issues of the practice setting.

This was also noted by Christoffersen et al. (2020) who explored how frontline managers provided follow-up support to midwives following critical incidents. Different leadership models were noted but some managers engaged in providing proactive relational support to help midwives cope. When following up after adverse incidents, these relational leaders were seen to prioritise individual support, incident debriefing and supporting personal development, a model that was described as distributed leadership. A review of leadership research in nursing found these types of behaviours to be associated with improved outcomes (Cummings et al., 2010).

Though transactional leadership is commonly observed in healthcare settings, transformational leadership has been widely promoted as leadership for change (Curtis and O'Connell, 2011) and is considered appropriate for leadership within midwifery (Byrom and Downe, 2010; Rumsey et al., 2017). However, Lee (2014) argues that it is time to move away from the transformational leadership model. The model, with its focus on visionary leaders, can be anti-democratic as it requires others to accept the vision advanced by those in senior roles, often with no contribution from those required to enact the change.

More recently, a model of distributed leadership is seen as a way to move forward. The King's Fund (2011) report on the future of leadership and management in the NHS highlighted that if organisational change is to be effected, leadership should be distributed away from the top of an organisation and shared by the individuals who will implement the change. The report recommends that service providers should focus on leadership practices rather than leadership roles and that those in positional leadership positions develop leadership at all levels (King's Fund, 2011). This is important as change requires multiple actors who have an understanding of the healthcare context and have relationships with those who share that context. Those engaged in leadership roles should work collaboratively, across organisational and professional boundaries, so that new practices or innovations can emerge.

This was demonstrated by Fitzgerald et al. (2013) who studied organisational change in healthcare settings. Their study included a number of maternity units where change was required to implement community-based caseload midwifery services. In the units where the change was most successful, effective leadership was in place at multiple levels with core teams supported by a range of collaborators. Senior leaders framed and resourced the change, while those in middle management drove forward the required changes through engagement with all staff and by creating policies to support local needs. Those leading the change were open to suggestions and a consultant midwife was key in implementing the change and supporting staff. A level of trust was apparent at all levels of the organisation. A distributed model of leadership was observed and the community teams were established successfully with flexible working hours to suit the needs of midwives and mothers. Change was less effective in settings where there was a lack of collaboration, trust or leadership at different levels in the organisation.

Though variable contextual features could enable or inhibit distributed leadership, Fitzgerald et al. (2013) found that service improvement was more likely to be successful where there were positive relationships between management and professional groups and leadership for change was widely distributed. The presence of effective flexible clinical leaders was associated with better outcomes. In organisations where there were leadership gaps or a lack of clarity about leadership roles, incomplete patterns of change leadership resulted in limited progress.

Distributed leadership based on relationships, unlike transformational leadership, encourages all workers to take a leadership role, to be involved in decision-making and with clear values central to both the delivery of care and also when change is required. Distributed leadership which involves collaboration and teamwork, essential for the delivery of quality and safety in maternity settings and the importance of good collegial relationships, was reported to be one of the most important aspects of sustaining midwives in practice (Crowther et al., 2016; Leversidge, 2016). It has also been shown that effective relational leadership styles can enhance recruitment and create healthy work environments (Cummings et al., 2010).

A distributed model of leadership was highly recommended for midwives by Deery and Fisher (2017), who stated that a leadership model that enacts midwifery values, and the value given to the contribution of midwives who seek to enhance the experiences of childbearing women and their colleagues, should be widely adopted. Midwifery leadership should be evident in all areas of practice, to ensure practice standards are maintained. The authors contend that a value-led approach to leadership may offer a good way to combat reluctance among some midwives to develop their practice beyond defensive practice (Deery and Fisher, 2017).

Conclusion

The benefits of distributed leadership can be seen in many units where midwifery values are enacted on a daily basis, providing woman-centred care, sharing the joy with parents when there is a good outcome while also supporting parents through more difficult birth experiences or during pregnancy loss. Distributed leadership is also apparent when midwives, who are increasingly required to provide guideline- and policy-directed care, have the opportunity to engage in policy development and innovation. While guidelines and policies are required to be evidence based, they can also reflect a values approach ensuring that the needs and views of women are central to the guideline development. Distributed leadership can also be recognised when midwives and others in senior roles encourage innovation and consult authentically with staff when changes are required.

Distributed leadership is also a key element in the management of emergency situations, where collective leadership is required among the members of the multidisciplinary team – the comments, suggestions and actions by even a junior member of the team can be valuable if errors are to be avoided. This can occur where there is a recognition that leadership is distributed among the team, there is a culture of safety and trust within a unit, and where each member of the team is valued.

Effective leadership is required every day, in every setting and at all levels of practice in maternity care. Where midwives can enact their values in the implementation of change and where there is trust and recognition of the roles of individuals in decision-making and provision of care, particularly in the management of emergency situations, quality in maternity care can be achieved. Optimal care can be focused in seeking to provide positive experiences for childbearing women as they receive care from midwives in the maternity services.

Key concepts discussed

- Effective leadership is a key element for midwifery practice and change in maternity care.
- For practice and service innovation, leadership at all levels is required and a model of distributed leadership is a useful approach to consider.
- While being open to new ways of working, midwives need to maintain their midwifery values and be aware of their personal contribution to leadership practices.

Key readings

- Byrom, S. and Downe, S. (2014) *Roar Behind the Silence: Why Kindness, Compassion and Respect Matter in Maternity Care*, London: Pinter & Martin.
- Downe, S. and Byrom, S. (2019) *Squaring the Circle: Normal Birth Research, Theory and Practice in a Technological Age*, London: Pinter & Martin.
- Downe, S., Byrom, S. and Simpson, L. (eds.) (2011) *Essential Midwifery Practice: Leadership, Expertise and Collaborative Working*, Chichester: Wiley-Blackwell.

Examples of empirical research

- Deery, R. and Fisher, P. (2017) Professionalism and person-centredness: Developing a practice-based approach to leadership within NHS maternity services in the UK, *Health Sociology Review*, 26 (2): 143–159.
- Fitzgerald, L., Ferlie, E., McGivern, G. and Buchannan, D. (2013) Distributed leadership patterns and service improvement: Evidence and argument from English healthcare, *Leadership Quarterly*, 24 (1): 227–239.
- Janssens, S., Simon, R., Barwick, S., Clipperton, S., Beckmann, M. and Marshall, S. (2019) Midwifery leadership in maternity emergencies: A video analysis, *Journal of Interprofessional Care*. Available at: https://doi.org/10.1080/13561820.2019.1675611.

References

Balatero, J.S., Spilker, A.F. and McNiesh, S.G. (2019) Barriers to skin-to-skin contact after cesarean birth, *American Journal of Maternal/Child Nursing*, 44 (3): 137–143.

Bannon, E.M., Alderdice, F. and McNeills, J. (2017) A review of midwifery leadership, *British Journal of Midwifery*, 25 (10): 655–661.

Byrom, S. and Downe, S. (2010) 'She sort of shines': Midwives' accounts of 'good' midwifery and 'good' leadership, *Midwifery*, 26 (1): 126–137.

Byrom, S. and Kay, L. (2011) Midwifery leadership: Theory, practice and potential, in S. Downe, S. Byrom and L. Simpson (eds.) *Essential Midwifery Practice: Leadership, Expertise and Collaborative Working*, Chichester: Wiley-Blackwell, 7–22.

Campbell, A. and O'Connell, R. (2020) Baby's first hug: Establishing skin-to-skin contact during caesarean birth using participatory action research, unpublished manuscript.

Campbell, O., Calvert, C., Testa, A., Strehlow, M., Benova, L., Keyes, E. et al. (2016) The scale, scope, coverage, and capability of childbirth care, *The Lancet*, 388 (10056): 2193–2208.

Casey, M., O'Connor, L., Cashin, A., Fealy, G., Smith, R., O'Brien, D. et al. (2019) Enablers and challenges to advanced nursing and midwifery practice roles, *Journal of Nursing Management*, 27 (2): 271–277.

Christoffersen, L., Teigen, J. and Rònningstad, C. (2020) Following-up midwives after adverse incidents: How front-line management practices help second victims, *Midwifery*, 85: 102669. Available at: https://doi.org/10.1016/j.midw.2020.102669 (accessed 20 October 2020).

Coghlan, D. and Brannick, T. (2014) *Doing Action Research in Your Own Organization*, 4th edition, London: Sage.

Commonwealth of Australia (2009) *Improving Maternity Services in Australia: The Report of the Maternity Services Review*, Canberra, ACR: Commonwealth of Australia. Available at: https://www1.health.gov.au/internet/main/publishing.nsf/Content/maternityservicesreview-report (accessed 20 October 2020).

Crowther, S., Hunter, B., McAra-Couper, J., Warren, L., Gilkison, A., Hunter, M. et al. (2016) Sustainability and resilience in midwifery: A discussion paper, *Midwifery*, 40: 40–48.

Cummings, G.G., MacGregor, T., Davey, M., Lee, H., Wong, C.A., Lo, E. et al. (2010) Leadership styles and outcome patterns for the nursing workforce and work environment: A systematic review, *International Journal of Nursing Studies*, 47 (3): 363–385.

Curtis, E. and O'Connell, R. (2011) Essential leadership skills for motivating and developing staff, *Nursing Management*, 18 (5): 32–35.

Deery, R. and Fisher, P. (2017) Professionalism and person-centredness: Developing a practice-based approach to leadership within NHS maternity services in the UK, *Health Sociology Review*, 26 (2): 143–159.

Dekker, S., Bergström, J., Amer-Wåhlin, I. and Cilliers, P. (2013) Complicated, complex, and compliant: Best practice in obstetrics, *Cognition, Technology and Work*, 15 (2): 189–195.

Department of Health (2016) Creating a Better Future Together: National Maternity Strategy 2016–2026, Dublin: Department of Health. Available at: https://www.gov.ie/en/publication/0ac5a8-national-maternity-strategy-creating-a-better-future-together-2016-2/ (accessed 20 October 2020).

Department of Health, Social Services and Public Policy (DHSSPS) (2012) *A Strategy for Maternity Care in Northern Ireland 2012–2018*, Belfast: DHSSPS. Available at: https://www.health-ni.gov.uk/sites/default/files/publications/dhssps/maternitystrategy.pdf (accessed 20 October 2020).

Divall, B. (2015) Negotiating competing discourses in narratives of midwifery leadership in the English NHS, *Midwifery*, 31 (11): 1060–1066.

Downe, S. and Byrom, S. (2019) *Squaring the Circle: Normal Birth Research, Theory and Practice in a Technological Age*, London: Pinter & Martin.

Elliott, N., Begley, C., Kleinpell, R. and Higgins, A. (2014) The development of leadership outcome-indicators evaluating the contribution of clinical specialists and advanced practitioners to health care: A secondary analysis, *Journal of Advanced Nursing*, 70 (5): 1078–1093.

Fealy, G.M., Casey, M., O'Leary, D.F., McNamara, M.S., O'Brien, D., O'Connor, L. et al. (2018) Developing and sustaining specialist and advanced practice roles in nursing and midwifery: A discourse on enablers and barriers, *Journal of Clinical Nursing*, 27 (19/20): 3797–3809.

Fitzgerald, L., Ferlie, E., McGivern, G. and Buchannan, D. (2013) Distributed leadership patterns and service improvement: Evidence and argument from English healthcare, *Leadership Quarterly*, 24 (1): 227–239.

Gaskell, L. and Beaton, S. (2015) Developing clinical competency: Experiences and perceptions of advanced midwifery practitioners in training, *Nurse Education in Practice*, 15 (4): 265–270.

Health Information and Quality Authority (HIQA) (2013) *Investigation into the safety, quality and standards of services provided by the Health Service Executive to patients, including pregnant women, at risk of clinical deterioration, including those provided in University Hospital Galway, and as reflected in the care and treatment provided to Savita Halappanavar*, Dublin: HIQA. Available at: https://www.hiqa.ie/sites/default/files/2017-01/Patient-Safety-Investigation-UHG.pdf (accessed 20 October 2020).

Hewitt, L., Priddis, H. and Dahlen, H.G. (2019) What attributes do Australian midwifery leaders identify as essential to effectively manage a midwifery group practice?, *Women and Birth*, 32 (2): 168–177.

Holohan, T. (2014) *HSE Midland Regional Hospital, Portlaoise perinatal deaths (2006-date)*, Dublin: Department of Health. Available at: http://www.lenus.ie/hse/bitstream/10147/313524/1/portlaoiseperinataldeaths.pdf (accessed 20 October 2020).

Janssens, S., Simon, R., Barwick, S., Clipperton, S., Beckmann, M. and Marshall, S. (2019) Midwifery leadership in maternity emergencies: A video analysis, *Journal of Interprofessional Care*. Available at: https://doi.org/10.1080/13561820.2019.1675611 (accessed 20 October 2020).

King's Fund (2011) *The Future of Leadership and Management in the NHS: No more heroes*, Report from The King's Fund Commission on Leadership and Management in the NHS, London: The King's Fund.

Kirkup, B. (2015) *The Report of the Morecambe Bay Investigation*, London: The Stationery Office. Available at: https://www.gov.uk/government/publications/morecambe-bay-investigation-report (accessed 20 October 2020).

Kumar, A., Sturrock, S., Wallace, E.M., Nestel, D., Lucey, D., Stoyles, S. et al. (2018) Evaluation of learning from practical obstetric multi-professional training and its impact on patient outcomes in Australia using Kirkpatrick's framework: A mixed methods study, *BMJ Open*, 8: e017451. Available at: https://bmjopen.bmj.com/content/8/2/e017451 (accessed 20 October 2020).

Lee, M. (2014) Transformational leadership: Is it time for a recall?, *International Journal of Management and Applied Research*, 1 (1): 17–29.

Leversidge, A. (2016) Why midwives leave – revisited, *Midwives Magazine*, 19 (4): 19.

Madeley, A.-M., Williams, V. and McNiven, A. (2019) An interpretative phenomenological study of midwives supporting home birth for women with complex needs, *British Journal of Midwifery*, 27 (10): 625–632.

Martin, T., Hauck, Y., Fenwick, J., Butt, J. and Wood, J. (2015) Midwives' experiences of working in a new service delivery model: The next birth after caesarean service, *Evidence Based Midwifery*, 13 (1): 10–14.

MBRRACE-UK (2016) Saving Lives, Improving Mothers' Care – Surveillance of maternal deaths in the UK 2012–14 and lessons learned to inform maternity care from the UK and Ireland Confidential Enquiries into Maternal Deaths and Morbidity 2009–14, Oxford: NPEU, University of Oxford.

NHS England (2016) *Better Births: Improving Outcomes of Maternity Services in England*, London: NHS England. Available at: https://www.england.nhs.uk/publication/better-births-improving-outcomes-of-maternity-services-in-england-a-five-year-forward-view-for-maternity-care/ (accessed 20 October 2020).

Pollard, K.C. (2011) How midwives' discursive practices contribute to the maintenance of the status quo in English maternity care, *Midwifery*, 27 (5): 612–619.

Read, J. (2019) The profile of professional midwifery leadership in England, *British Journal of Midwifery*, 27 (2): 120–127.

Rumsey, M., Catling, C., Thiessen, J. and Neill, A. (2017) Building nursing and midwifery leadership capacity in the Pacific, *International Nursing Review*, 64 (1): 50–58.

Rydenfält, C., Johansson, G., Odenrick, P., Åkerman, K. and Larsson, P. (2015) Distributed leadership in the operating room: A naturalistic observation study, *Cognition, Technology and Work*, 17 (3): 451–460.

Sandall, J., Benoit, C., Wrede, S., Murray, S.F., van Teijlingen, E.R. and Westfall, R. (2009) Social service professional or market expert? Maternity care relations under neoliberal healthcare reform, *Current Sociology*, 57 (4): 529–553.

Scottish Government (2017) *The Best Start: A Five-Year Forward Plan for Maternity and Neonatal Care in Scotland*, Edinburgh: The Scottish Government. Available at: https://www.gov.scot/publications/best-start-five-year-forward-plan-maternity-neonatal-care-scotland/ (accessed 20 October 2020).

Sheard, L., Jackson, C. and Lawton, R. (2017) How is success achieved by individuals innovating for patient safety and quality in the NHS?, *BMC Health Services Research*, 17 (1): 640–649.

Shoushtarian, M., Barnett, M., McMahon, F. and Ferris, J. (2014) Training (PROMPT) into maternity units in Victoria, Australia, *BJOG: An International Journal of Obstetrics and Gynaecology*, 121 (13): 1710–1718.

Siassakos, D., Draycott, T.J., Crofts, J.F., Hunt, L.P., Winter, C. and Fox, R. (2010) More to teamwork than knowledge, skill and attitude, *BJOG: An International Journal of Obstetrics and Gynaecology*, 117 (10): 1262–1269.

Turnbull James, K. (2011) *Leadership in Context: Lessons from new leadership theory and current leadership development practice*, London: The King's Fund. Available at: https://www.kingsfund.org.uk/sites/default/files/leadership-in-context-theory-current-leadership-development-practice-kim-turnbull-james-kings-fund-may-2011.pdf

Van Hecke, A., Goemaes, R., Verhaeghe, S., Beyers, W., Decoene, E. and Beeckman, D. (2019) Leadership in nursing and midwifery: Activities and associated competencies of advanced practice nurses and midwives, *Journal of Nursing Management*, 27 (6): 1261–1274.

Welsh Government (2019) *Maternity Care in Wales: A Five Year Vision for the Future (2019–2024)*, Cardiff: Welsh Government. Available at: https://gov.wales/maternity-services-strategy-2019-2024 (accessed 20 October 2020).

Winter, C., Crofts, J., Draycott, T.J. and Muchatuta, N. (2017) *PROMPT Course Manual*, 3rd edition, Cambridge: Cambridge University Press.

World Health Organization (WHO) (2018) *WHO Recommendations: Intrapartum care for a positive childbirth experience*, Geneva: WHO. Available at: https://www.who.int/reproductivehealth/publications/intrapartum-care-guidelines/en/ (accessed 20 October 2020).

Zwedberg, S., Blomquist, J. and Sigerstad, E. (2015) Midwives' experiences with mother–infant skin-to-skin contact after a caesarean section: 'Fighting an uphill battle', *Midwifery*, 31 (1): 215–220.

11 Nobody in charge – really?

David A. Buchanan

Chapter topics

- Distributed leadership as a spontaneous, naturally occurring phenomenon
- The need to move beyond binary thinking – leaders and followers, focused and distributed
- Leadership configurations
- The benefits of distributed leadership in rapidly changing and pressured contexts
- Conditions for encouraging distributed leadership in practice

Introduction: There must have been someone in charge

Leadership appears to be a key determinant of organisational effectiveness, whether we are discussing a hospital, an orchestra, a street gang, a political party, a mountaineering team or a multinational corporation. It is not surprising, therefore, that leadership is a focus of intense interest. This focus is a relatively recent phenomenon. In 1896, the United States Library of Congress had no books on leadership (Heller, 1997). The global literature on leadership is now vast – embarking on a comprehensive review of all this research and commentary will spoil your weekend.

Leadership is a controversial topic. We hear the complaint that 'we need more leadership', but at the same time, organisational hierarchies and formal authority structures that underpin leadership positions are also challenged. We equate leadership with positions of power, influence and status, but leadership can be seen at all levels of an organisation. Leaders have job titles and working conditions which symbolise their status. Yet flat structures, self-managing teams, knowledge work, and virtual and networked organisational forms weaken traditional leadership positions based on hierarchy and symbolism.

Who needs leaders anyway? In the *Human Relations* article by Buchanan et al. (2007), my colleagues and I describe how complex changes to improve cancer services in a British hospital (Grange – a pseudonym) were implemented by several people acting in concert, without project management plans, structures or leadership roles. Four key individuals, including two nurses, were heavily involved at different stages. But nineteen other people, together with twenty-six managerial, administrative and clinical groups, patients' representatives and other organisations also contributed in major ways to the change process. Their various contributions were informal and fluid, complementing each other, as responsibility for the changes 'migrated' around those individuals and groups. We concluded that dispersed or distributed leadership – implementing changes with 'nobody in charge' – can be just as successful as 'focused' (individual) change leadership or textbook change management approaches.

However, colleagues have challenged the title and argument of that article, suggesting that *somebody* must have been in charge, and that we have been guilty of exaggeration and oversimplification. The idea that change doesn't happen without leadership appears to be deeply embedded in our cultural consciousness. Was our title misleading? Was the argument overstated? With regard to service improvements in patient care, we *expected* to find project leaders – clinical and managerial – in charge of project teams, reporting to supervisory boards or advisory groups populated by senior leaders. But that is not what we found. NHS provider organisations have executive boards and chief executives, who are responsible for the performance of their organisations, and for the actions of their staff. The chief executive at Grange Hospital was, therefore, definitely 'in charge' for the duration of the change programme in question. However, he was not 'in charge' in the sense that he designed and led the change programme. He was not 'in charge' in the sense that staff had to wait until they had received his directions before acting. He was not 'in charge' in the sense that staff reported progress regularly to him for review before they could proceed further. Critically, he was not 'in charge' of the many individuals and groups who were not hospital employees, but whose contributions were also key to the change programme. However, he was 'in charge' of the overall conditions that allowed and encouraged a distributed approach to implementing this change programme to emerge and develop.

The UK National Health Service (NHS) has a Leadership Academy, based on the assumption that improvements in patient care rely on leadership – and that failures in care are due to poor leadership (www.leadershipacademy.nhs.uk). In 2019, NHS England announced a £2 million programme to boost leadership development, to 'grow a cadre of system leaders . . . with the right skills necessary to drive change and identify new ways of working' (www.england.nhs.uk). Development programmes are thus assumed to be capable of turning 'ordinary' staff members into leaders, without whom change will not happen. However, we also know that leadership effectiveness is contingent; a leader whose behaviours are successful in one context may not perform so well in a different setting. Beyond the definitions in academic textbooks, leadership is also a socially constructed concept – an IKIWISI idea: I'll know it when I see it'. Leadership development programmes assume a binary distinction between leaders and non-leaders (or followers), and that there is a core set of skills, knowledge and other attributes that can be taught and learned, in order to turn ordinary people into successful leaders. These assumptions are questionable.

The backstory

The aim of the research on which the 2007 article was based was to explore interactions between management and clinical staff in the implementation of improvements in healthcare service delivery. The methodology involved identifying a number of 'tracer' change projects in eleven different clinical settings. One of these tracers concerned the implementation of the dramatic improvements to male prostate cancer care services at Grange Hospital. The interview topic guide was designed to document the change process: problem, aims, actions, outcomes. Our particular interest lay with implementation, with those involved in putting the changes in place, and with the roles of clinical and managerial staff and their interactions in this process. How well did the 'grey suits' and 'white coats' collaborate in implementing such a major change?

The changes that were implemented involved a complex combination of new targets for cancer treatment, new equipment and facilities, new roles for clinical and administrative staff, new processes, and improved patient support mechanisms. The changes were successful with regard to meeting and exceeding the new targets. Previously, the referral-to-treatment time for non-urgent patients was over a year, and 140 days for urgent patients. Following the change initiative, all prostate cancer patients were seen within two weeks, with treatment beginning within one month.

Clearly, Grange Hospital was doing something right. How had they achieved these outcomes? Given our focus on implementation, the interview topic guide included questions about the project lead or leads, the members of a supervisory board or advisory group, and other roles and reporting structures. This was consistent with the standard categories in change leadership textbooks. Working my way through the twenty-one interview transcripts (recorded and then typed verbatim), I eventually came to the questions about project roles. In the first couple of transcripts that I examined, these sections were blank. Not a problem. 'Missing data' is a common feature of research projects of this kind. Some participants want to talk at length about particular topics, leaving little or no time for other questions on the schedule. One hopes that the combined information from a number of interviews will build up a comprehensive picture.

I began to panic when the third, fourth and subsequent transcripts were either blank or gave only short comments in response to the implementation questions. I had carried out only a small number of these interviews myself, so I had not previously seen the overall pattern of missing information. Had our research assistant – who I was not able to contact – made a mistake? Had we been let down by our transcription service? If any other section of the interview had been missing, that would not have been a major problem. But the questions on change implementation roles and structures were central to the research objectives. Panic seemed to be an appropriate response.

What was the explanation? There were no problems with the other questions on the interview topic guide. This problem had not arisen at any of the other 'tracer' sites. The non-response pattern was consistent across all of the managerial and clinical interviewees at Grange. I would have to return to the field. Standard research practice involves asking each organisation in a study of this kind to nominate a lead contact or liaison person, to help arrange interviews and rooms, and to monitor the activity of the research team in the organisation, particularly with regard to access to potentially sensitive or confidential information. The liaison at Grange was the human resources director. She was not directly involved with the cancer services improvements, and had therefore not previously been interviewed. I arranged an informal meeting to explain the problem and ask her advice.

The explanation was simple. There was no project lead, or project team, or project supervisory group. These were seen as unnecessary. Following recent senior management problems, Grange had a relatively new top team. The new chief executive consistently made clear his 'unashamed ambition' to improve the quality of patient care at Grange. The performance targets that the hospital was expected to achieve were well known. The chief executive expected staff to do what was necessary to meet and if possible exceed those targets. Having set the overall expectations, his role was to get out of the way. Interviews with two other staff, suggested by our liaison, confirmed this explanation.

According to Gronn (2002a), one of the defining features of distributed leadership is concertive action: steps initiated by one individual are developed through others. This involves the 'circulation of initiative' (Gronn, 2002b). Concertive action and the circulation of initiative were allowed to develop by the organisational conditions at Grange. The notion of concertive action implies a degree of consensus among those involved in change agency roles. However, it also appeared that at Grange, consensus over change substance and goals was accompanied by tensions concerning priorities, responsibilities (for actions and outcomes), the need to protect personal roles, and manoeuvring for position in evolving structures. In other words, the process of change at Grange, as in most other organisations, was influenced by organisation politics. Politics at work have a bad reputation, but Buchanan and Badham (2020) argue that political tactics can be used for positive, constructive, pro-social ends. Along with the circulation of initiative, the 'circulation of influence' – individuals persuading others of the need for action – also shaped the changes at Grange (Gronn, 2002b).

The conclusion, 'nobody in charge', was an emergent finding, indirectly related to the research aims. The title of our article was 'borrowed' from a book by Harlan Cleveland (2002), who argued that organisational issues are becoming too complex for single individuals or small teams to manage. The idea that any one individual can realistically be in charge, or in control, is today a myth. Box 11.1 develops Cleveland's theme, which attributes the need for distributed leadership to global shifts in working practices.

Box 11.1: Leadership throughout the organisation

Zheltoukhova (2014) argues that changes in the world of work are encouraging fresh ways of thinking about leadership. Recognising the need for leadership at all levels, organisations are exploring how to devolve decision-making, giving middle and junior managers, and other employees, leadership responsibilities. One of the main reasons for this shift concerns the need for organisational change, and to 'generate discretionary effort by staff, as well as to apply informal leadership techniques in order to influence internal and external colleagues who do not report to them directly' (Zheltoukhova, 2014: 2–3).

Leadership distribution and configuration

Traditionally, leadership theory has been characterised by simple dualities: leaders and followers, autocratic versus participative, focused or dispersed. This binary thinking, however, does not capture the complex and fluid realities of leadership in practice. It is now recognised that leadership is often a collective effort (Plowman et al., 2007; Gronn, 2011; Denis et al., 2012; Moore and Buchanan, 2013). This is not to claim that the lone, heroic, inspirational, visionary, powerful individual leader is redundant, but to recognise that this traditional stereotype is only one of many forms that leadership can take.

When first introduced in the early 1990s, the NHS Leadership Competencies Framework was aimed exclusively at board level executives. However, recognising the value of distributed leadership, recent versions of that framework are explicitly designed to apply to all staff, 'to guide team leaders at every level of the NHS to develop a critical set of improvement and leadership capabilities among their staff and themselves' (Department of Health, 2016: 2). So, is the argument from 2007 still valid? Distributed leadership continues to have numerous advantages that are relevant to the pressures that healthcare systems face today. First, better quality decisions are more likely to be taken by those closest to the action, such as nurses. Hospital managers typically have limited direct contact with patients, and often lack a detailed understanding of factors affecting patient flow and patient care (although they may have better access than other staff to aggregate patient data and financial information). The interactions that most doctors have with patients is episodic, and they also can have a limited view of the overall care process. Given the nature and breadth of their roles, nurses combine a detailed understanding of patient care with administrative and budgeting skills and knowledge – and are thus able to step into leadership roles when required. Band 5 nurses in the UK, below the rank of hospital ward sister, often have leadership responsibilities mentioned explicitly in their job descriptions, with regard to 'stepping up' in the absence of the ward sister, and providing leadership to support junior nurses.

Second, decisions can be made and acted upon more rapidly when they are taken at the point where the issue or problem arises. Having to wait for a senior leader to be briefed, to understand the situation, to make a decision and to give instructions is frustrating for those who know what has to happen anyway. Delayed decisions in any sector can be damaging, and in a healthcare setting can adversely affect the quality of patient care. Decisions taken in haste can of course also cause harm, but decisions taken by those closest to where an issue has arisen are more likely to be correct.

Third, distributed leadership, by definition, means engaging staff more fully and granting increased autonomy over how work is performed. Engagement and autonomy are both known to improve the quality of working life, job satisfaction, motivation and work performance (Deci et al., 2017; Meyer, 2017). Engagement and autonomy involve changes in management and staff behaviour, which incur no additional costs. With regard to improving performance, here is an approach that is free.

Fourth, when leadership is distributed, as it was at Grange Hospital, the change process is not dependent on key individuals or small teams. In some healthcare settings, responsibility for leading a change initiative is given to a specially appointed individual on a temporary contract or secondment from another role. When implementation is complete, the permanent staff are expected to take over. However, that does not always happen. 'Completion' is often an open-ended concept, projects are seen as being 'owned' by the temporary appointment, and the change process does not survive their departure as the permanent staff have no time, and lack the depth of understanding of the project lead.

The argument from 2007 thus has greater relevance today, given the changing nature of healthcare and the economic, financial, social, demographic, technological and epidemiological pressures with which the service now has to deal. Zheltoukhova (2014) identifies four trends shaping leadership roles in general, and not specifically in healthcare:

1. *Frequency and pace of change*: faster information-sharing and aggressive competition mean that decisions have to be taken faster, which means devolving responsibilities 'down the line'.
2. *Greater transparency and global consumer choice*: standards of business behaviour are now public and consumers can switch rapidly to competitors if they feel that an organisation is breaching those standards.
3. *Collaborative working*: flat structures and external partnerships mean that people have to influence others over whom they have no line management authority.
4. *Workforce diversity*: it is now more important to address different needs and motivations across the workforce, and appeal to a wider range of expectations than in the past.

These trends apply to public health systems as well as to commercial organisations. Public healthcare providers compete with each other, and with private providers, with regard to their performance standards (which are public knowledge), and they also compete for staff at all levels. It is NHS policy to extend greatly the scope of consumer (patient) choice in England (Department of Health and Social Care, 2019). Collaborative working in the NHS is mandated by the development of sustainability and transformation programmes, integrated care systems, and primary care networks, which involve close partnerships between organisations that have traditionally been in competition with each other. As one of the largest employing organisations in the world, the NHS workforce has significant gender, ethnic and cultural diversity, and managing an ageing, multigenerational workforce requires significant changes in human resource policy and practice.

These trends encourage a distributed approach to leadership which reacts rapidly to changing conditions and problems, without having to wait for bureaucratic processes to unfold, or for senior leaders to transmit orders down the hierarchy. Many senior managers have a problem with this distributed approach, based on a lack of trust. Can frontline staff – who are not as qualified and knowledgeable, and lack 'the big picture' – be trusted to make the right decisions? These doubts are expressed about staff who are qualified and knowledgeable in their areas of expertise, yet managers who don't see 'the detailed picture' are also likely to make bad decisions. Edmondson (2011) argues that not all mistakes and failures are bad. She explores the reasons for errors on a spectrum ranging from blameworthy to praiseworthy. At one extreme, deviance, breaking the rules deliberately, is blameworthy. At the other end of the spectrum, experiments to discover whether something new will work or not are praiseworthy. Do managers recognise this spectrum?

According to Edmondson (2011: 50), executives claim that only 2–5% of failures in their organisations are blameworthy. However, they also say that 70–90% are treated as blameworthy, which means that any lessons that could be learned are lost. Edmondson (2018) argues that organisations must be psychologically safe places, where experimentation is promoted, and individuals are not blamed when organisational circumstances have contributed to mistakes and failures. In addition, messengers who speak out with bad news, awkward questions or concerns, or make mistakes, should be rewarded rather than condemned. Box 11.2 encourages reflection about how organisations deal with people who try new things and make mistakes.

Box 11.2: Life and death mistakes

Clinical staff are familiar with life and death decisions. Occasionally, when mistakes are made, particularly when staff are under pressure, patients die. The military also have to deal with this issue. Theunissen and Maciejewski (2019: 7) report the perhaps surprising views of a British Army battalion commander on dealing with someone who has made a mistake: '[Y]ou do not hang someone out to dry. Sometimes mistakes are made in battle and people get killed. If you crucify people when a mistake is made in battle, they will freeze with fear the next time they're facing the enemy, and the consequences of that are far worse'. The aim is to learn from mistakes, and that doesn't happen if someone if afraid of punishment. In addition, the pressures facing soldiers in battle are immense, and anyone can make a mistake. Others do not rush to make judgements, therefore, knowing that it could be them who makes the next error.

How does your organisation respond when someone makes a serious mistake?

Misconceptions

Distributed leadership is subject to a number of misconceptions:

- *Distributed leadership is difficult to implement.* Not so. Distributed leadership is a naturally occurring phenomenon. People step into and out of leadership roles spontaneously, as the need arises. Distributed leadership happens in most if not all organisations without any planned management intervention. As we will discuss below, implementation simply involves setting the right conditions.
- *Everyone is a leader.* This is an inaccurate view of the concept, but in the right circumstances, everyone has the *possibility* of becoming a leader, if only for a short period. Taking on a temporary leadership role in this way does not necessarily require any special prior leadership development.
- *Chaos results if everyone is a leader.* This does not happen, because energies and activities – 'concertive actions' – are focused on a common framework of

objectives. In healthcare settings, these objectives typically relate to the quality and safety of patient care. However, in setting conditions that are favourable for distributed leadership it is important that the objectives and priorities are clear and consistent.

- *Distributed leadership means moving away from focused leadership.* Distributed leadership does not deny the need for formal, individual, senior, visionary figures who continue to exercise what are considered to be traditional leadership functions. However, we have to recognise that this is only one manifestation of leadership, and may not be appropriate in all circumstances.
- *It's either/or – traditional or distributed leadership, but not both.* There is no problem with sole, visionary, individual leaders co-existing and collaborating with a pattern of widely dispersed leadership which is decoupled from high office. This, after all, is close to the configuration which we observed at Grange, with a new, ambitious chief executive, and a large group of others who took responsibility for implementing the many changes that led to the improvements in cancer services.

Observe any healthcare setting closely, and you are likely to witness leadership distribution in action, occurring naturally and spontaneously. As the pressures on the service have intensified, and the need for rapid responses to opportunities and problems has increased, distributed leadership becomes more valuable, if not necessary. Although drawing on experience of settings beyond healthcare, Fraher (2011: 179–180) argues that in extreme contexts, a high-performing team 'allows the most qualified individual to emerge and lead as required by operational scenarios', and that, 'if a team has a number of tasks to manage, each member may exercise leadership at different times to accomplish the team's goals'. She concludes that teams that work well under pressure allow the most qualified individuals to lead as required, with different members exercising leadership at different times. Baran and Scott (2010: 65) similarly note that, 'leadership necessarily involves all members of the organization with respect to their roles and the context in which they operate'.

Noting that individual and collective or distributed forms of leadership are both significant, and can co-exist, Gronn (2009, 2011) argues that we should focus on *leadership configurations* as the unit of analysis. A configuration is defined as 'a pattern or an arrangement of practice' (Gronn, 2009: 383), which can involve different configurations of leadership attributes, behaviours and influence styles. This means that 'a hypothetical pattern of leadership in an organization may comprise some teams, networks and a series of individuals whose influence stems from their presumed charismatic inspiration' (Gronn, 2009: 383). These configurations may include focused and dispersed leadership patterns, but can adopt many other forms.

The concept of leadership configuration is less well defined than distributed leadership. However, Buchanan and Hällgren (2018) argue that different configurations or patterns of leadership may be suitable for different circumstances, and that different configurations can co-exist in the same setting. The 'wrong' leadership configuration in some settings can be particularly damaging. Their argument is based on an analysis of a movie, and the application to healthcare settings awaits further study.

Conclusion: Into practice

Will those who think this can't be done,
please get out of the way of those who are doing it already
– Chinese proverb

We have to recognise that change in some cases may more effectively be progressed with a small group of senior, powerful, formally appointed leaders, with clearly defined roles, following standard textbook procedures. This is the traditional approach advocated by, for example, Kotter (2007, 2012), and there is evidence to support this perspective (Appelbaum et al., 2012). Stace and Dunphy (2001) argue that autocratic, directive, perhaps even coercive leadership is appropriate where the changes that are required are major, when there is no time for participation, where there is no internal support for the changes, and where these are necessary for the survival of the organisation. At Grange hospital, the changes were major, but none of those other factors applied.

The argument from 'nobody in charge', therefore, is that *under certain conditions*, a distributed leadership approach will be more effective than a traditional focused perspective. The process of change may benefit from being more spontaneous, dispersed, fluid, migratory and influence-based rather than being formally defined and planned. At Grange, those conditions included:

- clear and consistent signalling of priorities by top management
- considerable autonomy granted to those who were involved in service improvement
- the absence of other strategic initiatives to distract attention and disperse energies
- good clinical–managerial relationships
- independence and high visibility of the cancer service at the heart of the initiative
- external resources and support were both recognised and utilised
- key hospital and network roles all had people in post
- change champions occupied key roles.

Is the idea of 'change champions' consistent with the concept of distributed leadership? As noted earlier, organisational change is a politicised process, and distributed leadership is characterised by the *circulation of influence*, as well as by the circulation of initiative (Gronn, 2002b; Buchanan and Badham, 2020). Change champions are key influencers, who are not necessarily in senior posts, but who encourage and persuade others to take on leadership and influencing roles. Duan et al. (2014) advise managers to identify and support the organisation's 'hidden influencers'. They are not likely to be in senior positions, and are not always the obvious choices. But they are known and respected, and are not seen as 'management messengers'. They convince others, who turn to them for advice, using informal influence. Change champions or hidden influencers are thus critical to supporting and developing concerted action and the distributed leadership phenomenon.

Putting the above combination of conditions in place sounds straightforward. However, those conditions are frequently absent in healthcare organisations today. Priorities can shift rapidly, depending on local events and national policy. Managers often withhold decision rights from frontline staff, and even from middle managers, not trusting them to act in the organisation's best interests (Buchanan et al., 2013). Politicians in the UK are unable to leave the healthcare system alone for long, and are constantly introducing major new policy initiatives with non-negotiable deadlines for implementation. These initiatives inevitably divert staff attention and energies from programmes that are already under way, unless senior staff are able to act as 'human shields' and buffer change leaders from those pressures. Performance targets and financial constraints mean that management and clinical staff come into conflict, not for personal reasons, but because clinical and managerial goals inevitably conflict in some circumstances. The clinical service that we studied at Grange was an independent department, not part of a larger service which could have diluted the energy and funds devoted to the care of prostate cancer patients. Chronic local and national staff shortages mean that key roles are not filled, or are filled by temporary or acting staff whose main commitments lie elsewhere. It is not always enough to have change champions, but it helps if those individuals are in the right places – or roles – at the right time. And healthcare providers do not always make full use of the resources and support of other organisations, either because they lack the time to do so or because they are not confident that others' experience is of value to them.

Ensuring that all or most of those conditions are in place for any significant length of time is not straightforward. The pressures and changes to which the healthcare system is subject do not create many periods of relative calm and stability. The introduction of fresh initiatives and the existence of national staff shortages are largely beyond the control of local management. How can distributed leadership be implemented in this context? Unfortunately, there are no ten-step McKinsey-style checklists. This is not because the guidelines haven't been developed, but because distributed leadership is a naturally occurring phenomenon. The main route to implementation, therefore, is to 'let it happen', by establishing and reinforcing where possible the conditions, such as those listed above, that allow and encourage distributed leadership to emerge spontaneously.

The main role of senior management thus involves setting consistent priorities and objectives, then standing back and getting out of the way. Top teams can also help to establish a psychologically safe environment in which people are allowed to experiment and to make 'praiseworthy' mistakes, from which individuals and the organisation can learn. Crucially, this means giving staff the autonomy to lead service improvements on their own, without prior permission or interference from senior management. For example, as part of the transformation programme at Nottingham University Hospitals, Guyler et al. (2014) describe the 'Just Do It' scheme. This encouraged staff to implement changes in their areas on their own initiative without lengthy approval processes. This worked well because staff were given permission to get on with the work of improving their services:

> In our experience the leadership role is to create change by enabling ideas to come from the front line and service users. Senior leaders must subscribe to the programme to reinforce their support through visible actions. (Guyler et al., 2014: 28)

One example from the 'Just Do It' initiative involved nurses on paediatric wards substituting full-size sheets and blankets with smaller cot-size items. Folding the larger sheets and blankets to fit children's cots took a considerable amount of time. The cot-sizes freed up nursing time to spend with patients. I challenged the transformation programme leader: 'Changing the size of blankets on a ward is hardly a good example of transformational change'. 'Yes it is', he replied, 'because before the programme and the Just Do It initiative were introduced, those nurses would not have felt able to make any changes, however small, on their own initiative. Now they know that they have permission to do this'.

The chief operating officer of a hospital in England once explained to me her disappointment with a nursing group who had been given significant budget responsibility, which they had then abused. What went wrong? On their own initiative, this nursing group placed a bulk order for hundreds of pens, all of which they would never be able to use. Irresponsible waste of money. 'They have no idea of the hospital's finances or budgeting', she explained. She did not offer those nurses training in finance and budgeting, but cancelled their budget responsibility instead. This example suggests that the single main barrier to distributed leadership is the attitude of management. The senior management view of empowerment is often negative, based on experiences similar to that of our chief operating officer.

Middle managers often resist the empowerment of subordinates because it diminishes their role. To retain the skills, knowledge and experience of middle managers, therefore, it may be necessary to redefine their positions, to become coaches and catalysts, with responsibility for supporting frontline teams, and ensuring that they have the support and resources that they need (De Smet et al., 2019).

Key concepts discussed

- Distributed leadership, also known as collective leadership, is a widely recognised perspective, which can be an effective approach in many circumstances.
- The traditional distinction between leaders and non-leaders, or followers, does not apply in all settings, and may in some cases be redundant.
- Distributed leadership has been shown to generate significant benefits for patients, staff and organisations in healthcare settings.
- The pressures facing healthcare today put distributed leadership at a premium, with regard to responding rapidly to problems and implementing necessary changes.
- The benefits of distributed leadership include faster, better quality decisions, engagement and autonomy, which increase job satisfaction and performance, and reduce dependence on formal change leaders.
- Distributed leadership is a naturally occurring, spontaneous phenomenon, defined by concertive action, and through the circulation of initiative and influence.
- Given the nature of their roles and the breadth of their frontline experience, nursing staff are often better equipped to step into leadership roles than are medical and other clinical staff.

- Leadership in the NHS is now recognised as a capability that staff at all levels should possess, in the interests of developing innovative approaches to improving patient care.
- Leadership effectiveness is highly contingent, and the assumption that there is a definable core set of leadership skills and knowledge that can apply to all circumstances is questionable.
- Traditional, focused, directive leadership may be successful in some settings, and particularly where the required changes are major, where time and internal support for change are in short supply, and where the changes are necessary for corporate survival.
- Current trends encourage a devolved, distributed approach to leadership: the pace of change, patient choice, collaborative working with flat structures, and differing needs across a diverse workforce.
- Distributed leadership has to be encouraged, rather than implemented, by setting the right conditions: clear priorities and goals, autonomy to act independently, the lack of other distracting initiatives (where possible).
- Senior and middle management resistance create the main barriers to distributed leadership. Middle management roles in particular need to be redefined to support distributed leadership.

Key readings

- Bolden, R. (2011) Distributed leadership in organizations: A review of theory and research, *International Journal of Management Reviews*, 13 (3): 251–269.
  Bolden reviews the literature on distributed leadership, exploring relationships and overlaps with shared, collective, collaborative, emergent and democratic leadership. He notes that interest in this area has grown since 2000, and is more popular in the UK than in the US. He also notes the significance of the concept of leadership configurations and concludes that the terminology of distributed leadership should be regarded as descriptive and not as normative – the universal advocacy of this approach to leadership in practice would be misguided.
- Denis, J., Langley, A. and Sergi, V. (2012) Leadership in the plural, *Academy of Management Annals*, 6 (1): 1–73.
  This article identifies four streams of thinking with regard to distributed leadership: sharing leadership in teams, pooling leadership at the top of the organisation, producing leadership through interaction, and spreading leadership across boundaries over time. Leadership in these perspectives is not a property of individuals and their behaviour but 'a collective phenomenon that is distributed or shared among different people, potentially fluid, and constructed in interaction' (2012: 2). This also means seeing leadership as a social process that takes place in and through interactions, through more mutual and less hierarchical practices.
- Guyler, T., Ward, P. and Buchanan, D.A. (2014) Transform a hospital from the front line up: Lessons from a whole hospital transformation, *Health Service Journal*, 26 September: 27–29.
  This article describes the transformation programme at Nottingham University Hospitals, from which the 'Just Do It' example in this chapter was drawn. The authors describe the many other aspects of that programme, and the ways in

which staff engagement and empowerment contributed to the success of the transformation.

- Moore, C. and Buchanan, D.A. (2013) Sweat the small stuff: A case study of small scale change processes and consequences in acute care, *Health Services Management Research*, 26 (1): 9–17.
  The authors describe a change initiative that was led by a small team of three people, none of whom were senior managers, who asked staff in one clinical service to identify their most annoying problems. These problems were then fixed, with little effort and at almost no cost, within five days. One of the key members of the project team was the 'who knows who knows what' person – a long-serving but relatively junior member of the administrative staff, who knew who to approach in the organisation in order to get information and to get things done quickly.
- Pfeffer, J. (2016) Getting beyond the BS of leadership literature, *McKinsey Quarterly*, 1 (January): 90–95.
  Pfeffer is critical of what he calls the 'leadership industry' for offering unhelpful advice on this topic based on wishful thinking that produces unrealistic images of leadership.

Useful websites

- https://www.youtube.com/watch?v=biPC_IJyiHo
  Professor Alma Harris discusses leadership practice, and the nature and role of distributed leadership (2016: 10 minutes).
- https://www.youtube.com/watch?v=oQI8H7XN4I4
  University of Hertfordshire animation explaining the phenomenon of distributed leadership (2016: 10 minutes).
- https://www.youtube.com/watch?v=tvh0xeodWys
  Interview with Deborah Ancona, head of MIT Leadership Centre, defining and describing what she calls collaborative, collective or distributed leadership (2017: 5 minutes).

References

Appelbaum, S.H., Habashy, S., Malo, J.L. and Shafiq, H. (2012) Back to the future: Revisiting Kotter's 1996 change model, *Journal of Management Development*, 31 (8): 764–782.

Baran, B.E. and Scott, C.W. (2010) Organizing ambiguity: A grounded theory of leadership and sensemaking within dangerous contexts, *Military Psychology*, 22 (1): 42–69.

Buchanan, D.A. and Badham, R.J. (2020) *Power, Politics, and Organizational Change*, 3rd edition, London: Sage.

Buchanan, D.A. and Hällgren, M. (2018) Surviving a zombie apocalypse: Leadership configurations in extreme contexts, *Management Learning*, 50 (2): 152–170.

Buchanan, D.A., Addicott, R., Fitzgerald, L., Ferlie, E. and Baeza, J. (2007) Nobody in charge: Distributed change agency in healthcare, *Human Relations*, 60 (7): 1065–1090.

Buchanan, D.A., Denyer, D., Jaina, J., Kelliher, C., Moore, C., Parry, E. et al. (2013) How do they manage? A qualitative study of the realities of middle and front-line management work in healthcare, *Health Services and Delivery Research*, 1 (4). Available at: https://www.ncbi.nlm.nih.gov/books/NBK259397/ (accessed 20 October 2020).

Cleveland, H. (2002) *Nobody in Charge: Essays on the Future of Leadership*, New York: Wiley.

Deci, E.L., Olafsen, A.H. and Ryan, R.M. (2017) Self-determination theory in work organizations: The state of a science, *Annual Review of Organizational Psychology and Organizational Behavior*, 4: 19–43.

Denis, J., Langley, A. and Sergi, V. (2012) Leadership in the plural, *Academy of Management Annals*, 6 (1): 1–73.

Department of Health (2016) *Developing People – Improving Care: A National Framework for Action on Improvement and Leadership Development in NHS-Funded Services*, London: National Improvement and Leadership Development Board.

Department of Health and Social Care (DHSC) (2019) *The NHS Choice Framework: What Choices are Available to Me in the NHS?*, London: DHSC.

De Smet, A., Smith, C. and Tofano, D. (2019) *How Companies can Help Midlevel Managers Navigate Agile Transformations*, London: McKinsey & Company.

Duan, L., Sheeren, E. and Weiss, L. (2014) Tapping the power of hidden influencers, *McKinsey Quarterly*, March: 1–4.

Edmondson, A. (2011) Strategies for learning from failure, *Harvard Business Review*, 89 (4): 48–55.

Edmondson, A. (2018) *The Fearless Organization: Creating Psychological Safety in the Workplace for Learning, Innovation, and Growth*, Hoboken, NJ: Wiley.

Fraher, A.L. (2011) *Thinking through Crisis: Improving Teamwork and Leadership in High-Risk Fields*, Cambridge: Cambridge University Press.

Gronn, P. (2002a) Distributed leadership as a unit of analysis, *Leadership Quarterly*, 13 (4): 423–451.

Gronn, P. (2002b) Distributed leadership, in K. Leithwood, P. Hallinger, K. Seashore-Louis, G. Furman-Brown, P. Gronn, W. Mulford et al. (eds.) *Second International Handbook of Educational Leadership and Administration*, Dordrecht: Kluwer, 653–696.

Gronn, P. (2009) Leadership configurations, *Leadership*, 5 (3): 381–394.

Gronn, P. (2011) Hybrid configurations of leadership, in A. Bryman, D. Collinson, K. Grint, B. Jackson and M. Uhl-Bien (eds.) *The Sage Handbook of Leadership*, London: Sage, 437–454.

Guyler, T., Ward, P. and Buchanan, D.A. (2014) Transform a hospital from the front line up: Lessons from a whole hospital transformation, *Health Service Journal*, 26 September: 27–29.

Heller, F. (1997) Leadership, in A. Sorge and M. Warner (eds.) *The Handbook of Organizational Behaviour*, London: International Thomson, 340–349.

Kotter, J.P. (2007) Leading change: Why transformation efforts fail, *Harvard Business Review*, 85 (1): 96–103 (originally published 1995).

Kotter, J.P. (2012) *Leading Change*, 2nd edition, Boston, MA: Harvard University Press.

Meyer, J.P. (2017) Has engagement had its day: What's next and does it matter?, *Organizational Dynamics*, 46 (2): 87–95.

Moore, C. and Buchanan, D.A. (2013) Sweat the small stuff: A case study of small scale change processes and consequences in acute care, *Health Services Management Research*, 26 (1): 9–17.

Plowman, D.A., Baker, L.T., Beck, T.E., Kulkarni, M., Solansky, S.T. and Travis, D.V.T. (2007) Radical change accidentally: The emergence and amplification of small change, *Academy of Management Journal*, 50 (3): 515–543.

Stace, D.A. and Dunphy, D. (2001) *Beyond the Boundaries: Leading and Re-Creating the Successful Enterprise*, 2nd edition, Sydney: McGraw-Hill.

Theunissen, R. and Maciejewski, J. (2019) How the British army's operations went agile, *McKinsey Quarterly*, October: 1–8.

Zheltoukhova, K. (2014) *Leadership: Easier Said than Done*, London: Chartered Institute for Personnel and Development.

12 Workshop formats for enacting distributed leadership practice

Vivienne Byers and Ruth Northway

Chapter topics

- The importance of developing and sustaining the knowledge and skills required for distributed leadership and management through discussion and practice
- The concept of a workshop as consisting of a group whose members share a common interest or problem, meeting together to improve their individual understanding of a subject through presentation, research, practice and discussion
- The learning theories underpinning the workshop concept
- The role of workshops in supporting the development of distributed leadership
- The practical implications of seeking to develop, deliver and evaluate such workshops

Introduction

Many different leadership theories and approaches have been proposed and whilst some (traits theories) argue that leaders possess particular personal qualities that make them effective leaders, other approaches offer the possibility that individuals can develop knowledge and skills to enhance their leadership potential. Leadership development has therefore become a key focus for both organisations and individuals. However, as the demands of leadership change so too do the requirements of leadership development. Accordingly, this chapter will explore the use of workshops as a strategy for supporting leadership development in the context of distributed leadership practice.

The importance of leadership development and lifelong learning

Previous chapters (see, for example, Chapter 2) have highlighted how changes in healthcare systems mean that changes in leadership approaches are required to meet the resultant complex and changing needs. A distributed leadership approach has been proposed as a way of meeting this leadership challenge and this is also evident in wider literature concerning healthcare leadership (e.g. King's Fund, 2011).

Changing the approach to leadership, however, also means that changes are required to the ways in which leadership development is provided. Indeed, De Brun et al. (2019) argue that if distributed leadership is to be enacted, then changes to leadership development have to occur. It has been suggested that, in general, the need for leadership development has never been more urgent (Moldoveanu and Narayandas, 2019), but at the same time there is some scepticism as to whether investment in such development is yielding the desired outcomes (Geerts et al., 2020). Consideration of potential ways forward thus needs to occur if distributed leadership is to become a reality in practice.

The King's Fund (2011) recognises that if a distributed leadership approach is to be adopted, then a wider range of people need to be included in programmes of leadership development. They thus argue that a range of clinicians (doctors, nurses and allied health professionals) should be provided with such developmental opportunities. However, they also note that leadership development should not just focus on the development of technical competence but rather that it should enable participants to develop a culture in which there is a focus on improving healthcare delivery and challenging poor practice where this occurs. Nonetheless, generally it is found that traditional leadership development programmes tend not to address what are often seen as 'soft' skills of communication and processes for effective collaborative working (Moldoveanu and Narayandas, 2019). This view is echoed in the context of healthcare by Hartviksen et al. (2019), who argue that traditionally leadership development has focused on skills training and the development of technical and conceptual knowledge rather than on fostering personal growth and awareness.

It has thus been stated that leadership development needs to focus on the development of roles, relationships and practices within a specific organisational context and needs to bring together people from within that context (King's Fund, 2011). This, in turn, highlights the need to view leadership development to support distributed leadership as something that cannot just be addressed within traditional academic programmes but rather that it needs to be viewed as part of continuing professional development requiring lifelong learning.

Approaches to leadership development

The focus of distributive leadership development can be seen to expand the collective capacity of organisational members in order to engage effectively in leadership roles and processes, through enhancing leadership skills and knowledge (Day, 2001). This expansion of collective capacity in leadership development, according to Van Velsor et al. (2010), includes the collective's capacity to produce direction, alignment and commitment. This is not a simple process, as transfer of learning from leadership development programmes does not always accommodate the development of critical thinking skills to manage issues that are actually occurring in the workplace (DeRue and Myers, 2014). According to Byers and Halligan (2017), the literature outlines three complementary approaches to leadership development (and education), based on the work of Stoller (2013), West et al. (2015) and Careau et al. (2014):

- curricular teaching
- mentorship and coaching
- experiential leadership opportunities.

Geerts et al. (2020) similarly identify a number of effective approaches to leadership development, including videotaped simulations followed by a debrief, coaching, action learning, mentoring and interactive workshops.

In order to expand the collective capacity for healthcare professionals to engage in leadership roles and processes, learners need to avail of the opportunity to learn from each other by working together, through service-learning and action-learning projects. The next section examines the development of interactive workshops in order to facilitate leadership development that supports distributed leadership utilising these types of approaches.

Learning theories underpinning the workshop approach

Using a distributive leadership framework for leadership development in healthcare calls for a shift in thinking. Distributed leadership development by its very nature calls for a blend of individual, team and organisational development activities due to their interdependence. It also requires a facilitator playing a role in drawing on expertise to see what needs to be developed both individually and collectively, in line with an organisational or healthcare system strategy (Byers and Halligan, 2017). This can be achieved through workshops and an interactive approach.

The use of workshops as an approach to leadership development is underpinned by positive anecdotal evidence, some sound pedagogic principles as well as available evidence (Belay et al., 2019). A review by Careau et al. (2014) investigated the content and competencies in education approaches to developing collaborative leadership in healthcare. Their paper reported on only a few sources regarding the use of workshops. However, they found that for competency-building for healthcare practitioners, location was positively correlated with workshops held in the workplace. However, the format of what are reported in the literature as workshops is often variable, and terms such as small-group teaching, tutorial, seminar, group discussion, problem-based-learning and workshop are used interchangeably (Belay et al., 2019). All these approaches have a number of things in common – namely, they emphasise participant inclusion and engagement, smaller group sizes, and they set tasks to tackle scenarios and problems in order to increase understanding and increase familiarity with knowledge and practices. Thus, a workshop approach that focuses on active experiential learning is defined as '. . . a short-term learning experience that encourages active, experiential learning and uses a variety of learning activities to meet the needs of diverse learners' (Brooks-Harris and Stock-Ward, 1999: 6).

Core to this definition are three interrelated elements: experiential learning, sensitivity to different learning styles and the use of a variety of learning activities.

These elements are also used in interactive leadership training, particularly team training interventions (Black and Westwood, 2004). The focus of these interventions is to engage an entire team to train them together to acquire the same skills. According to De Brun et al. (2019), interactive leadership training involves facilitated learning through seminars and/or learning sets and is delivered through workshops. Therefore, the term 'workshop' can denote the format used to deliver the training to a group and utilising the elements outlined above: experiential learning, sensitivity to different learning styles and a variety of learning activities. These elements are important for developing distributive leadership capacity, especially in an organisational context (Black and Westwood, 2004).

A systematic review comparing different approaches to medical education, including conferences, lectures, seminars, symposia, courses and workshops, showed that the interactive teaching methods in workshops are more effective than didactic lecture-based teaching (Forsetlund et al., 2009). Experiential and interactive learning facilitates the transfer of learning back into the organisational setting (Kolb, 2014). Experiential learning theory views ideas and concepts as formed and reformed by experience, rather than fixed and unchangeable. Thus, learning is viewed as a process, rather than achieved through select outcomes. The theory draws on the work of eminent scholars in the field of human learning and development, including John Dewey, Kurt Lewin, Jean Piaget, Carl Jung and Carl Rogers, to develop a holistic model of the experiential learning process (Kolb and Kolb, 2005).

Kolb's (2014) learning cycle involves four stages: concrete learning, reflective observation, abstract conceptualisation and active experimentation. His approach has been utilised in health professional workshops in order to progress the learner through the learning cycle (Manolson, 1992; Hanen Centre, 2020). The first stage of *concrete learning* is where the learner is introduced to a new experience through activities that help them apply personal learning to real-life situations. The second stage, *self-reflection*, involves activities and discussion that help the learner think about what the experience means to them. This stage is followed by activities such as presenting, leading discussions and role-playing to complete the third and fourth stages of *abstract conceptualisation* and *active experimentation*. Adopting this cyclical approach offers the potential to address the problems previously identified in this chapter, whereby the focus in more traditional leadership development programmes on technical and conceptual knowledge is at the expense of developing personal growth and awareness (Hartviksen et al., 2019)

Distributed leadership development thus lends itself to an experiential approach. Leadership development programmes need to take into consideration the dynamic relationships between health professionals, values, culture, capabilities and the organisational context (Friedrich et al., 2009; West et al., 2014; Eva et al., 2019). Workshop formats that present means to reflect, increase self- and organisational awareness and show how to meet organisational outcomes will facilitate the learner to appreciate their role in relation to others in their team and organisation. Transfer of learning will also occur between the various disciplines and at the different levels of hierarchy, as well as in identifying internal and external support mechanisms. Brooks-Harris and Stock-Ward (1999) see workshops as ideal in addressing individuals with different learning preferences. This is important with any group but perhaps even more so when bringing together people from different professional backgrounds (as is required in distributed leadership) who may have had very different previous educational experiences.

Planning, delivering and evaluating workshops

Effective workshops do not just happen. Fitzpatrick and Hunt (2019) argue that key to a successful workshop is the preparation that is undertaken beforehand. Based on their systematic literature review of research relating to leadership development amongst physicians, Geerts et al. (2020) advocate an evidenced-based approach to such development (including interactive workshops). An eight-stage approach is proposed:

1. Needs analysis
2. Selection of desired outcomes
3. Selection of explicit goals
4. Selection of participants
5. Selection of the programme structure, content, facilitators and activities
6. Devising an evaluation framework
7. Conducting an assessment of barriers to achievement of outcomes
8. Ensuring the principles of adult learning are addressed.

Each of these stages will be considered in turn in relation to workshops to support the development of distributed leadership.

An evidence-based approach to leadership development

The initial *needs analysis* should be undertaken with all key stakeholders with a view to exploring what the desired outcomes of the workshop(s) might be. It is possible that different stakeholders will have different views as to what these outcomes should be or that they may prioritise them differently. However, to maximise the potential for success it is important that such differences are identified and explored by all those involved. Such discussions might include board members, representatives of different professions, patient representatives, and those who will be charged with developing and delivering the actual workshops. Engagement of senior organisational management is particularly important since organisational support is essential if distributed leadership is to be successful (De Brun et al., 2019).

Having identified the needs in relation to leadership development, it is then important to *select the desired outcomes* for the workshop(s) so that these needs can be met. Geerts et al. (2020) suggest that outcomes need to be considered at a number of different levels – namely, the outcomes for individuals participating in the workshop, organisational outcomes and (given the specific context of healthcare) the outcomes for patients. This latter point is important given the links between leadership and patient outcomes (Northway, 2017).

Whilst the agreed outcomes will detail what the development workshops seek to achieve, it is also important that *specific and explicit* goals are identified.

Making them specific and measurable will provide the foundation for later evaluation of the workshops and hence using a SMART (specific, measurable, achievable, relevant and time-limited) approach is advocated. The goals will need to be considered and planned from the perspective of both participants and the organisation but Geerts et al. (2020) suggest that these need to be aligned with organisational strategy and priorities. This relates back to the importance of securing organisational support for distributed leadership (De Brun et al., 2019).

Geerts et al. (2020) also argue that adhering to the principles of adult learning (Stage 8) means that there should be opportunities for participants to select their own goals and outcomes. This suggests that whilst an eight-stage approach is advocated this should not be seen as strictly linear and that there needs to be movement forwards and backwards through the stages as the development programme progresses. They utilise Knowles's (1984) principles of adult learning, but they also suggest that it would be useful to investigate if these principles should be modified specifically for leadership development. Knowles's (1984) principles of adult learning include self-direction rather than self-reflection. However, Stage 8 could allow for *self-reflection*, which is an essential part of Kolb's (2014) learning cycle, and reflective practice can be seen as an essential modification of the key principles of adult learning.

Deciding who should participate in the workshop(s) needs careful consideration. Often leadership development courses have taken staff out of their usual work organisation and brought disparate groups of people together for a time-limited learning event. However, distributed leadership requires high levels of trust (Harris, 2014), and capacity and capability are developed through learning that is based on interaction (Hartviksen et al., 2019). In addition, it has been noted that whilst leadership in complex healthcare systems requires working in a multidisciplinary context, teams are often not provided with the opportunity to physically come together with the time to reflect (De Brun et al., 2019). There may, therefore, be value in considering bringing people from within an organisation together or people from organisations that need to work closely together to participate in leadership development workshops. This can then assist with supporting the development of a cooperative approach that is rooted in the context within which distributed leadership needs to be developed (Hartviksen et al., 2019).

There are, of course, many ways of delivering workshops and they can take many approaches, and so thought needs to be given to how they will be *structured*, what their *content* will be, who will *facilitate* them and what *activities* will be used.

In terms of structure, an important consideration is whether a 'one-off' workshop is to be held or whether a series of linked workshops will be developed. The former has a potential advantage in terms of limiting time away from the workplace and this may be an important factor influencing decision-making in organisations where both financial and human resources are stretched. However, a series of workshops offers the opportunity for trusting relationships to be developed amongst those attending and those facilitating, and this will enhance learning. In addition, this approach can also better support transfer of learning into the workplace since there is opportunity to apply new knowledge and skills between workshops and then to reflect on experience in subsequent events.

In order to facilitate a successful workshop that will truly impart experiential learning, there are a number of considerations that need to be taken into account (Brooks-Harris and Stock-Ward, 1999). Based on the earlier definition of workshops in this chapter, three interrelated elements are required: sensitivity to different learning styles, experiential learning and the use of a variety of learning activities (see previous section).

First, it is important to have an understanding of the participants themselves. Then to develop a comprehensive workshop design based on the subject area, such as implementing or understanding distributed leadership, and in relation to the particular group of participants within their work or discipline context. The third aspect is facilitating the workshop in order to promote active learning. Experiential learning theory can inform these approaches. The four stages of Kolb's (2014) learning cycle – concrete learning, reflective observation, abstract conceptualisation and active experimentation – that were outlined earlier is an experiential learning approach that been adopted to underpin running workshops (Belay et al., 2019; Hanen Centre, 2020).

This learning cycle outlines the four stages of learning. However, these stages accommodate the individual learning styles of participants. Utilising Kolb's Learning Style Inventory (Kolb and Kolb, 2011), participants can be assessed with regard to their individual learning styles. These styles reflect the stages of the learning process: those participants that accommodate and learn by feeling and doing (concrete learning stage), those that diverge and learn by feeling and watching (reflective observation stage), those that assimilate by thinking and watching (abstract conceptualisation stage) and finally those that converge by thinking and doing (active experimentation stage)

Geerts et al. (2020) comment that few of the leadership development programmes considered in their review had a clear evaluation strategy. This seems a significant gap given the investment of human and financial resources that is often associated with such programmes, the challenges faced by healthcare systems (Figueroa et al., 2019), and the severe consequences for patients, staff and population health where there are leadership failures (West et al., 2014). It is therefore important to develop an *evaluation framework* as part of the initial planning of leadership development workshops.

Such a framework needs to consider evaluation at a number of levels – the overall programme of workshops, the outcomes of individual activities, the outcomes for individual participants and the achievement of organisational outcomes (Geerts et al., 2020). This will be assisted by clear identification of clear outcomes and goals in the initial planning stages and requires the collection and analysis of both quantitative and qualitative (subjective) data. The timing of evaluation activities also needs to be carefully planned, the suggestion being that it should occur at baseline (before the start of the workshops), at the end of a workshop and at 6–9 months post workshop to determine the extent to which learning has been sustained and used in practice. This latter point is particularly important given the criticism of many leadership development approaches in which there are problems with transferring learning into the workplace (Moldoveanu and Narayandas, 2019).

Allen et al. (2017) utilised Kirkpatrick and Kirkpatrick's model (2006) to assess not only changes in attitude following a day workshop, but changes in behaviour for improving the comfort for clinical faculty in practising and teaching evidence-based medicine. Kirkpatrick and Kirkpatrick's (2006, 2013) model of evaluation distinguishes amongst four levels of outcome after a learning intervention: measuring the learner reaction, knowledge acquisition or changes in attitudes, changes in behaviours and, finally, changes in patient or organisational outcomes. In applying the model, Allen et al. (2017) utilised employee questionnaires both before and after the workshop, as well as observations and interviews. The changes were mapped against the desired organisational outcomes.

Their findings indicated that comfort in teaching and practising evidence-based medicine (EBM) can be improved by a one-day workshop, with most of this improvement being maintained 3–6 months later. The methodology that they adopted for teaching and practising EBM – the Population Intervention Comparator Outcome (PICO) approach – to question framing for teaching and/or clinical practice could be learnt at this one-day workshop. The acquired use of the PICO methodology in the workshop was associated with a self-reported change in clinical and teaching practice 3–14 months later. Utilising Kirkpatrick and Kirkpatrick's model of evaluation (2006), the authors found that this represented change at both level 2 (attitudes) and level 3 (behaviours).

Whilst there may be an expressed commitment to the development of distributed leadership within an organisation, it has been suggested that operational pressures may militate against this happening in practice (Anandaciva et al., 2018). If leadership development workshops are to achieve their desired outcomes, it is important that an *assessment of the barriers to achievement of outcomes* is undertaken as part of the planning process. If problems can be anticipated, then it may be possible to prevent them or (where this is not possible) to incorporate strategies to address then and to mitigate their impact.

Hopefully engaging all of the key stakeholders from the beginning of the process as detailed above will assist in ensuring that there is organisational commitment. However, other factors need to be considered, including prevailing views of power within an organisation whereby even if there is a stated commitment to empowerment of leaders at all levels, this might differ from the perceptions of some within that organisation (Martin et al., 2014). If not addressed, such perceptions could undermine attempts to support development of distributed leadership. Organisational culture is thus a key issue that needs to be considered (Geerts et al., 2020).

The eighth stage proposed by Geerts et al. (2020) is ensuring that the *principles of adult learning are addressed.* However, as already noted above, this needs to run through and inform each of the preceding stages. This chapter has therefore addressed how experiential learning can be incorporated in planning, delivering and evaluating workshops through utilising approaches such as Kolb's (2014) learning cycle.

Conclusion

If distributed leadership is to become a reality, then it is essential that strategies are put in place to ensure appropriate leadership development is provided. However, traditional approaches to training and development may not support development of the knowledge, skills and personal qualities required for distributed leadership and hence alternative approaches are required. This chapter has therefore proposed that the use of workshops offers the potential to support development of distributed leadership given their use of experiential learning approaches and their focus on interaction, problem-solving and transfer of learning to day-to-day practice. However, effective workshops do not just happen and key to their success is the preparation that is undertaken beforehand. Nonetheless, there is a paucity of available literature addressing the use of workshops for enacting distributed leadership practice.

Geerts et al. (2020) note in their systematic literature review of leadership development approaches that interest in the area is substantial, yet it remains unclear which interventions or approaches are most reliably associated with positive outcomes. However, workshops are used extensively in leadership development with much anecdotal and some research evidence of their success. This chapter has highlighted the benefits of this approach as well as the importance of self-reflection and/or reflective practice as an important part of this overall interactive and experiential learning. Workshops supporting distributed leadership development also need to take into consideration the dynamic relationships between health professionals, their capabilities and their values, as well as organisational culture and context. They require very careful planning and it is important that their effectiveness for individuals, the organisation and the impact on patient care are evaluated. A framework for planning and evaluating such an approach has been outlined.

Key concepts discussed

- Academics and practitioners promote the importance of developing and sustaining knowledge and skills required for distributed leadership through discussion and practice.
- A workshop can be defined as a short-term learning experience that encourages active, experiential learning and uses a variety of learning activities to meet the needs of diverse learners.
- Workshops are designed for groups whose members share a common interest or problem, meeting together to improve their individual understanding of a subject through presentation, research, practice, self-reflection and discussion.
- A workshop has three interrelated elements: experiential learning, sensitivity to different learning styles and the use of a variety of learning activities.
- Experiential and interactive learning underpins the workshop concept and format by facilitating the transfer of learning back into the organisational setting.
- Although there is a paucity of available literature examining the use of workshops to support the development of distributed leadership, a number of studies in the wider literature outline key factors that have been successful in the transfer of learning from workshops.
- Key steps are outlined to develop, deliver and evaluate workshops.

Key readings

- Belay, H.T., Ruairc, B.Ó. and Guérandel, A. (2019) Workshops: An important element in medical education, *British Journal of Psychological Advances*, 25 (1): 7–13.
  This paper outlines the evidence for workshops in medical education and reviews the principles governing how to conduct workshops and the use of technology to enhance their delivery. Data collected from an undergraduate psychiatry course delivered in an Irish university are used to illustrate how applying these principles contributes to optimising the use of workshops from both the learners' and facilitators' perspective.
- De Brun, A., O'Donovan, R. and McAuliffe, E. (2019) Interventions to develop collectivistic leadership in healthcare settings: A systematic review, *BMC Health Services Research*, 19: 72. Available at: https://doi.org/10.1186/s12913-019-3883-x.
  This paper reports on a systematic review conducted to explore interventions that develop collectivistic leadership in healthcare settings. The authors found that collectivistic leadership interventions have demonstrated positive outcomes but there is a need for more rigour and consistency in their evaluation.
- Geerts, J.M., Goodall, A.H. and Agius, S. (2020) Evidence-based leadership development for physicians: A systematic literature review, *Social Science and Medicine*, 246: 112709. Available at: https://doi.org/10.1016/j.socscimed.2019.112709.
  This paper systematically reviews physician leadership development and identifies which interventions are most reliably associated with positive outcomes. The authors apply a validated instrument used for medical education to the included studies. This paper is reported as a first review in this research area that creates a tiered rating system to assess the best available evidence.

Example of empirical research

- Allen, D., Abourbih, J., Maar, M., Boesch, L., Goertzen, J. and Cervin, C. (2017) Does a one-day workshop improve clinical faculty's comfort and behaviour in practising and teaching evidence-based medicine? A Canadian mixed methods study, *BMJ Open*, 7: e015174. Available at: https://bmjopen.bmj.com/content/bmjopen/7/7/e015174.full.pdf (accessed 20 October 2020).

Useful websites

- Health Innovation Hub Ireland: https://hih.ie/engage/education-workshops/
  Health Innovation Hub Ireland runs a connected series of innovation workshops designed specifically for healthcare professionals who want to make a measurable difference in how healthcare will be delivered into the future. One-day workshops are designed specifically to build participants' insights into the latest thinking on practical implementation of new processes ideas, new product ideas, and creative approaches to re-thinking healthcare from within.

- The King's Fund: https://www.kingsfund.org.uk/projects/review-leadership-nhs *The King's Fund have a specific focus on leadership and leadership development and their website contains details of both their leadership programmes and other resources.*

References

Allen, D., Abourbih, J., Maar, M., Boesch, L., Goertzen, J. and Cervin, C. (2017) Does a one-day workshop improve clinical faculty's comfort and behaviour in practising and teaching evidence-based medicine? A Canadian mixed methods study, *BMJ Open*, 7: e015174. Available at: https://bmjopen.bmj.com/content/bmjopen/7/7/e015174.full.pdf (accessed 20 October 2020).

Anandaciva, S., Ward, D., Randhava, M. and Edge, R. (2018) *Leadership in Today's NHS: Delivering the Impossible*, London: The King's Fund.

Belay, H.T., Ruairc, B.Ó. and Guérandel, A. (2019) Workshops: An important element in medical education, *British Journal of Psychological Advances*, 25 (1): 7–13.

Black, T.G. and Westwood, M.J. (2004) Evaluating the development of a multidisciplinary leadership team in a cancer-center, *Leadership and Organization Development Journal*, 25 (7): 577–591.

Brooks-Harris, J.E. and Stock-Ward, S.R. (1999) *Workshops: Designing and Facilitating Experiential Learning*, London: Sage.

Byers, V. and Halligan, P. (2017) Leadership education for healthcare professionals, in E.A. Curtis and J.G. Cullen (eds.) *Leadership and Change for the Health Professional*, London: Open University Press.

Careau, E., Biba, G., Brander, R., van Dijk, J.P., Paterson, M. and Tassone, M. (2014) Health leadership education programs, best practices, and impact on learners' knowledge, skills, attitudes, and behaviors and system change: A literature review, *Journal of Healthcare Leadership*, 6: 39–50.

Day, D.V. (2001) Leadership development: A review in context, *Leadership Quarterly*, 11 (4): 581–613.

De Brun, A., O'Donovan, R. and McAuliffe, E. (2019) Interventions to develop collectivistic leadership in healthcare settings: A systematic review, *BMC Health Services Research*, 19: 72. Available at: https://doi.org/10.1186/s12913-019-3883-x (accessed 20 October 2020).

DeRue, D.S. and Myers, C.G. (2014) Leadership development: A review and agenda for future research, in D.V. Day (ed.) *The Oxford Handbook of Leadership and Organizations*, New York: Oxford University Press, 832–855.

Eva, N., Wolfram Cox, J., Tse, H.H. and Lowe, K.B. (2019) From competency to conversation: A multi-perspective approach to collective leadership development, *Leadership Quarterly*, 101346. Available at: https://doi.org/10.1016/j.leaqua.2019.101346 (accessed 20 October 2020).

Figueroa, C.A., Harrison, R., Chauhan, A. and Meyer, L. (2019) Priorities and challenges for health leadership and workforce management globally: A rapid review, *BMC Health Services Research*, 19: 239. Available at: https://doi.org/10.1186/S12913-019-4080-7 (accessed 20 October 2020).

Fitzpatrick, R. and Hunt, D. (2019) *How to Design and Teach Workshops that Work Every Time*, London: Robfitz Ltd. Available at: http://workshopsurvival.com (accessed 20 October 2020).

Forsetlund, L., Bjorndal, A. and Rashidian, A. (2009) Continuing education meetings and workshops: Effects on professional practice and health care outcomes, *Cochrane Database of Systematic Reviews*, 2: CD003030. Available at: https://doi.org/10.1002/14651858.CD003030.pub2 (accessed 20 October 2020).

Friedrich, T.L., Vessey, W.B., Schuelke, M.J., Ruark, G.A. and Mumford, M.D. (2009) A framework for understanding collective leadership: The selective utilization of leader and team expertise within networks, *Leadership Quarterly*, 20 (6): 933–958.

Geerts, J.M., Goodall, A.H. and Agius, S. (2020) Evidence-based leadership development for physicians: A systematic literature review, *Social Science and Medicine*, 246: 112709. Available at: https://doi.org/10.1016/j.socscimed.2019.112709 (accessed 20 October 2020).

Hanen Centre (2020) *Workshops for Speech-Language Pathologists: Turning Theory into Practice*, Toronto: The Hanen Centre. Available at: http://www.hanen.org/Professional-Development/Workshops-For-SLPs.aspx (accessed 12 June 2020).

Harris, A. (2014) *Distributed Leadership Matters: Perspectives, Practicalities and Potential*, Thousand Oaks, CA: Corwin.

Hartviksen, T.A., Aspfors, J. and Uhrenfeldt, L. (2019) Healthcare middle managers' experiences of developing capacity and capability: A systematic review and meta-synthesis, *BMC Health Services*, 19: 546. Available at: https://doi.org/10.1186/s12913-019-4345-1 (accessed 20 October 2020).

King's Fund (2011) *The Future of Leadership and Management in the NHS: No More Heroes*, London: The King's Fund. Available at: https://www.kingsfund.org.uk/sites/default/files/future-of-leadership-and-management-nhs-may-2011-kings-fund.pdf (accessed 20 October 2020).

Kirkpatrick, D. and Kirkpatrick, J. (2013) *Kirkpatrick Four Levels®: Audio recordings study guide*, Newnan, GA: Kirkpatrick Partners. Available at: https://www.kirkpatrickpartners.com/Portals/0/Products/Kirkpatrick%20Four%20Levels%20-%20Audio%20Recordings%20Study%20Guide.pdf (accessed 13 June 2020).

Kirkpatrick, D.L. and Kirkpatrick, J.D. (2006) *Evaluating Training Programs: The Four Levels*, 3rd edition, San Francisco, CA: Berrett-Koehler.

Kolb, A.Y. and Kolb, D. (2005) Learning styles and learning spaces: Enhancing experiential learning in higher education, *Academy of Management Learning and Education*, 4 (2): 193–212.

Kolb, A.Y. and Kolb, D.A. (2011) *The Kolb Learning Style Inventory version 4: A Comprehensive Guide to the Theory, Psychometrics, Research on Validity and Educational Applications*. Available at: https://learningfromexperience.com/downloads/research-library/the-kolb-learning-style-inventory-4-0.pdf (accessed 13 June 2020).

Kolb, D.A. (2014) *Experiential Learning: Experience as the Source of Learning and Development*, Englewood Cliffs, NJ: Financial Times Press.

Knowles, M.S. (1984) *Andragogy in Action*, San Francisco, CA: Jossey-Bass.

Manolson, A. (1992) *It Takes Two to Talk: The Hanen Program for Parents of Children with Language Delays*, Toronto: The Hanen Centre.

Martin, G., Beech, N., MacIntosh, R. and Bushfield, S. (2014) Potential challenges facing distributed leadership in healthcare: Evidence from the UK National Health Service, *Sociology of Health and Illness*, 37 (1): 14–29.

Moldoveanu, M. and Narayandas, D. (2019) The future of leadership development, *Harvard Business Review*, 97 (2): 40–48.

Northway, R. (2017) Leadership and patient care outcomes, in E.A. Curtis and J.G. Cullen (eds.) *Leadership and Change for the Health Professional*, London: Open University Press, 149–160.

Stoller, J.K. (2013) Commentary: Recommendations and remaining questions for health care leadership training programs, *Academic Medicine*, 88 (1): 12–15.

Van Velsor, E., McCauley, C.D. and Ruderman, M.N. (eds.) (2010) *The Center for Creative Leadership Handbook of Leadership Development*, San Francisco, CA: Jossey-Bass.

West, M., Eckert, R., Steward, K. and Passmore, B. (2014) *Developing Collective Leadership for Healthcare*, London: The King's Fund.

West, M., Armit, K., Loewenthal, L., Eckert, R., West, T. and Lee, A. (2015) *Leadership and Leadership Development in Healthcare: The Evidence Base*. London: Faculty of Medical Leadership and Management.

13 Making sense of empirical research on distributed leadership tendencies

John G. Cullen

Chapter topics

- What is distributed leadership?
- Is there a difference between collective leadership and distributed leadership in the literature (and does it matter)?
- What do we know about distributed leadership from empirical research?
- In what contexts has distributed leadership been studied, and what is known about distributed leadership in nursing and healthcare settings?
- What do we need to know about distributed leadership in nursing and healthcare?

Introduction

Distributed leadership (DL) has become something of a touchstone for management and organisational researchers who address the many shortcomings of existing leadership theory. There is a tendency for leadership discourse to examine minute aspects of leadership in a disconnected and abstracted way or to celebrate the 'heroic' achievements of business executives without acknowledging the huge amount of invisible work that was done by other employees (Daniels, 1987; Hatton, 2017) or their family members (McGee, 2005) to ensure they can take all the praise for their partial achievements. Distributed leadership was initially proposed as an 'alternative to the current focus, which is primarily on the deeds of individual leaders' (Gronn, 2002: 423). Distributed leadership recognises that the roles of leader and follower are interchangeable, malleable and centred on creating synergies that result in new outcomes for organisations. Are these claims backed up in practice though? It is perhaps easy to see why DL attracted the attention of researchers. Many have puzzled for years as to why a small group of individuals in organisations ('leaders') were studied in a way which assumed that other employees ('followers') were not as creative, ethical or inspiring as those who were privileged to finish their career in more senior positions. The reputations of most organisations are made by those who work within them, rather than the 'focused leaders' (Gronn, 2002: 424) at their apex, and the cultural leadership practices of many employees were rarely accounted for in the business sections of newspapers. The lens of DL, it would appear, gets us closer to how leadership is done in organisations, which is often in spite of, rather than because of, those who sit at its head.

Distributed leadership sounds good, but it is important to ask what we actually know about it before making claims for it, and risk it becoming another irrelevancy in the vast cannon of leadership research that gathers dust in the archives of obscurity. On the surface, it looks very appealing, particularly to pressed leaders in healthcare organisations, and works such as this book will do much to make it more acceptable and of interest to those organisations and departments who need it. In order to do this, however, we need to briefly glance backwards to see where our research on the subject has taken us so far.

What does the literature on distributed leadership tell us about it?

Because this chapter will make reference to evidence, it is important to outline what sources are used. The key resource used is the Social Sciences Citation Index (SSCI). Over a number of decades the SCCI has grown to be the optimal multidisciplinary indexer of research-based literature in the social sciences (Wang et al., 2012). Most of the evidence was collected and analysed in the early months (January to March) of 2020. Because new sources are added to this massive database on an almost daily basis, search results can change and grow rapidly, so general trends are reported. The SSCI was also chosen as a resource above other health-related ones (such as CINAHL and PubMed) as it relates findings on DL in its broadest sense, although attention will be given to health fields also.

For example, a title search using the string 'Distributed Leader*' on the SSCI in very early March 2020 returned 134 'hits', of which 117 were reviewed research articles. Eighty-four (nearly 63%) of all returns were in categories related to educational research and 36 (nearly 27%) were in management and business. Only six (less than 4.5%) were in the areas of health and health policy. In other words, there is relatively little empirical DL research in fields related to health services, so our exploration of that work must be reviewed in relation to other work. The reason for the DL focus in the education category may be due to policy decisions that emphasised its implementation and utility in an educational context (Bolden, 2011), and that its main populariser and one of its earliest theorists, Professor Peter Gronn, was an education academic.

The most cited of these articles are Peter Gronn's 'Distributed leadership as a unit of analysis' (2000) and Richard Bolden's 'Distributed leadership in organisations: A review of theory and research' (2011). Gronn's work has been used more in academic research, with almost two and a half times the amount of citations of Bolden's, although it must be recognised that the latter was published more recently, which has obviously limited the amount of time available for it to be cited. Gronn (2002) begins from a position that claims pre-existing forms of leadership were not suited to new divisions of workplace activity.

Gronn (2002) distinguishes between two forms of DL: *numerical action* and *concertive action*. By *numerical action*, Gronn means the commonplace understanding of DL as involving the distribution of numerous leaders throughout the organisation. *Concertive action*, in contrast, implies that leadership is a practice that happens as a result of there being a number of people engaging with each other in everyday workplace projects, which produces forms of leadership that are a result of employees working in concert with each other. Gronn sees these as emerging in three ways: (1) through spontaneous workplace collaboration: (2) the emergence of shared understandings, which arises intuitively as a result of collaboration amongst colleagues; and (3) formal institutionalised practices which regularise distributed action. He demonstrates how new workplace imperatives generate different forms of interdependence between employees that require distributed models of coordination in the workplace.

Bolden's review article (2011) roughly takes Gronn's work as a starting point and notes a growth in both citations and peer-reviewed publications since the beginning of the millennium; the research undertaken for this chapter confirms that this acceleration has continued, although Bolden noted that not all variants of DL had received the same amounts of attention since then. Interestingly, he found the concept of 'shared leadership' had received much more attention in the nursing and medicine literature, but that this trend had pre-existed the emergence of DL.

Forms of distributed leadership

Bolden noted that DL was most commonly researched in the education and education management journals, and this is another trend that has continued in the years since his review was published. Bolden's review highlights that there have been many definitional 'tussles' over what DL is and how it can be accomplished. In some senses the division between co-performance and collective performance as outlined by Gronn (2002) still exists and, perhaps as a result, different taxonomies of collective leadership have emerged over time. Gronn (2000) cites a work by Hodgson, Levinson and Zaleznik (1965) which predates contemporary interest in DL considerably. This was a study of the 'role constellation' that emerged between three psychiatric hospital administrators.

> This conjoint work unit represented more than the aggregated efforts of three self-contained individuals enacting their own particular roles. It evolved from a process of adaptation negotiated between the three men as they intermeshed their personalities while reworking a pre-existing set of relationships following a leadership succession process. (Gronn, 2000: 332)

Is this an example of co-leadership or collective leadership? The definition of this practice is perhaps unimportant, as the outcome was increased productivity. It is interesting to note that the DL-related processes happened in the aftermath of a leadership succession process. Bion (1961), for example, noted that co-leadership often occurred in groups in the aftermath of their realisation that their current leader would no longer serve as an adequate 'object' for the group (De Board, 1978/2014). When there is a small group of individuals working together in an unofficial, but tangible leadership capacity with the resources and authority to make decisions, co-leadership is more appropriate.

On the other hand, when leadership is something which is done throughout the organisation, then collective leadership might be a more appropriate designation. On a surface level the idea of collective leadership may appear to have shared similarities with the idea of 'strong cultures' celebrated by 1980s management gurus (Peters and Waterman, 1984). Raelin (2011), however, posits that if organisations genuinely adopt democratic principles which acknowledge that all employees are inherently capable of contributing to the growth and flourishing of those organisations, opportunities should be provided to them through what has become known as 'leaderful' practice. When teams or organisations find themselves working together in a manner that flows and is fruitful, they are experiencing a working situation that is characterised as *leaderful* (even through there is no one leader!). 'Everyone is participating in the leadership of the entity both collectively and concurrently; in other words, not just sequentially, but all together and at the same time' (Raelin, 2011: 203). Leadership is thus not an activity that is done by leaders, but one which can be done by any individual at any point in time. As such, to allow such activities to genuinely take place, leadership conversations need to be taken out of the hands of 'official leaders' and placed into the sphere of those who can legitimately influence them. For example, when the founder of Interface Inc., Ray Anderson, attempted to radically re-orient his company to a carbon-zero position, he also created a company ethos and culture where all employees shared his belief that changing his company would result in the world being saved (Anderson, 1998; Bakan, 2004; Werbach, 2009). By allowing employees to share and act on the same concerns as those that would be held by a traditional leader, Anderson allowed his organisation to become one which was 'full' of leadership or leaderful (Raelin, 2011).

Many DL theorists urge a healthy cynicism or critical mindset on the topic. Bolden advocates for a critical approach to DL which is not descriptive or normative but which 'facilitates reflection on the purpose(s) and discursive mechanisms of leadership and an awareness of the dynamics of power and influence in shaping what happens within and outside organisations' (2011: 263). The idea of replacing the person of a leader with an ethos or a concept has been utilised by ideologues to radicalise isolated people and turn them into terrorists who commit atrocities. This concept, which is known as 'leaderless resistance' is a very extreme and orchestrated attempt to seduce vulnerable people into adopting dangerous ideas by individuals who then do not take responsibility for subsequent actions.

In the *Protestant Ethic and the Spirit of Capitalism* (1930/1992), Max Weber wrote about the way in which religious beliefs influenced a work ethic that in turn led to the development of highly motivated individuals who had a very high propensity for work and attainment, but also espoused the principles of personal frugality. This led to ideal conditions for the emergence of capitalistic growth in regions where such beliefs were prevalent. Although having a 'calling' or 'vocation' is often lionised as a good career orientation for an individual to have (Bellah, 1985; Wrzesniewski et al., 1997; Wrzesniewski and Dutton, 2001; Berkelaar and Buzzanell, 2015), the idea of a collective ethic or purpose needs to be critically appraised as a way of understanding a distributed work ethic as an enabler of DL.

Anthony Heyes' article 'The economics of vocation or "why is a badly paid nurse a good nurse"?' (2005) demonstrates how thinking about a profession as a calling or a vocation can be used to reduce salaries. As nursing is often considered a 'vocation' by non-nurses, a belief has emerged that if nurses were paid according to the true value of the work that they do, then people who were just 'in it for the money' would be attracted to the role, but the standard of the work which nurses do would then decline.

To return to the topic of DL, the research literature suggests that in the aftermath of poor experiences of being led (due to leader toxicity, absence or unethical behaviour, for example), the appetite for participating in the leadership of the organisation by members is increased. The first consultative stage of *planful action* suggested by Leithwood et al. (2006, see below) might be best enacted during this time of organisational anomie, and could assist in the healing of employees following the experience of 'moral injury' that often arises as a result of poor leadership (Shay, 1994, 2002, 2014).

In a later article titled 'The future of distributed leadership', Gronn suggested that the word 'leadership' had become overused in discussions of DL and that the word 'hybrid' might be more appropriately suited to represent 'diverse patterns of practice which fuse or coalesce [hybrid] elements of emergent activities' (2008: 155). This perhaps demonstrates a fundamental shift away from the idea of a single, focused individual leader towards one where 'any organization in which there may be evidence of persons and units leading, that configuration is simply one of "leadership", unqualified and unembellished' (Gronn, 2009: 390).

What does the literature on distributed leadership tell us about it in nursing and healthcare?

Because most of the empirical research on DL has been undertaken in the context of education, there is a limited understanding on how it impacts patient outcomes and this is a clear research need. Healthcare is an entirely different operating system to education, so caution needs to be exercised when relating research which discusses how DL influences outcomes for learners rather than patients. Bolden (2011) reports on a number of studies in educational management which support positive relationships between DL and improved student outcomes. Leithwood et al. (2006) provide a taxonomy of four types of DL:

- *Planful alignment* happens when resources and responsibilities are deliberately allocated to those in the organisation who can best lead a particular function or task.
- *Spontaneous alignment* occurs when leadership tasks and roles are distributed in a way which is not researched or planned, but on the basis of intuitive decisions.
- *Spontaneous misalignment* is when spontaneous alignment goes wrong.
- *Anarchic misalignment* happens when leaders follow their own goals without reference to that of others.

The outcomes of the final two forms perhaps require no comment, but Leithwood et al. found that planful alignment was most conducive to organisational productivity, and spontaneous alignment (and planful alignment) resulted in short-term organisational productivity. Implementing DL, then, requires a thoughtful, consultative understanding of its outcomes to achieve specific goals and outcomes.

As more leadership research in the area of healthcare and nursing has been conducted in relation to shared or collective leadership, it is important to determine what this body of work investigates and what it has to 'say' to the field of nursing and healthcare management. Bolden (2011) noted that most DL research was conducted in the UK context and this would appear to be the case for DL in health leadership, although studies have also been conducted in Kenya (Nzinga et al., 2018), Denmark (Jonasson et al., 2018) and Canada (Markle-Reid et al., 2017). There was a mix in the qualitative and quantitative methodologies used, but the most prevalent form of data collection used was qualitative interviews. Distributed leadership is often studied in the context of health service change (Chreim et al., 2010; Johnson et al., 2011; Best et al., 2012; Chreim and MacNaughton, 2016; Nzinga et al., 2018) or service mergers (Jonasson et al., 2018). Although research on DL in the health service context is quite limited when compared to other sectors, it also provides insights into how it can be practically accomplished. Nzinga et al. (2018) found that context, power and relationships between professional groups moderated the ability of DL participants to bring about change – this is an important finding because it does not portray the healthcare setting as a politically neutral space. This is echoed by Jonasson et al. (2018), who found a variety of forms of DL across organisational boundaries, with the implication that appropriate forms of DL must be investigated and understood across partner units prior to mergers. Johnson et al. (2011), study, provides some additional context on this. The authors found that active participation in DL tasks was positively associated with self-efficacy, innovation and job satisfaction and this was most observable amongst permanent employees, chief physicians and employee representatives. Almost all of the literature on DL, both in general and in the healthcare context, begins by claiming that the leadership literature celebrates individual leaders and ignores the collective context. Distributed leadership is discussed as a positive way to ensure that organisational goals and patient outcomes are obtained. However, the lionisation of DL is not cognisant of the fact that the rise of precarious work contracts (Standing, 2011) means that individuals who are not employed in senior positions or hold permanency or tenure feel isolated and vulnerable, and the massive austerity measures in the forms of redundancies and salary cuts that were inflicted on healthcare professionals around the world during the global financial crisis remain in recent memory. Cynicism towards DL is understandable amongst employees, who may feel they are participating in a form of leadership where their personal worth and occupational capital is 'invisibilised' by being part of a collective. In short, the words 'team member' is less valuable than 'team leader' on the CV of somebody who is not protected by seniority and tenure. This is a critical point that must be considered by all organisations that wish to engage with DL. The winners in the 'war for talent' (Michaels et al.,

2001) are those who develop 'CV capital' in each of their employment choices. If DL does not allow this, individuals with ambitions to move into senior or more secure positions may be de-motivated as a result.

Healthcare research on DL indicates concerns about the value that participating in it generates for employees and organisations. Chreim and MacNaughton (2016) point out that the emergence of leadership role constellations can result in overlaps, duplication and ambiguities for teams. The need to establish responsibility for certain deliverables in confused work situations can add to a greater level of work for members, but this can be addressed if leaders agree who ultimately 'owns' each area of responsibility (McKee et al., 2013). Many articles stress that confusion and ambiguity can be an unintended result of DL and articulate the need to alternate between centralised leaders and constellation-based approaches as appropriate. Chreim and MacNaughton (2016) advocate for the appointment of a designated change agent to manage organisational transformational processes that are dependent on a DL-based approach.

Although most of the health services DL literature focuses on change initiatives, some mention its impact on patient outcomes. Distributed leadership has been particularly useful in developing services for patients who have specific needs that require the intervention of multiple stakeholders (Markle-Reid et al., 2017; McEvoy et al., 2017). McEvoy et al. (2017), for example, mention the role of DL in allowing a self-selected group of stakeholders to use their knowledge of local and cultural traditions to engage with a specific religious group in order to improve their access to mental healthcare services.

Recently, reviews of collective leadership have grown again in popularity in the social sciences. In their review of collective leadership theory, Ospina et al. (2020) present an up-to-date framework of where literature in the field of collective leadership research and theory is at present. It does this by presenting a dual-axis matrix: the first axis inquiries into the *locus of leadership* and asks if it is theorised as belonging to a group or within an organisational or social system; the second axis interrogates the notion of *collective leadership* and seeks to determine if it is a type of leadership or a theoretical approach to studying leadership. When these two axes come together, they suggest a map of four different approaches to the study of leadership:

- The first sees collective leadership as involving plural forms of leadership which reside in interpersonal relationships (such as co-leadership, shared leadership, team leadership, etc.).
- The second type refers to plural forms of leadership which reside in systems (such as distributed leadership).
- The third type refers to theoretical approaches which see leadership as something that is a practice rather than, for example, a position or title (Raelin, 2007, 2011).
- The fourth and final type sees leadership as something that is theoretical and resides in systems dynamics and often involves critical leadership studies.

We can see from this model that there are a number of different ways of thinking about collective leadership. In the same issue of the leading social sciences journal where this article was published, *Human Relations*, another article states that the most popular term used in studies of collective leadership was *distributed leadership*, which appeared in 41% of all studies reviewed (Fairhurst et al., 2020). Distributed and collective leadership are often considered to be the same thing by researchers in the field. This is also the case in recent reviews of research such as De Brún and colleagues' (2019) systematic review of interventions to develop collectivist leadership in healthcare settings, which used the keyword 'distributed leadership' amongst other terms such as 'collective leadership' and 'shared leadership'.

De Brún and colleagues' (2019) review explored a range of interventions such as team training approaches, co-leadership, service improvement initiatives and co-design team development interventions. The findings of the studies on all of these approaches reported positive results in the facilitation of collective leadership, staff engagement, satisfaction and team performance. De Brún et al. point out that collaborative decision-making and problem-solving in particular resulted in higher levels of staff engagement and empowerment. Why is this the case, given the suggestion raised earlier in this chapter, that the success and acceptance of DL might potentially impact on staff employed in more precarious positions? Isabel Menzies' (1960) study of the generation of organisational anxiety examined why high-performing nurses left a teaching hospital as a result of strict rules about structures and processes that had been put in place to manage the reality of working with patients who were suffering. The organisational defences against anxiety that had been put in place actually ended up making it very difficult for the staff members to fulfil their roles as nurses. By distributing leadership (and its responsibilities) amongst staff members, anxiety about violating organisational controls (or defences) are transferred from the individual to the collective.

Conclusion

In summary, DL was initially proposed as an alternative to the ongoing focus on individual leaders and their traits, behaviours and communication styles that had come to dominate mainstream leadership research. Distributed leadership was an acknowledgment not only that these leaders' 'successes' depended on the innovation and 'leaderly' activities of subordinates, but that much leadership theory and 'products' relied on bolstering the self-fulfilling fantasies of individuals (Svengingsson and Larsson, 2006) who found themselves at the head of organisations (Ladkin, 2015).

The vast majority of research on DL has been in the educational sector (in particular the education management sector) and most has been conducted in UK settings and is primarily qualitative in nature. The qualitative aspect to this research is welcome, as the development of DL as both a field of practice and a theoretical lens (Fairhurst et al., 2020; Ospina et al., 2020) is dependent on developing nuanced understandings of how to make it work in a way that is conscious of the need to work with the grain of local organisational cultures.

There have been several attempts to conceptualise DL and there are various understandings of what it actually is. The central division in thinking sees it as involving either the distribution of leaders throughout a group or an organisation, or the distribution of opportunities for doing leadership throughout the organisational system. Some theorists see DL as a sub-set of collective leadership and others see it as interchangeable with it and most of the health services research views it as a mixture of both approaches.

Findings on the benefits of DL in healthcare are most reported in relation to organisational or change-related outputs, and it is particularly noted to have produced strong patient outcomes when applied to issues requiring multiple-stakeholder engagement. However, implementing or including DL in such initiatives requires a deeper understanding of who the members of the 'collective' where the leadership will be distributed are.

The research on DL and collective forms of leadership in the context of nurses and healthcare is generally conducted through qualitative methods (Bolden, 2011; Fairhurst et al., 2020; Ospina et al., 2020), and this chapter proposes that this is positive. Large-scale quantitatively oriented studies of leadership may be appropriate in developing generalisations about concepts, but qualitative research methods have a much greater utility in unpacking the lived experiences of nurses and health professions in their workplaces. Most of the research conducted, however, suggests the positives of DL in improving staff engagement and satisfaction in team-based scenarios (and particularly those engaged with change), and stresses improvements in patient outcomes where optimal care provision is dependent on multiple stakeholders. A key research need, however, is understanding the relationship between employment contract type and engagement in DL.

Distributed leadership is often considered in the literature to be the same thing (or at least interchangeable with) collective leadership, but it is important to be clear what we mean by the 'collective'. Management and organisational theory remains rooted in late-nineteenth- or early-twentieth-century understandings of what the workplace is and how it functions. Even the advances made in understanding socio-technical systems and human relations theory assumes a cohesive cultural whole to which all employees feel some sense of attachment to. Workers at the 'edges' of the organisational cultures (who are often the ones who provide unseen or unacknowledged support to other workers) are often not considered to be part of this collective. Petriglieri et al. (2019) found that members of precarious workforces often experience emotional distress as a result of being disconnected from the benefits of full organisational or professional membership. Given that so much research appears to assume the role of a collective organisational memory (Abrahamson, 2004) or shared cultural intelligence (Spiller et al., 2019) in facilitating the distribution of leadership capabilities, the fact that there is significant usage of locum and temporary workers in healthcare settings means that new understandings of how to 'do' DL with new types of workforces are necessary.

In other words, the research on DL in healthcare settings is small, but it appears to report that it is has positive outcomes for groups of patients or healthcare workers. What we don't know is how this works for the voices that are not often heard in this research – the excluded or marginalised workforce in healthcare who are made up of agency, temporary or otherwise precariously employed staff. We do not know what they contribute to DL, or whether their work has the potential to change the leadership profile or effectiveness of an organisation.

In practice, DL is something that healthcare managers should investigate and explore when seeking 'distributed outcomes'. The focus of DL research and theory has been one way in which leadership can be positively dispersed throughout teams, units and organisations, but there is also an opportunity to see how it can change work cultures by developing new forms of collectives. As many DL research papers begin by decrying the bulk of research which focuses on the individual leader, future DL research may risk ignoring and excluding *all* of the future potential leaders of organisations.

Key concepts discussed

- established understandings of DL and forms of DL (e.g. 'leaderfulness', 'distributed leadership practice', 'post-heroic', 'collective leadership', 'team leadership', 'co-leadership' and 'democratic leadership'
- 'organising' concepts of DL: descriptive DL, normative DL, critical DL
- key research in context (which has been primarily in the field of education)
- the cultural challenge of practising DL.

Key readings

- Bolden, R. (2011) Distributed leadership in organisations: A review of theory and research, *International Journal of Management Reviews*, 13 (3): 251–269.
  A comprehensive overview of empirical research on the theory and practice of DL.
- Gosling, J., Bolden, R. and Petrov, G. (2009) Distributed leadership in higher education: What does it accomplish?', *Leadership*, 5 (3): 299–310.
  A critical analysis of the impact of DL in organisations.
- Kelly, S. (2014) Towards a negative ontology of leadership, *Human Relations*, 67 (8): 905–922.
  A psychoanalytic structural review of the condition of 'leaderlessness'.
- Kelly, S., White, M.I., Martin, D. and Rouncefield, M. (2006) Leadership refrains: Patterns of leadership, *Leadership*, 2 (2): 181–201.
  An article that compares DL with other forms of leadership.
- Raelin, J. (2011) From leadership-as-practice to leaderful practice, *Leadership*, 7 (2): 195–211.
  This article introduces the practical concept of 'leaderfulness' to the literature on DL.
- Spiller, C., Maunganui Wolfgramm, R., Henry, E. and Pouwhare, R. (2019) Paradigm warriors: Advancing a radical ecosystems view of collective leadership from an Indigenous Māori perspective, *Human Relations*, 73 (4): 516–543.
  A recent article that powerfully introduces and unpacks the concept of collective leadership as a cultural trope.

References

Abrahamson, E. (2004) *Change Without Pain: How Managers Can Overcome Initiative Overload, Organisational Chaos, and Employee Burnout*, Boston, MA: Harvard Business School Press.
Anderson, R.C. (1998) *Mid-course Correction: Toward a Sustainable Enterprise – The Interface Model*, Atlanta, GA: Peregrinzilla Press.

Bakan, J. (2004) *The Corporation: The Pathological Pursuit of Profit and Power*, London: Constable.

Bellah, R.N. (1985) *Habits of the Heart: Individualism and Commitment in American Life*, Berkeley, CA: University of California Press.

Berkelaar, B.L. and Buzzanell, P.M. (2015) Bait and switch or double-edged sword? The (sometimes) failed promises of calling, *Human Relations*, 68 (1): 157–178.

Best, A., Greenhalgh, T., Lewis, S., Saul, J.E., Carroll, S. and Bitz, J. (2012) Large-system transformation in health care: A realist review, *Milbank Quarterly*, 90 (3): 421–456.

Bion, W.R. (1961) *Experiences in Groups, and Other Papers*, London: Tavistock.

Bolden, R. (2011) Distributed leadership in organisations: A review of theory and research, *International Journal of Management Reviews*, 13 (3): 251–269.

Chreim, S. and MacNaughton, K. (2016) Distributed leadership in health care teams: Constellation role distribution and leadership practices, *Health Care Management Review*, 41 (3): 200–212.

Chreim, S., Williams, B.E., Janz, L. and Dastmalchian, A. (2010) Change agency in a primary health care context: The case of distributed leadership, *Health Care Management Review*, 35 (2): 187–199.

Daniels, A.K. (1987) Invisible work, *Social Problems*, 34 (5): 403–415.

De Board, R. (2014) *The Psychoanalysis of Organisations: A Psychoanalytic Approach to Behaviour in Groups and Organisations*, classic edition, London: Routledge (originally published 1978).

De Brún, A., O'Donovan, R. and McAuliffe, E. (2019) Interventions to develop collectivistic leadership in healthcare settings: A systematic review, *BMC Health Services Research*, 19: 72. Available at: http://dx.doi.org/10.1186/s12913-019-3883-x (accessed 20 October 2020).

Fairhurst, G.T., Jackson, B., Foldy, E.G. and Ospina, S.M. (2020) Studying collective leadership: The road ahead, *Human Relations*, 73 (4): 598–614.

Gronn, P. (2000) Distributed properties: A new architecture for leadership, *Educational Management and Administration*, 28 (3): 317–338.

Gronn, P. (2002) Distributed leadership as a unit of analysis, *Leadership Quarterly*, 13 (4): 423–451.

Gronn, P. (2008) The future of distributed leadership, *Journal of Educational Administration*, 46 (2): 141–158.

Gronn, P. (2009) Leadership configurations, *Leadership*, 5 (3): 381–394.

Hatton, E. (2017) Mechanisms of invisibility: Rethinking the concept of invisible work, *Work Employment and Society*, 31 (2): 336–351.

Heyes, A. (2005) The economics of vocation or 'why is a badly paid nurse a good nurse'?, *Journal of Health Economics*, 24 (3): 561–569.

Hodgson, R.C., Levinson, D.J. and Zaleznik, A. (1965) *The Executive Role Constellation: An Analysis of Personality and Role Relations in Management*, Boston, MA: Harvard University Graduate School of Business Administration.

Johnson, P.A., Bookman, A., Bailyn, L., Harrington, M. and Orton, P. (2011) Innovation in ambulatory care: A collaborative approach to redesigning the health care workplace, *Academic Medicine*, 86 (2): 211–216.

Jonasson, C., Kjeldsen, A.M. and Ovesen, M.S. (2018) Dynamics of distributed leadership during a hospital merger, *Journal of Health Organisation and Management*, 32 (5): 691–707.

Ladkin, D. (2015) Leadership, management and headship: Power, emotion and authority in organisations, in B. Carroll, J. Ford and S. Taylor (eds.) *Leadership: Contemporary Critical Perspectives*, London: Sage, 3–25.

Leithwood, K., Day, C., Sammons, P., Harris, A. and Hopkins, D. (2006) *Successful School Leadership: What It Is and How It Influences Pupil Learning*, Nottingham: DfES Publications.

Markle-Reid, M., Dykeman, C., Ploeg, J., Stradiotto, C.K., Andrews, A., Bonomo, S. et al. (2017) Collaborative leadership and the implementation of community-based fall prevention initiatives: A multiple case study of public health practice within community groups, *BMC Health Services Research*, 17: 141. Available at: http://dx.doi.org/10.1186/s12913-017-2089-3 (accessed 20 October 2020).

McEvoy, P., Williamson, T., Kada, R., Frazer, D., Dhliwayo, C. and Gask, L. (2017) Improving access to mental health care in an Orthodox Jewish community: A critical reflection upon the accommodation of otherness, *BMC Health Services Research*, 17: 557. Available at: http://dx.doi.org/10.1186/s12913-017-2509-4 (accessed 20 October 2020).

McGee, M. (2005) *Self-Help, Inc.: Makeover Culture in American Life*, New York: Oxford University Press.

McKee, L., Charles, K., Dixon-Woods, M., Willars, J. and Martin, G. (2013) 'New' and distributed leadership in quality and safety in health care, or 'old' and hierarchical? An interview study with strategic stakeholders, *Journal of Health Services Research and Policy*, 18 (2 suppl.): 11–19.

Menzies, I.E. (1960) A case-study in the functioning of social systems as a defence against anxiety, *Human Relations*, 13(2): 95–121.

Michaels, E., Handfield-Jones, H. and Axelrod, B. (2001) *The War for Talent*, Boston, MA: Harvard Business School Press.

Nzinga, J., McGivern, G. and English, M. (2018) Examining clinical leadership in Kenyan public hospitals through the distributed leadership lens, *Health Policy and Planning*, 33 (suppl. 2): 27–34.

Ospina, S.M., Foldy, E.G., Fairhurst, G.T. and Jackson, B. (2020) Collective dimensions of leadership: Connecting theory and method, *Human Relations*, 73 (4): 441–463.

Peters, T.J. and Waterman, R.H. (1984) *In Search of Excellence: Lessons from America's Best-run Companies*, New York: Warner Books.

Petriglieri, G., Ashford, S.J. and Wrzesniewski, A. (2019) Agony and ecstasy in the gig economy: Cultivating holding environments for precarious and personalized work identities, *Administrative Science Quarterly*, 64 (1): 124–170.

Raelin, J.A. (2007) Toward an epistemology of practice, *Academy of Management Learning and Education*, 6: 4. Available at: https://doi.org/10.5465/amle.2007.27694950 (accessed 20 October 2020).

Raelin, J. (2011) From leadership-as-practice to leaderful practice, *Leadership*, 7 (2): 195–211.

Shay, J. (1994) *Achilles in Vietnam: Combat Trauma and the Undoing of Character*, New York: Atheneum/Oxford: Maxwell Macmillan International.

Shay, J. (2002) *Odysseus in America: Combat Trauma and the Trials of Homecoming*, New York: Scribner.

Shay, J. (2014) Moral injury, *Psychoanalytic Psychology*, 31 (2): 182–191.

Spiller, C., Maunganui Wolfgramm, R., Henry, E. and Pouwhare, R. (2019) Paradigm warriors: Advancing a radical ecosystems view of collective leadership from an Indigenous Māori perspective, *Human Relations*, 73 (4): 516–543.

Standing, G. (2011) *The Precariat: The New Dangerous Class*, London: Bloomsbury Academic.

Sveningsson, S. and Larsson, M. (2006) Fantasies of leadership: Identity work, *Leadership*, 2 (2): 203–224.

Wang, G.G., Gilley, J.W. and Sun, J.Y. (2012) The 'science of HRD research': Reshaping HRD research through scientometrics, *Human Resource Development Review*, 11 (4): 500–520.

Weber, M. (1992) *The Protestant Ethic and the Spirit of Capitalism*, trans. T. Parsons, London: Routledge (originally published 1930).

Werbach, A. (2009) *Strategy for Sustainability: A Business Manifesto*, Boston, MA: Harvard Business School Press.

Wrzesniewski, A. and Dutton, J.E. (2001) Crafting a job: Revisioning employees as active crafters of their work, *Academy of Management Review*, 26 (2): 179–201.

Wrzesniewski, A., McCauley, C., Rozin, P. and Schwartz, B. (1997) Jobs, careers, and callings: People's relations to their work, *Journal of Research in Personality*, 31 (1): 21–33.

14 Towards a sociology of distributed leadership: A lesson from higher education

Aidan Seery

Chapter topics

- Introduction
- Distributed leadership and social systems
- Three key ideas in Luhmann's work and distributed learning
- Case study: Sexual consent education in a university
- Luhmann's three key ideas in the context of the case study
- Conclusion

Introduction

Leadership cultures both in healthcare and education can be placed along a continuum marked by the tension between managerialism at one end of the spectrum and collegiality at the other. This fundamental tension and the debate about leadership styles and approaches in these professions arise especially from the historical condition that both were for long times marked by stringent hierarchies, dispositions of compliance, and a widespread intolerance of the questioning of authority. At the same time, both professions have always, at the horizontal level, been marked by a strong sense of solidarity and collegiality and a healthy querying, if not suspicion, of traditional hierarchies and authority. In the last couple of decades, however, there have been very targeted public policies and educational endeavours to change both the self-understandings of professionals in healthcare and education, and at the same time change the style and culture of leadership within these professions. Both non-doctor healthcare and education workers have learned to view themselves as professionals with a claim to be recognised as professionals equally with solicitors and doctors. It is not the place here to trace how this development has come about, but it is connected to the expertise and qualification demands that have arisen and been adopted into preparation, training and further education in these professions. As a result of the particular cultures of these two professions and also of their more recent history of a growing sense and self-understanding of professionalism, they provide interesting arenas in which to examine the practice or practices of distributed leadership that have become influential in the wider context of business and economic activity in recent years.

A first intention in this chapter is to argue that the particular circumstances of diverse roles, actors and stakeholders in the education and healthcare professions lend themselves to adopting a more systems theory approach to understanding the sociology of distributed leadership within them. More specifically, the approach, or three aspects of the approach developed by Niklas Luhmann are suggested here as a way of understanding certain sociological dimensions of distributed leadership and their performance in these fields. A second aim of the chapter is to present a case study of an intervention initiative in an institution of higher education in Ireland that adopted distributed leadership as the most effective way of building a social system that can learn and support learning in the manner described by Luhmann. Finally, in the final section of the chapter, an attempt is made to examine how the three aspects of a sociology of distributed leadership that were discussed in the case study in higher education might apply to certain situations in healthcare settings that might also benefit from a similar sociological perspective on distributed leadership.

Distributed leadership and social systems

There are a number of well-rehearsed reasons why distributed leadership (DL) has been seen recently as providing a more attractive and potentially effective way of developing leadership capacity, especially in public service institutions such as those of higher education and healthcare. Its appropriateness or effectiveness in higher education, for instance, has been the focus of research for at least twenty years (Gronn, 2000, 2003, 2009; Bolden et al., 2012). Some of these reasons suggest that DL is a promising approach to leadership in the field. They also point to the value of a social systems heuristic for understanding contemporary leadership. One of the reasons for the attractiveness of a DL approach in higher education is the continual rise in the number of demanded and required metrics and outputs for institutions (Siemens et al., 2013), and the impossibility for any single 'heroic' leader to respond to all of the demands. In addition to the output, productivity and transparency demands in current higher education, educational leaders are burdened with the pressing demand from politics and society for radical reform and re-structuring of the sector (Gunter, 2012) and burdened also with internal crises of self-understanding of what a university is for, or can be, in contemporary society (Boulton and Lucas, 2008). Despite the attractiveness of DL, however, leadership in higher education in most of the world seems to be holding on to a more traditional leader-centric approach and concentrating efforts to develop the leadership capacity of individuals while, at the same time, relying more and more on information technology sources to generate data on ever more detailed metrics and productivity measures (Jones et al., 2017).

In this context, it is not surprising that an approach to leadership that shifts the focus from the influence and actions of a small number of individuals holding titled positions to one that emphasises wide engagement, shared purposive action and an appreciation of distinct expertise would gain considerable attention and acceptance, even if this acceptance would seem to be slow. This shift has, most pointedly and most relevantly for the argument and case study here, been described as a decentralisation of leadership away from an individual or individuals to the idea that leadership is an outcome of *practices* (Youngs, 2017) and agency on the part of many in an organisation. Leadership as practice can be described succinctly as 'immanent collective action emerging from mutual, discursive, sometimes recurring and sometimes evolving patterns in the moment and over time amongst those engaged in the practice' (Raelin, 2016: 3). It is this concept that provides the link between DL and Luhmann's theory of social systems in a way that demonstrates particularly the continuing relevance of the latter.

Three key ideas in Luhmann's work and distributed leadership

Niklas Luhmann is regarded not only as a key figure in the development of sociological systems theory but the thinker who developed this theory to its most sophisticated formulation (Schmidt, 2000; Meyer and Boxenbaum, 2010; Seidl and Mormann, 2015). Building on the structural-functional systems theory of Talcott Parsons, he adopts ultimately an evolutionary genetic-functional approach that incorporates ideas from biological systems that highlight the interaction between systems and environment and the ability of certain systems to self-produce, self-sustain and self-regenerate in this relationship. He then takes this model of self-referential systems and applies them to social systems. In a late work, Luhmann discusses organisations specifically as social systems (Luhmann, 2018).

Three key ideas in Luhmann's work, I argue, are useful in providing a deeper understanding of what might be termed the sociology of DL and the way in which human actors can be seen as leaders in practice and the ways in which DL can sometimes flourish or fail. The first idea is that behaviour is not the most useful unit of inquiry when trying to understand how organisations and leaders within them work. Luhmann replaces the foundational idea of behaviour with the concept of the '*operation*', which shifts the emphasis from person-centred actions to the network and social dynamics of practice. This move has the almost counter-intuitive consequence of not considering human beings to be the elemental units of society or of an organisation. So much of leadership and organisational literature has focused on the importance of the individual and of their agency. Here, however, the suggestion is that there is much to be gained by considering the *communication* between human beings as the elemental operation or practice that constitutes an organisation or a system. This is not to say, as critics of systems theory have claimed, that human beings are completely disregarded in the theory (Habermas, 1987; Mingers, 2002; Thyssen, 2003). There can be no human communication without human beings, but in Luhmann's theory they appear as 'persons' – that is, as constructed identities that are the origins and recipients of communication, and only then as actors in the interaction between the two structurally connected systems of physical bodies and consciousness. In the context of this chapter and a discussion of leadership, this perspective is indeed at a radical distance from heroic individual human beings spearheading activity, purpose and direction while also distinct and ahead of others.

A second key idea in Luhmann that lends itself to an understanding of DL and will be useful in the discussion of the case study is that of the self-producing, self-sustaining and regenerating system. This is an idea (autopoiesis) that Luhmann takes from the work of Maturana and Varela (1980) and applies to social systems. Within these systems, operations or practices can emerge and establish themselves only within a network of those same operations, and the network itself comes about only through the operations that constitute the network. An example of such an operation is the social function of offering and receiving favours, which is a feature of organisational and working lives and not just private lives. In circumstances where the proffering and acceptance of favours is ubiquitous, if one is asked for a favour, it is almost impossible to refuse the request and so the network of favours is sustained by the very operation that constitutes it. Focusing, as Luhmann does, on the functions and operations within a system gives a very different view of networks and relations from the information that might be given from an organisational chart. Formally drawn relations and connections in organisations often live side-by-side with informal networks of practice that are very powerful but often not immediately visible. Also, a member of an organisation may have a formal right to be part of a network but if she is not part of the functional system, she may nevertheless be excluded. Finally, this feature of Luhmann's system theory emphasises that social systems contain an 'inverted' control concept in that they resist overt external influence and rely substantially on their self-referential and autopoietic nature.

Applied to leadership and specifically DL, this central Luhmannian idea of self-sustaining networks and systems of functions rather than individuals and their traits helps to understand how certain distributed leadership initiatives can flourish or not, and how formal trait- and individual competency-based leadership may also either flourish or fail. It does so by focusing on an empirical feature of most contemporary organisations that have polycentric internal systems or relatively autonomous units that connect to the larger organisation. This is in contrast to classical organisations that have a single centre or central unit together with a strong hierarchical structure. Once again, it is not that human beings in their complexity and intentional actions are eliminated from this theory but the change of focus to the function of communications between individuals and how these functions establish self-sustaining and adaptable networks can throw light on how organisations and leadership within organisations work. This is especially the case in public service bodies in which there is a very high level of functional differentiation between sections of the organisation. In the case of higher education, for instance, the functional networks among academics can be quite different from those that exist among administrative or technical staff and these networks are different again from those that exist among the student body and their representative bodies.

Before moving to a discussion of the case study in this chapter, one final feature of Luhmann's system theory and how it can help in the understanding of DL and organisational networks is worth mentioning in the context of educational and healthcare institutions and the case study. The place and role of values is sometimes overlooked in the discussion of function-differentiation and autopoiesis in systems. However, this aspect is particularly important in the context of this chapter and book. In social systems of functionally differentiated communications, values provide the common basis for the communication and shared orientation in the selection of action based on this communication. Our immediate conscious states are not available to each other, and communication between individuals can be understood not only on the basis of a shared language but also on some shared values that make this language accessible and understandable to all parties. Furthermore, there is a complex and sometimes tense relationship between values and norms in communications in social systems. For Luhmann, values have normative meanings and norms have inbuilt value. In the interaction not only of individuals but also of an organisation as system and the environment, there is a constant exchange of value- and norm-based communications that can lead to challenge and even conflict. In the realm of leadership and especially DL, the treatment of the complexity of personal values and norms and the values and norms of others and the external environment is of great significance and deserving of close consideration, as these aspects of communication and action in organisations can determine levels of engagement from individuals and ultimately the success or failure of projects. As should be clear from the case study presented below, the leadership and communications within the initiative were characterised by a mutually developed value-language that brought people together to decide and act on an issue that held value for them. The example is from higher education, but it would seem reasonable to assume that within a health professional context there are also many initiatives, programmes and campaigns that require leadership and focused communications that are crucially value-based.

This first section of the chapter has described briefly three features of Luhmann's systems theory that seem to offer a useful way in which to understand the sociology of distributed leadership as a system of communications. It differs fundamentally from approaches that take agents and agency as the central elements of organisations, in the sense that actions from this perspective are artefacts that emerge *later* in attribution on the basis of communications. Viewing communications as the fundamental element of investigation can help avoid some of the difficulties in identifying the basic unit of an act made by an individual agent. For instance, does an organisational behavioural act include the motivation or the intention of the actor or can it be regarded purely as a phenomenon on its own grounds? The view presented here is arguably more holistic and constructivist than provided for in action or agency theory.

The first suggestion, then, is to view DL relations, in the aspects of both governance and leadership, as a system of functions/operations or practices, rather than the perspective of the decisions, actions and agency of individuals. Secondly, it can be useful to consider the workings of DL as an autopoietic system rather than one simply reacting to external impulses and influences. Finally, the place of values and normative demands in any distributed leadership situation is important for the way in which both communication and actions are understood and shared. The next section describes a case of what can be argued to be the implementation of a distributed leadership approach to the governance and leadership of a new non-formal educational initiative in an institution of higher education. The circumstances and the substance of the initiative will be described and the leadership model that was employed will be discussed employing the ideas developed above. While this example is taken from the sphere of higher education, it will be clear, hopefully, that the features of semi-autonomous operations and groups, the existence of self-learning autopoietic units and the value-laden-ness of communications will be familiar to researchers and practitioners in healthcare settings. These three systems-theoretical features will now be examined individually in the context of the case study below.

Case study: Sexual consent education in a university

The issues of consensual sexual relations and that of the converse of sexual harassment have come to prominence in many institutions of higher education and in many parts of the world (see, for example, Byfield and East, 2018; Lay, 2019). The responses to reports of high levels of sexual harassment being suffered by very many female students and some male students in universities have ranged from the introduction of mandatory classes and training on the one hand, to inaction and transposition of the issue to the general public domain on the other. However, in recent years, most public universities have made attempts to address these issues in some educational way and, indeed, in some countries addressing these issues has become a politically required institutional requirement (Witze, 2018).

The initiative described here was developed as a result of a 'bottom-up' campaign of information and awareness that resulted in a call for action and response. In 2015, the students' union in the university conducted a survey on the prevalence of sexual harassment among students. The study found that one in four female and one in twenty male students had experienced non-consensual sexual encounters in the previous four years. The experiences were of varying nature and severity and concerning enough that the students' union approached the college authorities to discuss a response. This response had, and continues to have, both an operational and a leadership/governance aspect whereby in this description the emphasis will be placed on the latter. Nevertheless, the operational side of the initiative contains the substantive value or norm load of the project and will be discussed briefly also.

From a leadership perspective, the initial response was informal and a small group of five was formed to explore the idea of developing an educational intervention for incoming first-year students who were to live together in one college accommodation location. The group comprised the Welfare Officer of the students' union, an Annual Officer of the college, a clinical student counsellor and two members of the Common Room of the college accommodation, representing the students living there. It was agreed at a first meeting that the Officer of the College would chair meetings in the initial phase. In the summer of 2016 with the aid of colleagues in another university who had trialled an intervention, all members of the informal committee as well as a number of academic staff members and students underwent training as facilitators of Sexual Consent Workshops. The model adopted was that workshops to be offered to incoming students would be led by a team of two facilitators, one academic and one student. It is worth pausing here in the description to note that it was not the academic staff member who led the facilitation. Both in the training and the facilitation itself, tasks and leadership in the exercises that formed part of the workshops were shared or at least each team of two decided for itself how it would manage workshops and any 'leading' within them. The workshops were then conducted in September 2016 with 400 students taking part on a voluntary basis but with lots of encouragement and peer influence. Student feedback was sought after each workshop and the data generated was collated and later reviewed.

In March/April of 2017, a review was conducted of the September 2016 trial on the basis of the data generated from the post-workshop surveys and the anecdotal evidence of workshop facilitators. This was carried out informally by the establishing committee. The review established two main outcomes: first, that the content of the workshops required re-designing as some elements did not work in context and, secondly, that this intervention had been a clear success with students and demanded mainstreaming into the induction of students to college or at least to those who were taking up residence in college accommodation. It was this second conclusion that gave rise to considerable discussion about the leadership, governance, management and place of this project in the structures of the college. What developed out of this review and discussion was aided in no small way by the evolution of a partnership agreement between the students' union and the college that was eventually signed in 2018. Under this agreement, the Sexual Consent Workshop project was accepted as the first partnership project under this agreement and therefore could be integrated into established governance and management structures. The steering committee, now formally established, reports now to a sub-committee of a committee of the university's Academic Council and has a wider membership to include staff from the area of diversity and inclusion. Also, the leadership of the project is shared between the students' union representative and the college's representative at the level of an Officer of the College. The project, now in its fourth year has expanded its educational offerings to other groups in the university and a full-time intern role was established in the project two years ago. The project continues to have success and gain acknowledgment and respect but equally, as it has become established in both institutional culture and structures, it has had to negotiate its place among other health initiatives that have somewhat different governance and management structures. This will be discussed in a little more detail below.

Luhmann's three key ideas in the context of the case study

The descriptive background of this project outlined above gives the context and the some of the bounds of the case study in leadership, distributed leadership and systems thinking. Not all aspects of the dimensions of distributed leadership or systems theory can be examined here and so the discussion is limited and based to a large extent on a consideration of the theoretical points discussed earlier but now in the specific context of this case.

It is perhaps important at the outset to point to some of the particularities and idiosyncrasies of this case. Probably most noteworthy are two aspects – the collaboration between academic staff and students as equal partners in what has become a formal part of the operations of the college, and the educational nature of the project with its very particular theme. The two aspects, however, are connected. One of the reasons why the collaboration between staff and students could work in a way that did not give primacy to the expertise and experience of staff over students lay in the fact that neither group held an advantage in knowledge of what was required or of how the project should necessarily proceed. It was a significant feature of the initial meetings, planning and ultimate establishment of a formal group that the research, design and execution of the project was carried out *ab initio* by all involved and together in a mutually respectful and supportive process. It is this aspect, perhaps more than any other, that leads to the conclusion that it can be considered as an example in a public service context of a distributed leadership approach, as it satisfies the conditions or requirements that are sometimes cited as necessary for identifying distributed leadership. These include that participants are fully involved, that the process is supportive, that professional development is provided and resources are available (Jones and Harvey, 2015), and this project fulfilled at least two if not three of these criteria. Those who took part in the project did so voluntarily, with enthusiasm and without any overt sense of anyone wishing to dominate or to lead in a traditional, heroic manner. The structure of the project was completely flat in that those who designed, planned and managed were also those who operationalised the project and conducted the workshops. This kind of structure, culture and activity is perhaps naturally more likely to be amenable to a distributed leadership approach. Nevertheless, it is also worth noting that the college in its normal operations of governance and management is regarded as quite traditional and hierarchical, and there was and is a certain tension between the leadership and management of this project and the overall culture of management in the college. It manages to still fit in and find a place in the college largely as a consequence of the almost contradictory co-existence of a strongly collegial structure on the one hand, but one that constructs and re-constructs its own quite hierarchical culture on the other, regardless of the fact that those elected to positions of leadership and authority exercise this only for limited time.

Clearly, this case study of what I argue is an example of distributed leadership within the context of the overall leadership of an institution is insufficient to draw conclusions about the appropriateness or effectiveness of a DL approach in other contexts and settings. However, I suggest that an initiative that brings people together in a way that there is no clear owning of expertise, in which those involved come from different parts of an organisation to achieve something together, and who take on the dual tasks of management and operations, may be more conducive to DL approaches than other initiatives or types of organisational activity.

The educational nature of this project is, I believe, also significant when considering the applicability and appropriateness of DL as a leadership approach. By their very nature, educational endeavours do not lend themselves to specific, predetermined and guaranteed outcomes. Despite all efforts to formulate educational outcomes in this manner, they are not rule-led ordered systems but systems of social agency. Educational initiatives are essentially communicative, they very often involve semi-autonomous units that are designed to promote both learning and self-learning, and they are fundamentally value-based. Thus, they lend themselves to the kind of systems thinking that is proposed here and to the application of distributed leadership as a social dynamic. What is suggested here is that the leadership type that might be adopted best in means-outcomes settings is likely to be less amenable to a distributed approach that lends itself especially to educational and healthcare settings. In our case, leadership in the project was greatly influenced by a shared understanding among the participants that all educational encounters are personally and professionally relational and not primarily outcome-object based. In such settings the normative rather than regulative perspective dominates, and the logic of appropriateness rather than the logic of instrumentality is applied (Scott, 2001). The setting therefore would seem to be also an important factor in the possible success or not of a DL approach to leadership.

This last consideration of the influence of the nature of the project on the leadership approach leads to the discussion of whether the sociology of DL is amenable to an interpretation from the perspective of systems theory. Specifically, the systems-theoretical features that were presented earlier can be examined to guide this discussion, and the case study of the Sexual Consent Workshop project can be used to illustrate the three aspects of the functional-differentiation of Luhmann's social systems, the autopoiesis of systems in their independence and interaction with the environment, and the role of values and norms.

As was pointed out, the educational initiative of the Sexual Consent Workshops and the organisational structure that was constructed in order to develop and provide these was not based on the expertise or authority of a guiding individual leader. It was, and remains the case, that the tasks of design, content selection, organisation of events, training and facilitation, oversight, evaluation and feedback were not attached to individuals but are more effectively and appropriately described as a set of functions, operations and practices that are networked in a way that is almost independent of the human agents that carry them out at any one time. This is an important feature of the project and of organisational systems that have a high turnover of participants. In the consent project, there is some turnover of staff participants in each year, although the turnover in student participants is almost 100%. This is, of course, a feature of very many student projects in a university setting and it demands that initiatives and structures are maintained in such a way that they can be sustained over time and with a strong independence from individuals. Regarding the project as a system of differentiated functions that can be described and maintained in an almost independent network does suggest a way of 'leading' the project in a way that is highly distributed in a functional way.

Luhmannian systems are founded on communication as the fundamental and elemental function in the system. The case study offers a good example of the development of a shared language and the construction of a new network of communication that was at its core grounded in communication at a number of functional levels. First, the theme or issue of education in sexual consent was not one that was familiar at the outset to any of the participants. Indeed, it is an issue that more generally in society would not have had a language until very recently. Therefore, the content-language was new to those participating. Secondly, the language of consent workshops specifically: how these can be done most effectively, their scope, and the training required for facilitators to work in this new area has also to be developed. Once again, these developments were not produced by individuals with particular traits or expertise and not by a charismatic leader. They were developed within the group and with little reference to individuals. This experience certainly suggests that what was described above as an almost counter-intuitive way of looking at organisations and leadership without leaders or even human agents as the elemental object of inquiry can make sense and give valuable insights into how groups, projects and organisations work.

Some of the description above of the genesis of this project and the way in which it initially and eventually found its place in the existing structures of the organisation should give some indication of the argument presented now that this project can be viewed as an example of an autopoietic system. This second idea from Luhmann, discussed earlier in the chapter, seems particularly apt in this case study. Initially, of course, the stimulus for the creation of the project came from the environment and the response was in some way at least a response to this external stimulus. However, the stimulus alone is completely insufficient in order to explain the response. The stimulus provided by reports of sexual harassment and the response to these disclosures could well have been one that saw the development of procedures on reporting, investigating, conduct and discipline. However, this was not the direction taken. In the event, and as described above, the response was to enter into an educational enterprise that changed the focus from negative behaviour and experiences into what was designed to be positive behaviour enhancing and affirming.

The status of the project as a first concrete manifestation of the college–students' union partnership also lent it a degree of independence and allowed it to develop a life of its own without very much intervention from the wider organisation. With this space, it was possible not only to develop the language of communications as stated, but also to begin to form relations and an internal network that could be self-sustaining also in the face of large-scale changes in personnel. This has indeed proven to be the case as the group and its activities continue to grow; structures have been strengthened even though there is now just one of the original members of the steering committee remaining after just two years.

One of the characteristics of autopoietic systems is that they can learn and can also contribute to supporting learning. This case study of an educational intervention is a clear example of a learning system. In the first pilot year, the learning was to some large extent from others outside the institution, but it is a feature of the project that the learning moved internally very quickly. Within one year, much of the content of the workshops had been changed and their structure redesigned. In the last two years, the learning of the first years has led to the creation of new interventions for different groups and with different objectives. Almost all of this learning has been internal to the group, involving very little external input or even influence. This distinguishing feature stands in contrast to view that the life and workings of organisational groups is characterised by adaptive behaviour in response to outside environmental influence.

The governmental and managerial independence of the consent project and group has been sustained to a great extent on the basis of two factors. The first is the relative success of the project with students, as evidenced by formal feedback and informal social media comment. This success influences, but does not explain fully, the second factor of the college's unspoken but tangible stance of non-interference in micro-governance or management. An autopoietic system is one that is self-sustaining and renewing and has a high degree of independence from its environment. However, no such system can survive massive and unchecked influence from the outside and all such systems with their culture of distributed leadership, collaborative working and supportive processes are also fragile at least in the event of major upheaval. This is worth some consideration within such systems as there are conditions to autonomy and relative independence that need to be monitored and evaluated as they can change with major consequences.

In the case of the consent education project, a recent intervention by a government minister on the wide issue of sexual behaviour in colleges and universities and consequent action by the Higher Education Authority in Ireland on the issue could be seen as a possible major outside influence on the project that could impact the project in a way that changes its nature, culture, governance and management in the institution. The organic life of autopoietic systems can be endangered and can be forced to unforeseen and perhaps undesired adaptations.

A final aspect of a systems-view of the sociology of DL concerns the value-laden and normative basis of communication as function. As discussed in the first part of the chapter, communication is possible only on the basis of a set of common values and meanings, otherwise speech acts in groups remain at the very least opaque, if sometimes even incomprehensible. The experience of the consent project was one in which it was very clear that the language of the group was shaped by a common set of values both moral and educational. Given the specific issue that the project was addressing, this set of values as a medium of all communication also had a strong normative aspect. The actions that were undertaken as part of the project were designed to influence and shape behaviour in a clear value-informed manner. As such, this is a good example of this dimension of communicative social systems and of the exercise of distributed leadership seen in a systems light.

Conclusion

This chapter has attempted to view some aspects of the sociology of distributed leadership through the lens of aspects of systems theory to be found in the work of Niklas Luhmann. In particular, it was argued that the aspects of involvement and supportive processes in leadership can be illuminated by viewing involvement as functionally differentiated communication and viewing supportive processes in leadership as an autopoietic system. In the context of leadership in public service, the roles of values and norms as the medium of communication and the basis of a systems view of distributed leadership were discussed in the first half of the chapter. The second section was given over to the examination of a case study of a project that demonstrates distributed leadership in a systems-interpreted way.

The case study is from higher education and it is necessary to reflect finally on the relevance of this case and the analysis made of the system of leadership and governance to healthcare settings. Beginning with the first suggestion of considering distributed leadership as a system of communications and only second-order actions and agency, the case study shows that this perspective seems very useful when understanding educational initiatives and projects. However, for healthcare workers, it is worth considering how many projects in their settings have a similar structure and that a consideration of the social system of communications might be more revealing of leadership than a consideration of a person's or leader's actions. Alone the consideration of communications in projects and initiatives between medical staff, administrative staff, patients and other stakeholders reveals a clear parallel to the complex and diverse groups of participants in education projects. Secondly, the points made above on the role of values and norms in constructing the language of communications should be evident in the case study and will surely also be familiar to health workers. Both educational and healthcare settings share the characteristic of what was described here as a 'functionally differentiated' system. In both the case study and healthcare settings, multidisciplinary teams were and are a feature. Very often the disciplines in these teams have different 'languages' and there is need for some common basis for understanding each other. The suggestion made in this chapter is that it is the shared language of values and norms that can provide the basis or mutual understanding and the possibility for distributed leadership. Finally, with regards to the systems feature of autopoiesis, it is hopefully evident in the case study that the group that took on the leadership, governance and operations of the sexual consent education project became a self-sustaining, self-maintaining and self-referential system within a larger organisational context. The enactment of leadership within the group was one of the promotion of learning and self-learning. Such a situation with this particular feature would surely also be familiar to healthcare workers involved, for instance, in a research group, or in a care-management group. In both, the sense of self-referentiality and the way in which such groups reproduce their functions and grow within their own parameters will be familiar. They very often define their own work, induct their own new members themselves, form quite a closed entity though one capable of change and growth, and hold a kind of systemic intelligence that is not found in the wider organisation.

Hopefully, the argument has been made and illustrated here that there are definite situations and settings in education and healthcare that lend themselves to being led by distributed leadership but viewed from a sociological systems perspective that gives primacy to communications, values-based shared understanding and autopoietic learning, self-maintenance and reflexive reproduction. If healthcare and education workers attend to these aspects of working groups, it could lead to a deeper understanding and acceptance of how such systems work in such groups. This view allows for a different perspective on how leadership is enacted in these situations that should be advantageous to growth.

Key concepts discussed

- sociology of distributed leadership
- leadership in social systems organisations
- Niklas Luhmann's systems theory
- systems of communications and values
- autopoiesis in systems
- centrality of communications in education and healthcare.

Key readings

- Gronn, P. (2009) Leadership configurations, *Leadership*, 5 (3): 381–394.
  Peter Gronn is one of the most influential and reflective commentators on distributed leadership in education.
- Luhmann, N. (2018) *Organization and Decision*, trans. D. Baecker and R. Barrett, Cambridge: Cambridge University Press (originally published in German 2011).
  This is the key text from Luhmann on organisations as social systems.
- Maturana, H.R. and Varela, F.J. (1980) *Autopoiesis and Cognition: The Realisation of the Living*, Boston, MA: Riedel.
  This text is the classic source of the concept of autopoiesis in biology which was adapted by Luhmann to social systems.

Examples of the theory of applied research studies

- Jones, S. and Harvey, M. (2015) *Developing a cross-institutional network of experts in the use of benchmarks for distributed leadership to improve learning and teaching*, Canberra, ACT: Australian Government Office for Learning and Teaching.
- Jones, S., Harvey, M., Hamilton, J., Bevacqua, J., Egea, K. and McKenzie, J. (2017) Demonstrating the impact of a distributed leadership approach in higher education, *Journal of Higher Education Policy and Management*, 39 (2): 197–211.

Useful websites

- https://eadh.org/projects/niklas-luhmann-archive
  This is the Niklas Luhmann archive of the European Association of Digital Humanities and provides an extensive resource of materials.
- https://niklas-luhmann-archiv.de/
  This is the definitive archive on Luhmann in German.
- http://www.distributedleadership.com.au/
  This provides valuable information and resources on distributed leadership in higher education in Australia.

References

Bolden, R., Gosling, J., O'Brien, A., Peters, K., Ryan, M. and Haslam, A. (2012) *Academic Leadership: Changing conceptions, identities and experiences in UK higher education* (Final Report, Research and Development Series), London: Leadership Foundation for Higher Education.

Boulton, G. and Lucas, C. (2008) *What are universities for?*, Leuven: League of European Research Universities. Available at: https://www.leru.org/files/What-are-Universities-for-Full-paper.pdf (accessed 21 October 2020).

Byfield, Z. and East, L. (2018) Sexual assault and harassment in Australian universities, *Australian Nursing and Midwifery Journal*, 25 (9): 42.

Gronn, P. (2000) Distributed properties, *Educational Management Administration and Leadership*, 28 (3): 317–338.

Gronn, P. (2003) Leadership: Who needs it?, *School Leadership and Management*, 23 (3): 267–291.

Gronn, P. (2009) Leadership configurations, *Leadership*, 5 (3): 381–394.

Gunter, H. (2012) *Leadership and the Reform of Education*, Bristol: Policy Press.

Habermas, J. (1987) Excursus on Luhmann's appropriation of the philosophy of the subject through systems theory', in J. Habermas, *The Philosophical Discourse of Modernity: Twelve Lectures*, Cambridge: Polity Press.

Jones, S. and Harvey, M. (2015) *Developing a cross-institutional network of experts in the use of benchmarks for distributed leadership to improve learning and teaching*, Canberra, ACT: Australian Government Office for Learning and Teaching.

Jones, S., Harvey, M., Hamilton, J., Bevacqua, J., Egea, K. and McKenzie, J. (2017) Demonstrating the impact of a distributed leadership approach in higher education, *Journal of Higher Education Policy and Management*, 39 (2): 197–211.

Lay, J.C. (2019) Policy learning and transformational change: University policies on sexual harassment, *Journal of Women, Politics and Policy*, 40 (1): 156–165.

Luhmann, N. (2018) *Organization and Decision*, trans. D. Baecker and R. Barrett, Cambridge: Cambridge University Press (originally published in German 2011).

Maturana, H.R. and Varela, F.J. (1980) *Autopoiesis and Cognition: The Realisation of the Living*, Boston, MA: Riedel.

Meyer, R.E. and Boxenbaum, E. (2010) Exploring European-ness in organization research, *Organization Studies*, 31 (6): 737–755.

Mingers, J. (2002) Can social systems be autopoietic? Assessing Luhmann's social theory, *Sociological Review*, 50 (2): 278–299.

Raelin, J. (ed.) (2016) *Leadership-as-Practice: Theory and Application*, New York: Routledge.

Schmidt, J. (2000) Die Differenz der Beobachtung. Einleitende Bemerkungen zur Luhmann-Rezeption, in H. de Berg and J. Schmidt (eds.) *Rezeption und Reflexion. Zur Resonanz der Systemtheorie Niklas Luhmanns außerhalb der Soziologie*, Frankfurt am Main: Suhrkamp.

Scott, W.R. (2001) *Institutions and Organisations: Ideas, Interests and Identities*, Thousand Oaks, CA: Sage.

Seidl, D. and Mormann, H. (2015) Niklas Luhmann as organization theorist, in P. Adler, P. du Gay, G. Morgan and M. Reed (eds.) *Oxford Handbook of Sociology, Social Theory and Organization Studies: Contemporary Currents*, Oxford: Oxford University Press.

Siemens, G., Dawson, S. and Lynch, G. (2013) Improving the quality and productivity of the higher education sector, *Policy and Strategy for Systems-Level Deployment of Learning Analytics*, Canberra, ACT: Society for Learning Analytics Research for the Australian Office for Learning and Teaching.

Thyssen, O. (2003) Luhmann and management: A critique of the management theory in Organisation und Entscheidung, in T. Hernes and T. Bakken (eds.) *Autopoietic Organization Theory: Drawing on Niklas Luhmann's Social Systems Perspective*, Copenhagen: Copenhagen Business School Press.

Witze, A. (2018) US science agency will require universities to report sexual harassment, *Nature*, 554 (7692): 287–288.

Youngs, H. (2017) A critical exploration of collaborative and distributed leadership in higher education: Developing an alternative ontology through leadership-as-practice, *Journal of Higher Education Policy and Management*, 39 (2): 140–154.

15 Synthesising practical insights and empirical data

Siobhán Corrigan

Chapter topics

- The complexity of healthcare systems – a socio-technical systems perspective
- A call for a different type of leadership
- Empirical research on distributed leadership
- Synthesis and pathway for future research

Introduction

Simply put we need to move beyond the theoretical discussions on distributed leadership (DL) and generate a strong empirical evidence base for its potential effectiveness. This will be easier said than done.

The idea of DL has been absorbed enthusiastically by some, but it needs to move on to more applied concerns with capacity-building and focused supporting structures and policies so that practitioners are better placed to enact DL and secure lasting improvements in healthcare. To date academic researchers have had little to say about the practicalities of establishing and sustaining such initiatives. Their efforts have focused largely on assessing the theoretical implications of DL and evaluating the potential advantages of moving in this direction. Meanwhile, training consultants and providers of leadership development courses have generally failed to move beyond traditional forms of executive skill-building, with little of this covering DL. As a result, there is understandable frustration about this among practitioner groups.

This frustration has been evident from healthcare participants who attended a series of leadership seminars over a nine-year period in the School of Nursing and Midwifery, Trinity College Dublin and also from a number of focus groups carried out as part of an exploratory research study in the Faculty of Health Science, University of Malta in March 2019. Healthcare workers, mainly nurse practitioners, highlighted that they are looking for more focused guidance on the everyday challenges of making DL work, on limiting the adverse effects of traditional leadership and management thinking, and helping them to make the most of available opportunities while working under limiting constraints and ever demanding circumstances.

This chapter will explore the existing evidence base on both the possibilities and challenges of implementing DL healthcare. While it is widely accepted that there is a dearth of empirical literature in this area, what is available suggests that there is a connection between DL and improved delivery in the quality of healthcare. However, anecdotal evidence is also highlighting the very real challenges of implementing DL and the methodological challenges in conducting the type of serious empirical work that is required.

The complexity of healthcare systems: A socio-technical systems perspective

Before delving into the evidence base on DL it is important to examine and understand the complexity of safety systems such as healthcare. Complexity in healthcare systems and implications for leadership have been introduced in Chapter 2 of this book. The discussion here focuses on one specific approach to complexity and its impact on safety and healthcare performance. A range of diverse views about complexity in healthcare have been put forward over the years. The one proposed by Plsek and Greenhalgh (2001) still by and large holds true, as they described healthcare as a complex adaptive system that has the following characteristics:

- System boundaries are 'fuzzy and ill defined' (page 626): individuals that are members of the system (or subsystem) change and may belong to multiple systems.
- Individuals in the healthcare system (e.g. physicians, nurses, patients) use rules and mental models that are internalised and may not be shared with or understood by others. In addition, these rules and mental models change over time.
- People and system(s) adapt to local contingencies.
- Systems are embedded within other systems and 'co-evolve and interact over time' (page 626). Those interactions between multiple systems may produce tension and conflict that do not necessarily need to be resolved or can be resolved. In addition, the 'system interactions continually produce new behaviours and new approaches to problem-solving' (page 626).
- The system interactions are non-linear and often unpredictable. This lack of predictability is, however, accompanied by general patterns of behaviour.
- Self-organisation is inherent through simple locally applied rules.

Overall complex work systems are characterised by high uncertainty, multiple interacting elements and dynamic change (Vicente, 1999; Carayon, 2006). Our healthcare professionals have been under enormous pressure over the past few years. Long waiting lists, emergency services at breaking point, problems in staff recruitment and high rates of staff attrition are only some of the most common concerns that we have heard about. The Covid-19 emergency has created another layer of disruption that has also posed a range of challenges and complexities for healthcare leadership and will continue to do.

Employing a socio-technical systems (STS) approach to understanding complex safety systems reflects a growing belief that many dimensions of safety are emergent properties of such systems (Carayon et al., 2015). Broadly speaking, STS is an approach that considers the interplay of human, social and organisational factors as well as technical factors in the design and everyday operations of organisational systems.

Ongoing and evolving interactions are critical to the STS approach and healthcare is very different from other sectors because of the intensity and interplay of interactions of humans, processes, information/knowledge flows, technology and hierarchical structures. Therefore, when analysing, planning, implementing and evaluating healthcare systems, these interactions need to be fully understood as the respective interactions between the different levels as they contribute to a more effective and integrated analysis of the current operational practice (Robertson et al., 2015). This clearly emphasises the need for a socio-technical systems approach and the consideration of human factors and organisational issues related to healthcare quality and patient safety.

Increased complexity and ambiguity combined with the need to respond faster to complex and ever-changing conditions has led to 'new emerging patterns of accountability, inter-dependency and co-ordination which constitute a shift in the division of labour within organisations' (Fitzsimmons et al., 2011: 318). Arguably a major contributing factor for these issues are the outdated leadership practices, such as leader-centricity, linear thinking and poor readiness for innovation, that are being used in healthcare organisations (Weberg, 2012). These outdated leadership styles presume a knowable and predictable world, but top-down power dynamics and concentrated hierarchical leadership are no longer effective for dealing with the increasing complexity and adaptive challenges facing healthcare (Porter-O'Grady and Malloch, 2008; Uhl-Bien et al., 2008; Weberg, 2012). There is broad agreement that relying upon traditional leaderships structures and the concentrated knowledge of those at the top of managerial hierarchies is unrealistic and potentially damaging (Currie and Lockett, 2011; Chreim et al., 2013). A new type of leadership is required based on the need to be more adaptive to rapidly changing circumstances and unpredictable problems, and to understanding the role of external influences and how they impact the internal organisational culture and ways of doing things (Berwick, 2003; Shearer and Reed, 2004; Porter-O'Grady and Malloch, 2008; Uhl-Bien et al., 2008).

A call for a different type of leadership

The different approaches to traditional leadership and their limitations in the current context of healthcare were explored in Chapter 2, highlighting how DL has emerged as a result of the failures of the traditional leadership models. Before we move into an exploration of the evidence base of DL, this section will provide an outline of the some of the seminal academic thinking in this area.

There has been a consistent call for the role of effective leadership to lead and drive change and reform at all levels of the health system. Distributed leadership has emerged as one of the possible leadership styles that could drive sustainable improvements in healthcare as it constructs leadership as a shared responsibility 'rather than the elusive prerogative of those in executive positions' (Beirne, 2017: 264). The King's Fund, for example, has argued for leadership that extends 'from the board to the ward', with partnership arrangements that devolve decision-making to nurses and doctors who do not think of themselves as leaders (King's Fund, 2011; West et al., 2014). The complexity of healthcare has also undermined the faith traditionally invested in traditional hierarchical leadership (Grint and Holt, 2011; Martin et al., 2015). This reliance on traditional leadership practices and structures is considered unrealistic and potentially damaging due to the growing complexity of this sector (Currie and Lockett, 2011; Chreim and MacNaughton, 2016).

It is not surprising considering the scandals and shortfalls in performance by many enquiries and investigative reports that a greater emphasis has been given to devolved and distributed forms of clinical leadership, as a viable alternative to the top-down, hierarchical and 'heroic' variants (Beirne, 2017). Distributed leadership takes a more systemic perspective, whereby leadership responsibility is dissociated from formal organisational roles, and the action and influence of people at all levels are recognised as integral to the overall direction and functioning of the organisation. Spillane suggests that a distributed perspective 'puts leadership practice centre stage' (2006: 25), thereby encouraging a shift in focus from the traits and characteristics of 'leaders' to the shared activities and functions of 'leadership'. Distributed leadership is differentiated from traditional approaches to leadership as it focuses on influence, knowledge and expertise rather than the leader's formal position. In effect this should mean that the capacity to lead, which involves the ability to communicate effectively, make critical and timely decisions, devise responsive action plans and lead the implementation of interventions, is not just confined to those in formal leadership roles.

The trends in the academic literature support that these characteristics are more widely distributed and can be expected to influence organisational practice in one way or another (Spillane, 2006; Beirne, 2017). Crosby and Bryson claim that new and distributed leadership has a range of benefits for organisations characterised by complex problems that 'cross the boundaries of organisational responsibility, multiple professional groups with divergent identities, norms and accountabilities, and ambiguous or multifaceted aims' (2005: 364). Traditional leadership approaches focusing on the individuals in positional authority seem to reduce the likelihood of effective change and progress because it is more difficult to cross institutionalised professional and clinical boundaries (Hartley and Allison, 2000). Academics argue that it is particularly challenging in healthcare organisations, where quality and safety are so reliant on the collaborative efforts of multiple parties separated by such boundaries (Crosby and Bryson, 2005). Ongoing efforts to implement and sustain much needed improvements in healthcare are susceptible to disappointment and failure if there is an insistence on depending on the older traditional forms of leadership rather than 'recognising, valuing and mobilising new forms of leadership that are distributed throughout the organisation' (Martin et al., 2009; Powell et al., 2009).

Empirical research on distributed leadership

Despite the resolve and ambitions, empirical research on DL in healthcare is very limited compared with other sectors, most notably the education sector. There are only a handful of studies on how DL has been enacted in practice in healthcare.

Research in DL from both mental health nursing (Cleary et al., 2011) and acute clinical wards (Tomlinson, 2012) has provided evidence of a positive link between autonomous influence, quality of working life and organisational performance. Other benefits evident from empirical research include more effective and timely decision-making to secure cost savings and improve patient outcomes (Richardson and Storr, 2010; McKee et al., 2013; Whitlock, 2013), better use of frontline knowledge resulting in higher levels of job satisfaction, staff engagement and more supportive clinical environments (Dean, 2014). Paynton (2008) suggests that the distributed influence of nurses through both formal and informal patterns of devolved authority can have a significant impact on patient-centred care.

Fitzgerald et al. (2013) conducted a qualitative empirical study exploring DL patterns and its impact on service improvement in the NHS. They carried out semi-structured interviews (160 in total), observations at meetings and documentation analysis covering three groups involved in service improvement (cancer, diabetes and maternity services). Three key themes emerged from their research:

1. *Emerging patterns of distributed change leaderships was linked to delivering improvement in service outcomes.* Their definition of DL included 'senior leaders with the capability and the interest to support change, credible opinion leaders at middle levels with general management or hybrid roles, and other staff engaged in change efforts who also became change leaders' (Fitzgerald et al., 2013: 239). All were found to be essential to delivering improvements.
2. *Professional/managerial hybrids demonstrated crucial lateral facilitation activities, modifying their roles and responsibilities to meet contextual demands.* Shortcomings in the understanding of DL meant that some of the proposed initiatives lacked the 'cumulative impact of senior leaders framing and resourcing activities and middle management translating, tailoring, engaging and linking' (2013: 240). Certain actions, behaviours and processes were often carried out in parallel rather than sequentially, and at times appeared disorganised, but their ongoing impact accumulated. The role of the middle manager was critical and involved 'proactively translating and adapting national mandates to meet local agendas, occasionally acting entrepreneurially to engage staff. Supporting activities included fluid group formation, influencing through evidence-based arguments, and linking hierarchical levels and professions' (2013: 241).
3. *Pre-existing relationships underpinned the capacity of DL to implement service improvements.* Effective DL was underpinned by good working relationships. The ability and willingness of staff to collaborate was found to be critical. Other factors critical to supporting this new way of working included 'consistently signaled strategy, autonomy for change leaders, and the visibility of the target service' (2013: 241).

The findings from this study reflect what Pierson (2003) referred to as 'cumulative effects' when trying to explain the impact and influence of DL on organisational change and service improvement. The cumulative effects approach highlights that a combination of factors needs to be considered and that these are highly interdependent, complex, dynamic and fluid as opposed to being ordered and sequential.

McKee et al. (2013) conducted an empirical qualitative study that focused on interviewing 107 key strategic stakeholders in the NHS. They found that the key stakeholders felt that the healthcare system saw a strong role for DL and highlighted the importance of 'leadership coalitions between managers and clinicians' (2013: 16). However, they highlighted that this was not an easy task, particularly in the healthcare domain as different professional and managerial groups endure an uneasy co-existence, their interests competing amid messy power relations (Martin et al., 2009; Currie and Lockett, 2011). Therefore, the roll out and acceptance of DL required very careful management based on the traditional hierarchical approach complementing the distributed leadership approach in order to avoid two key pitfalls that emerged in their study in relation to a 'nobody in charge' mode (Currie and Lockett 2011) or the mere re-branding of yet another leadership approach.

Chreim et al. (2010) conducted a longitudinal qualitative case study over a four-year period focusing on the roll out of multidisciplinary primary healthcare teams in Canada. This study provided an interesting insight into the change process and how leadership practices emerged. Seventy-four participants took part in research interviews and this was supplemented by several observations. Even though the senior physicians and senior administrators were originally identified as the key leaders, over the life of the project 'a number of other participants also became engaged and stepped into various leadership roles, championing a variety of new initiatives related to implementing the new model' (2010: 197). This was evidence of a leadership approach that was more distributed and spread out both vertically and horizontally in a less formal manner across the levels of the organisations. One of the noteworthy findings from this study was that these new leaders did not explicitly recognise themselves as leaders and very much downplayed the importance of the vital role they played. This study also highlighted the critical role of social capital that needs to be appreciated both as a substitute for bureaucratic and formal control mechanisms. The issue of trust, a component of social capital (Leana and Van Buren, 1999), was continually mentioned by stakeholders as an integral element allowing different agents to exert influence. Leana and Van Buren stated that social capital is 'an asset that inheres in social relations and networks' and that it creates 'value by facilitating successful collective action' (1999: 538).

One of the first comprehensive quantitative studies of perceived agency in DL was conducted by Günzel-Jensen et al. (2018). They carried out a large-scale organisational survey (1,147 participants) at one of Scandinavia's largest public hospitals focusing on how DL impacts organisational efficacy. One of their key findings was that when leaders felt empowered, this had a positive impact on staff participation through self-efficacy and established a firm foundation for the successful implementation of DL practices. The authors argued that this impact might be 'especially strong in healthcare settings as empowering leaders can provide autonomy and freedom in a very hierarchical, complex and predefined setting where these attributes are crucial in the performance of daily tasks. Additionally, empowering leadership might let employees gain confidence to perform in interdisciplinary teams and across hierarchical boundaries' (2018: 115).

Boak et al. (2015) carried out an empirical study that analysed the introduction of a new initiative to improve waiting times in a physiotherapy department in a UK-based healthcare organisation. Qualitative and quantitative data was gathered from the physiotherapy department over a period of 24 months and they found that DL and team working were central to several system changes that were initiated by the department, which led to improvements in patient waiting times for therapy. They found six factors that enabled the effective enactment of DL.

1. Agreed consensus on the key problem that needed to be addressed.
2. The focus of the change within one profession, which is likely to be less challenging to DL than a setting occupied by multiple professions (Currie and Lockett, 2011; Drotz and Poksinska, 2014).
3. Ongoing and active engagement and positive attitude of all staff in the changes.
4. Considerable time was required for the scoping and planning phase before the teams were formally established to ensure the full engagement of all staff – taking on board all options and alternatives.
5. Standardised procedures enabling the department to move from an individual model of working to one that was more team based and distributed.

Teams were given an active and distributed leadership role. A range of responsibilities and resources were given to the specialised teams and they could develop their own way of working. Timely information on key aspects of service delivery was provided enabling effective decisions to be made. Ongoing monitoring and evaluation of their practices was also embedded in the new way of working to continually improve their service.

Drawing on qualitative data over a three-year period, Martin et al. (2015) analysed the benefits and challenges on how three co-located healthcare organisations implemented DL. Fifty-six focus groups across the three co-located organisations were undertaken as part of this study. The authors found three separate types of disconnect that posed significant problems for DL (power, distance and values).

Power disconnect

Rather than an empowering effect of DL, Martin et al. found many instances where views of the power of others were questioned. These 'constructions created perceptions that the voices of senior non-clinical managers and clinical staff in leadership roles were unlikely to be heard, resulting in misalignment' (2015: 19). In addition, there was a strong belief that the real power was beyond the local culture or environment and that the external constraints, some of which were beyond the control of local staff (e.g. legislation and regulations), played a huge role also. Hence, managers and clinicians were often positioned as subject to the power of policy-makers, with little ability to influence policy or practice on the ground.

Distance disconnect

Perceptions of distance in terms of physical, attitudinal and temporal aspects created a range of difficulties. There were mixed perceptions from frontline staff and managers/senior clinicians in relation to the degree and quality of contact between these different groups. The findings from the interviews with non-clinical senior leaders showed that they believed they 'made strenuous efforts to be seen within and beyond the organisation because they saw themselves as figureheads' (Martin et al., 2015: 22). It was felt that professional boundaries exacerbated this distance as well as the large number of staff dispersed across three sites. It should also be noted that this study did also highlight examples of engagement and collaboration between different professional groups. Examples of these included the establishment of new training and development programmes, new teams that delivered new services and taking a more partnership approach

Values disconnect

One of the key findings was the perceptions of two competing institutionalised logics: a 'medical logic', which valued patients and care provision, and a 'managerial logic', which was concerned with resources and targets (Reay and Hinings, 2009).

Overall this study in its attempt to analyse the introduction of DL highlighted significant disconnects in relation to the concepts of empowerment and engagement.

The empirical literature, albeit very limited, does point to a mostly prescriptive and somewhat enthusiastic potential for the role DL has to offer. The exception to this is Martin et al. (2015), who highlighted a more sceptical and pessimistic outlook on the value of DL. These less than positive views have also been reflected in discussions with healthcare professionals who point to the very real challenges in effectively implementing this approach to leadership and who feel that DL is more desired than experienced. It is felt that the challenges are compounded by the complexity of the healthcare systems, the socio-political make-up, traditional hierarchical structures spanning different professions/siloed approaches to working, and the 'wicked' or 'toxic' culture that healthcare has often been portrayed as (Grint and Holt, 2011). So, what does the future hold for DL?

Synthesis and pathway for future research

Chreim et al. (2010) strongly argue that the empirical evidence indicates that the notion of DL and change agency warrants serious consideration and that the issues need to become more prevalent and can no longer be ignored by those who attempt to understand and to manage complex healthcare organisations. As already noted, there are only a limited number of studies on how DL has been enacted in healthcare and even those with a positive message have argued that the complexity of the professional and policy institutions in healthcare renders attempts to endorse new forms of leadership very difficult (Currie and Lockett, 2011).

The empirical research available has provided some insights into the potential effectiveness of DL and aspects that are required for its enactment. The key aspects appear to be focused around: (i) the importance of social relations and social capital in facilitating the creation of effective coalitions across professional boundaries; (ii) provision of the necessary support and commitment from institutional and national policy level; (iii) promoting empowering structures and practices; (iv) acceptance that it will be something that evolves organically as opposed to a planned linear process; (v) requirement for an overall consensus for new ways of working; (vi) interpersonal trust; (vii) perceived autonomy and accountability; and

(viii) combining the best aspects of old and new, concentrated and distributed leadership in ways which are situationally and contextually sensitive.

In many ways these are highly prescriptive and do not provide any substantial coverage to what happens in operational practice. Martin et al. (2015) do tackle the very real 'disconnects' and challenges that healthcare organisations face in their attempts to roll out DL but none of the empirical research to date gives serious consideration to the complexity and deep-rooted cultural aspects of our healthcare systems. Healthcare is constantly changing and is inherently more complex than the educational sector which pioneered the concept of DL, so the process of transfer requires considerably more research validation and enhancement. A failing of much of the empirical literature on DL is its focus on the micro-foundations of healthcare organisations. However, healthcare is embedded in the complexity of professional and policy institutions and specific societal and political rationalities. These aspects constrain the agency of those who may seek to exercise leadership (Thornton et al., 2013). Blackler (2006) and Blackler and Kennedy (2004) argue that the structural constraints on the agency of healthcare CEOs (NHS in this case) made their jobs unsustainable, so questioning their capability to implement a new style of leadership.

Given the scale, range and diversity of interconnected elements involved in healthcare, understanding this complexity and viewing it as a socio-technical system is vital. This perspective understands the emergent, self-organising/organic and unfixed nature of change (Suchman, 2011; Puustinen and Lehtimäki, 2016), its instability and unpredictability (Shore and Kupferberg, 2014), the often hidden and tacit knowledge (Montgomery et al., 2015; Baker et al., 2016), and the appreciation that 'command and control' modes often elude health system leaders working where no *one* perspective or oversight is possible (Heldal, 2015).

Therefore, the unpredictability of change is viewed as the norm in the change process so leaders must develop a skill set that allows them to manoeuvre and navigate ambiguity, paradox and uncertainty (Till et al., 2016). They must learn to expect the unexpected (Boustani et al., 2010). The Covid-19 pandemic is an example of the unexpected. This emergency has created another layer of disruptive transformation that requires a completely different mindset. Performance in a crisis is more susceptible to error and safety failure than normal operations. The Covid-19 emergency has resulted in new and redeployed staff, unprecedented demands and rigorous performance standards. Ensuring the best possible quality, safety and patient outcomes will therefore require more effective leadership, accountability and governance in order to adapt and improve through the crisis and into a recovery period.

One interesting argument that could be further explored is that by using the complexity principles of emergence, self-organisation, non-linearity and paradox to frame and drive change (Caffrey et al., 2016), would there be a greater chance of sustained improvement, or a meaningful, transformative change and improvement in the quality of care?

The implication of this approach is that a greater distribution of leadership at each level and in diverse organisational settings is required for process-driven and context-specific change (Fitzgerald et al., 2013) as it operates optimally when effectively networked (Boustani et al., 2010). Different practices of distributed leadership include inter-organisational collaboration (Audet and Roy, 2016), teamwork (Bleakley et al., 2012) and many new forms of healthcare partnerships (Bamford-Wade and Moss, 2010; Byrne-Davis et al., 2017). Fundamentally it is a social rather than 'command and control' system and as such can only change through a complex process of engagement that is relational, context-attuned and flexible (Damschroder et al., 2009).

Effective leadership, therefore, is less about the individual personality and more about the strength and vitality of the social and networking relationships within healthcare – future research needs to further explore this emerging theme (Fitzgerald et al., 2013; McKimm and Till, 2015; West et al., 2015; Chreim and MacNaughton, 2016; Till et al., 2016).

In this vein, understanding how effective change and improvement is actioned through a DL approach is critical and inevitably this type of leadership does and will continue to meet with resistance. A very clear agenda for further empirical research is required. Future research needs to explicitly address the complexities of the healthcare system and to view it as a socio-technical system, as leadership at whatever level requires dealing with technical and social relational problems. The research to date has been at a localised level focusing primarily on the theoretical insights within geographical regions or among relatively narrow professional groupings. This needs to be expanded to include the system-of-systems approach – local intuitions, regulators, national bodies, government bodies, etc. The overall methodological approach also needs careful consideration in order to build a clear evidence base for the effectiveness of DL. Due to the complexity and the ever-changing dynamics of healthcare, longitudinal case studies using a mixed-methods approach would be highly effective in order to capture the intricacies, interactions and interdependencies of change.

Complementing this research is the need to focus on what the practical challenges are in initiating and sustaining DL and how this will impact what type of learning support is required in terms of educating healthcare staff (Corrigan and Curtis, 2017). For example, how effective are traditional educational programmes on leadership? What role does informal and more collaborative learning play? In balancing this emphasis on practical challenges, it is also critical to understand what is currently working well within healthcare and how this can facilitate a more distributed approach.

Hewitt-Taylor highlights that considering 'how people will perceive and be affected by an innovation, including what individuals and teams will gain or lose, who the opinion leaders will be, and the influence of workplace culture' (2013: 37) are all essential. The author presents a distinction between *change* as the observable things that happen or are done differently, and *transition* as what people feel, experience and see as important. This transition phase is almost always overlooked, as much of the research fails to take adequate account of the systemic emotional dynamics at play during a change transition. This is particularly relevant as a shift to shared or DL does impact established role relations and traditional professional boundaries.

To ensure that all state-of-the-art research findings, theoretical insights and development initiatives are effectively disseminated to policy-makers, the involvement of all levels of health service staff, professional bodies and patient associations is essential. This dissemination needs to take many different formats but needs to be based on the development of an applied evidence base of the enabling and constraining factors on DL and to support future applied research on a sustainable pathway that engages practitioners and supports their 'ordinary' leadership contributions. Overall, more needs to be done to build bridges between theoretical conceptions and an empirical evidence base on the one hand and policy-making, diffusion and widespread implementation on the other.

Conclusion

We have heard the callings for a new type of leadership but embedding any level of change in healthcare is very difficult. There is a future for DL in our healthcare systems but much more research and proactive collaboration between practitioners, healthcare service users and academics is urgently required. A degree of caution is recommended in relation to translating the findings of DL empirical research from the educational sector into healthcare. Unquestionably because of the lack of DL empirical research in healthcare we have got to rely on the educational sector. However, they are two very different sectors and the complexity of healthcare needs to be considered. Leadership does not function in isolation to everything else that is happening in an organisation, and DL will only make an impact if it is examined and understood as part of the wider socio-technical system.

Key concepts discussed

- socio-technical systems
- complexity of the healthcare sector
- human factors
- challenges of implementing change
- importance of the right level of dissemination that provides both theoretical insights and practical guidance.

Key readings

- Beirne, M. (2017) The reforming appeal of distributed leadership, *British Journal of Healthcare Management*, 23 (6): 262–270.
- Currie, G. and Lockett, A. (2011) Distributing leadership in health and social care: Concertive, conjoint or collective?, *International Journal of Management Reviews*, 13: 286–300.
- Fitzsimons, D., Turnbull-James, K. and Denyer, K. (2011) Alternative approaches for studying shared and distributed leadership, *International Journal of Management Reviews*, 13 (3): 313–328.
- Puustinen, A. and Lehtimäki, H. (2016) Success and failure?, *Emergence: Complexity and Organization*, 18 (3/4): 1–9.
- Weberg, D. (2012) Complexity leadership: A healthcare imperative, *Nursing Forum*, 47 (4): 268–277.

- West, M., Armit, K., Loewenthal, L., Eckert, R., West, T. and Lee, A. (2015) *Leadership and Leadership Development in Health Care: The Evidence Base*, London: The King's Fund.

Examples of empirical research on distributed learning

- Chreim, S. and MacNaughton, K. (2016) Distributed leadership in health care teams: Constellation role distribution and leadership practices, *Health Care Management Review*, 41 (3): 200–212.
- Fitzgerald, L., Ferlie, E., McGivern, G. and Buchanan, D. (2013) Distributed leadership patterns and service improvement: Evidence and argument from English healthcare, *Leadership Quarterly*, 24 (1): 227–239.
- Günzel-Jensen, F., Jain, A.K. and Kjeldsen, A.M. (2018) Distributed leadership in healthcare: The role of formal leadership styles and organisational efficacy, *Leadership*, 14 (1): 110–133.
- Martin, G., Beech, N., MacIntosh, R. and Bushfield, S. (2015) Potential challenges facing distributed leadership in health care, *Sociology of Health and Illness*, 37 (1): 14–29.
- Richardson, A. and Storr, J. (2010) Patient safety: A literature review on the impact of nursing empowerment, leadership and collaboration, *International Nursing Review*, 57 (1): 12–21.
- Tomlinson, J. (2012) Exploration of transformational and distributed leadership, *Nursing Management*, 19 (4): 30–34.

Useful websites

- The Faculty of Medical Leadership and Management with The King's Fund and the Centre for Creative Leadership: www.ccl.org/Leadership
- The Faculty of Medical Leadership and Management with The King's Fund and the Centre for Creative Leadership: www.fmlm.ac.uk
- The King's Fund: www.kingsfund.org
- Health Service Executive Ireland – Leadership and Management development: www.hse.ie
- Centre for Innovative Human Systems, School of Psychology, Trinity College Dublin: https://www.tcd.ie/cihs/
- Impact of collective leadership on team performance and healthcare safety: http://www.ucd.ie/collectiveleadership/

References

Audet, M. and Roy, M. (2016) Using strategic communities to foster inter-organizational collaboration, *Journal of Organizational Change Management*, 29 (6): 878–888.

Baker, N.J., Suchman, A. and Rawlins, D. (2016) Hidden in plain view: Barriers to quality improvement, *Physician Leadership Journal*, 3 (2): 54–57.

Bamford-Wade, A. and Moss, C. (2010) Transformational leadership and shared governance: an action study, *Journal of Nursing Management*, 18 (7): 815–821.

Beirne, M. (2017) The reforming appeal of distributed leadership, *British Journal of Healthcare Management*, 23 (6): 262–270.

Berwick, D.M. (2003) Disseminating innovations in healthcare, *Journal of the American Medical Association*, 289 (15): 1969–1975.

Blackler, F. (2006) Chief executives and the modernisation of the English National Health Service, *Leadership*, 2 (1): 5–30.

Blackler, F. and Kennedy, A. (2004) The design and evaluation of a leadership programme for experienced chief executives from the public sector, *Management Learning*, 35 (2): 181–203.

Bleakley, A., Allard, J. and Hobbs, A. (2012) Towards culture change in the operating theatre: Embedding a complex educational intervention to improve teamwork climate, *Medical Teacher*, 34 (9): e635–e640.

Boak, G., Dickens, V., Newson, A. and Brown, L. (2015) Distributed leadership, team working and service improvement in healthcare, *Leadership Health Service*, 28 (4): 332–334.

Boustani, M., Munger, S., Gulati, R., Vogel, M., Beck, R. and Callahan, C. (2010) Selecting a change and evaluating its impact on the performance of a complex adaptive health care delivery system, *Clinical Interventions in Aging*, 5: 141–148.

Byrne-Davis, L., Bull, E., Burton, A., Dharni, N., Gillison, F., Maltinsky, W. et al. (2017) How behavioural science can contribute to health partnerships: The case of The Change Exchange, *Globalization and Health*, 13: 30. Available at: https://doi.org/10.1186/s12992-017-0254-4 (accessed 21 October 2020).

Caffrey, L., Wolfe, C. and McKevitt, C. (2016) Embedding research in health systems: Lessons from complexity theory, *Health Research Policy and Systems*, 14: 54. Available at: https://doi.org/10.1186/s12961-016-0128-x (accessed 21 October 2020).

Carayon, P. (2006) Human factors of complex sociotechnical systems, *Applied Ergonomics*, 37 (4): 525–535.

Carayon, P., Hancock, P., Leveson, N., Noy, Y., Sznelwar, L. and van Hootegem, G. (2015) Advancing a sociotechnical systems approach to workplace safety: Developing the conceptual framework, *Ergonomics*, 58 (4): 548–564.

Chreim, S. and MacNaughton, K. (2016) Distributed leadership in health care teams: Constellation role distribution and leadership practices, *Health Care Management Review*, 41 (3): 200–212.

Chreim, S., Williams, B.E., Janz, L. and Dastmalchian, A. (2010) Change agency in a primary health care context: The case of distributed leadership, *Health Care Management Review*, 35 (2): 187–199.

Chreim, S., Langley, A., Comeau-Vallée, M., Huq, J.-L. and Reay, T. (2013) Leadership as boundary work in healthcare teams, *Leadership*, 9 (2): 201–228.

Cleary, M., Horsfall, J., Deacon, M. and Jackson, D. (2011) Leadership and mental health nursing, *Issues in Mental Health Nursing*, 32 (10): 63–639.

Corrigan, S. and Curtis, E.A. (2017) Facilitating informal learning in nursing, *British Journal of Healthcare Management*, 23 (1): 22–27.

Crosby, B.A and Bryson, J.M. (2005) *Leadership for the Common Good: Tackling Public Problems in a Shared-Power World*, San Francisco, CA: Jossey-Bass.

Currie, G. and Lockett, A. (2011) Distributing leadership in health and social care: Concertive, conjoint or collective?, *International Journal of Management Reviews*, 13: 286–300.

Damschroder, L., Aron, D., Keith, R., Kirsh, S., Alexander, J. and Lowery, J. (2009) Fostering implementation of health services research findings into practice: A consolidated framework for advancing implementation science, *Implementation Science*, 4: 50. Available at: https://doi.org/10.1186/1748-5908-4-50 (accessed 21 October 2020).

Dean, E. (2014) Opinion divided on extent of cultural shift in health service, *Nursing Management*, 21 (4): 10–12.

Drotz, E. and Poksinska, B. (2014) Lean in healthcare from employees' perspectives, *Journal of Health Organization and Management*, 28 (2): 177–195.

Fitzgerald, L., Ferlie, E., McGivern, G. and Buchanan, D. (2013) Distributed leadership patterns and service improvement: Evidence and argument from English healthcare, *Leadership Quarterly*, 24 (1): 227-239.

Fitzsimons, D., Turnbull-James, K. and Denyer, K. (2011) Alternative approaches for studying shared and distributed leadership, *International Journal of Management Reviews*, 13 (3): 313–328.

Grint, K. and Holt, C. (2011) *Followership in the NHS: A report for The King's Fund Commission on Leadership and Management in the NHS*, London: The King's Fund. Available at: www.kingsfund.org.uk/leadershipcommission (accessed 21 October 2020).

Günzel-Jensen, F., Jain, A.K. and Kjeldsen, A.M. (2018) Distributed leadership in healthcare: The role of formal leadership styles and organisational efficacy, *Leadership*, 14 (1): 110–133.

Hartley, J. and Allison, M. (2000) The role of leadership in the modernization and improvement of public services, *Public Money and Management*, 20 (2): 35–40.

Heldal, F. (2015) Managerial control versus professional autonomy in organizational change: Tearing down the walls and fighting fire with fire, *Journal of Change Management*, 15 (3): 18–209.

Hewitt-Taylor, J. (2013) Planning successful change incorporating processes and people, *Nursing Standard*, 27 (38): 35–40.

King's Fund (2011) *The Future of Leadership and Management in the NHS: No more heroes*, London: The King's Fund. Available at: http://www.kingsfund.org.uk/publications/future-leadership-and-management-nhs (accessed 10 March 2020).

Leana, C.R. and Van Buren, H.J., III (1999) Organizational Social Capital and Employment Practices, *The Academy of Management Review*, 24 (3): 538–555.

Martin, G., Currie, G. and Finn, R. (2009) Leadership, service reform and public-service networks: The case of cancer-genetics pilots in the English NHS, *Journal of Public Administration Research and Theory*, 19 (4): 769–794.

Martin, G., Beech, N., MacIntosh, R. and Bushfield, S. (2015) Potential challenges facing distributed leadership in health care, *Sociology of Health and Illness*, 37 (1): 14–29.

McKee, L., Charles, K., Dixon-Woods, M., Willars, J. and Martin, G. (2013) 'New' and distributed leadership in quality and safety in health care, or 'old' and hierarchical? An interview study with strategic stakeholders, *Journal of Health Services Research and Policy*, 18 (suppl. 2): 11–19.

McKimm, J. and Till, A. (2015) Clinical leadership effectiveness, change and complexity, *British Journal of Hospital Medicine*, 76 (4): 239–243.

Montgomery, J., Doulougeri, K. and Panagopoulou, E. (2015) Implementing action research in hospital settings: A systematic review, *Journal of Health Organisation and Management*, 29 (6): 729–749.

Paynton, T. (2008) The informal power of nurses for promoting patient care, *OJIN: The Online Journal of Issues in Nursing*, 14: 1. Available at: http://ojin.nursingworld.org/MainMenuCategories/ANAMarketplace/ANAPeriodicals/OJIN/TableofContents/Vol142009/No1Jan09/ArticlePreviousTopic/InformalPowerofNurses.html (accessed 21 October 2020).

Pierson, P. (2003) Big, slow-moving, and . . . invisible, in J. Mahoney and D. Rueschemeyer (eds.) *Comparative Historical Analysis in the Social Sciences*, Cambridge: Cambridge University Press, 177–207.

Plsek, P.E. and Greenhalgh, T. (2001) Complexity science: The challenge of complexity in healthcare, *British Medical Journal*, 323 (7313): 625–628.

Porter-O'Grady, T. and Malloch, K. (2008) Beyond myth and magic: The future of evidence-based leadership, *Nursing Administration Quarterly*, 32 (3): 176–187.

Powell, A.E., Rushmer, R. and Davies, H.T.O. (2009) *A systematic narrative review of quality improvement models in health care*, Edinburgh: NHS Quality Improvement Scotland.

Puustinen, A. and Lehtimäki, H. (2016) Success and failure?, *Emergence: Complexity and Organization*, 18 (3/4): 1–9.

Reay, T. and Hinings, C.R. (2009) Managing the rivalry of competing institutional logics, *Organization Studies*, 30 (6): 629–652.

Richardson, A. and Storr, J. (2010) Patient safety: A literature review on the impact of nursing empowerment, leadership and collaboration, *International Nursing Review*, 57 (1): 12–21.

Robertson, M., Hettinger, L., Waterson, P., Noya, I.Y., Dainoff, M., Leveson, N.G. et al. (2015) Sociotechnical approaches to workplace safety: Research needs and opportunities, *Ergonomics*, 58 (4): 650–658.

Shearer, N.B. and Reed, P.G (2004) Empowerment: Reformulation of a non-Rogerian concept, *Nursing Science Quarterly*, 17 (3): 253–259.

Shore, D.A. and Kupferberg, E.D. (2014) Preparing people and organizations for the challenge of change, *Journal of Health Communication*, 19 (3): 275–281.

Spillane, J.P. (2006) *Distributed Leadership*, San Francisco, CA: Jossey-Bass.

Suchman, A.L. (2011) Organizations as machines, organizations as conversations: Two core metaphors and their consequences, *Medical Care*, 49 (suppl.): S43–S48.

Till, A., Dutta, N. and McKimm, J. (2016) Vertical leadership in highly complex and unpredictable health systems, *British Journal of Hospital Medicine*, 77 (8): 471–475.

Tomlinson, J. (2012) Exploration of transformational and distributed leadership, *Nursing Management*, 19 (4): 30–34.

Thornton, P.H., Ocasio, W. and Lounsbury, M. (2013) *The Institutional Logics Perspective: A New Approach to Culture, Structure and Process*, Oxford: Oxford University Press.

Uhl-Bien, M., Marion, R. and Mckelvey, B. (2008) Complexity leadership theory: Shifting leadership from the industrial age to the knowledge era, in M. Uhl-Bien and R. Marion (eds.) *Complexity Leadership Part 1: Conceptual Foundations*, Charlotte, NC: Information Age Publishing, 185–224.

Vicente, K.J. (1999) *Cognitive Work Analysis: Towards Safe, Productive, and Healthy Computer-Based Work*, Mahwah, NJ: Lawrence Erlbaum.

Weberg, D. (2012) Complexity leadership: A healthcare imperative, *Nursing Forum*, 47 (4): 268–277.

West, M., Eckert, R., Steward, K. and Pasmore, B. (2014) *Developing Collective Leadership for Health Care*, London: The King's Fund. Available at: http://www.kingsfund.org.uk/publications/developing-collective-leadership-health-care?gclid=COqK_fX6gMsCFSLlwgod3BcG1g (accessed 10 March 2020).

West, M., Armit, K., Loewenthal, L., Eckert, R., West, T. and Lee, A. (2015) *Leadership and Leadership Development in Health Care: The Evidence Base*, London: The King's Fund.

Whitlock, J. (2013) The value of active followership, *Nursing Management*, 20 (2): 20–23.

16 Nurturing, implementing and sustaining distributed leadership

Elizabeth A. Curtis

Chapter topics

- Why is leadership important?
- Distributed leadership – terms, definition and goals
- Nurturing and supporting distributed leadership in the workplace
- Antecedents of distributed leadership
- Positive outcomes and challenges
- How might distributed leadership be implemented?
- Sustainability of distributed leadership

Introduction

As a subject, leadership has generated much interest over the years (Yukl, 1998, 2013; Cullen and O'Connell, 2017), is of huge concern to us (Cullen and Curtis, 2017; Curtis, 2019) and should leave us in no doubt about its importance and relevance in healthcare. To further support this viewpoint, Hughes et al. remind us that 'leadership is everyone's business and everyone's responsibility' (2006: 19). Yet, its importance and influence in sustaining team or organisational success is often overlooked and this was eloquently expressed by Warren Bennis in 2007 when he said, 'In the best of times, we tend to forget how urgent the study of leadership is. But leadership always matters, and it has never mattered more that it does now' (2007: 2). These views, although expressed in 2007, remain relevant in healthcare given that in the last two decades several shortcomings in care and unnecessary patient deaths have been reported in media coverage and scholarly literature both nationally and internationally. Examples include the maternal death of Savita Halappanavar in Ireland (HSE Report, 2013) and the Mid Staffordshire NHS Public Enquiry in England (Francis, 2013). Commissioned reports following these, and similar cases have called for improved leadership. For example, the Winterbourne View report confirmed a 'lack of local leadership and weak accountability' (Bubb, 2014: 25) and the Áras Attracta Report contained a section entitled 'Strengthening and Enhancing the Leadership and Management' with a key recommendation to implement a leadership development programme (Áras Attracta Swinford Review Group, 2016: 13). Further support for improved leadership was echoed in publications by Ahmed et al. (2015) and West et al. (2015) with both calling for a different approach to leadership in healthcare. Distributed leadership (DL) is one approach put forward to help address the failures associated with traditional heroic, single-leader leadership.

This chapter does not offer a comprehensive account of DL. Rather, its purpose is to introduce health professionals to the topic and draw attention to key considerations for nurturing, implementing and sustaining DL in healthcare practice. It begins with some background information on DL, provides a definition of the term, and draws attention to the key objectives driving the development and implementation of DL. Next, the chapter discusses how healthcare environments can nurture and support DL using three key components contained in the Irish Health Services People Strategy Framework. These are leadership, talent and capability. Precursors or antecedents of DL have been reported in the literature as critical to the success of implementation, so this is discussed next. Three approaches to implementing DL are given and potential challenges that could occur during implementation outlined. The chapter concludes with suggestions for sustaining improvement initiatives such as distributed leadership.

Distributed leadership: Terms, definition and goals

Given recent interest and an increase in literature on distributed leadership, you may well come to the conclusion that it a relatively new concept. In fact, it is the opposite; its origins can be traced back to 1250 BC making it one of the oldest leadership approaches used for achieving organisational goals (Oduro, 2004). The theoretical roots of the concept are, however, more recent – emerging around the early 1920s (Bolden, 2011).

Distributed leadership is an approach to leadership that endorses work practices that combine knowledge, abilities and skills of many individuals and a move away from concentrated leadership. It acknowledges that specialised knowledge can come from several employees and not just those in senior positions, thus creating opportunities for leadership to emerge from individuals at all grades and levels within a team or organisation. In their overview of the literature on DL, MacBeath and colleagues (2005) reported the use of many different terms, some of which are used interchangeably while other writers choose to explain their differences. These terms include, 'shared leadership', 'collaborative leadership', 'delegated leadership' and 'democratic leadership' (MacBeath et al., 2005, Harris, 2013). Clarifying differences in term usage is useful as it reduces vague, imprecise meanings and prevents unconfirmed assumptions being drawn. This view is shared by Harris (2013), who suggests that the use of several terms not only results in mixed-up meanings but also potential problems when researching the concept. Furthermore, to imply that DL is the opposite of hierarchical leadership or a component of a hybrid prototype confuses the meaning of the term even further. According to Bennett et al., 'There are few clear definitions of distributed leadership . . . and those that exist appear to differ from each other, sometimes widely and sometimes more in nomenclature than in essence' (2003: 6). Although this reference is seventeen years old, similar definitional problems about DL have been reported by others, including Currie and Lockett (2011) and Feng et al. (2017). Spillane defines DL as follows:

> From a distributive perspective, leadership involves mortals as well as heroes. It involves the many and not just the few. It is about leadership practice, not simply roles and position. And leadership practice is about interactions, not just the actions of heroes. (2006: 4)

This definition raises optimism about leadership in healthcare and supports the development and implementation of DL in teams and organisations. For example, DL encourages greater participation in leadership, greater team and organisational effectiveness and efficiency, improved interaction to achieve goals (Jain and Jeppesen, 2014), and is considered an alternative approach to individual, heroic leadership. No one individual should have monopoly of, or responsibility for, leadership. Instead, a more cooperative approach that embraces participation from all grades and levels of staff is recommended (Bolden, 2011; Currie and Lockett, 2011). For an overview of the theoretical roots of DL and a discussion of its potential benefits, see Chapters 4 and 6 in this book.

Nurturing and supporting distributed leadership in the workplace

Contemporary evidence from healthcare suggests that leadership is fundamental in grooming the culture of an organisation; making leadership development a priority is vital, therefore, for improving health services (West et al., 2015). Additionally, research has shown associations between leadership and variables such as quality, safety and patient outcomes (Kaufman and McCaughan, 2013; Wong, 2015), that ineffective (poor) leadership has the potential to impact negatively on patient safety (Department of Health and Children, 2008), and that work cultures that embrace learning, trust and honesty can help to reduce errors and adverse events (de Zulueta, 2016). Hospitals considered to be effective are those that engage in distributed leadership and promote staff participation in a meaningful way (McKee et al., 2010). Such compelling evidence leaves one in no doubt that health services need to improve standards so that care becomes patient- and client-focused. To do so requires moving away from traditional positional, heroic leadership to a distributed model. Although it has been acknowledged that traditional forms of leadership in healthcare need to be replaced and that research on DL is taking place, there is little or no reference to how DL might be nurtured and supported in the workplace. Consequently, it was decided to use a section contained in the 'Irish Health Services People Strategy 2019–2024' (HSE, 2019) to guide discussions about nurturing and supporting DL.

The Irish Health Services People Strategy framework reports on future developments of healthcare services for the nation and is premised on a shared HSE goal to deliver improved healthcare for all. It identifies three important components: 'Leadership, Talent and Capability' (HSE, 2019). In addition, the framework reports nine priorities that are affiliated with the three components of leadership, talent and capability. In Box 16.1, these three key components along with some of the priorities will be used to demonstrate how healthcare environments can nurture distributed leadership in practice.

Box 16.1: Nurturing and supporting distributed leadership

Component 1: Leadership – *Working collectively for better and safer healthcare*
Working collectively is essential to improving leadership and creating a culture where empathy, kindness and caring is obvious to all (HSE, 2019). This view that collaborative working is essential within health services is also reported by Eljiz et al. (2018) and Regan et al. (2016). In practical terms, changing the culture of work environments can be challenging but through DL and individual autonomy it is possible. Distributed leadership promotes the view that employees should combine knowledge, abilities and skills to achieve goals rather than operate through heroic (single-person), concentrated approaches to leadership where one individual is in charge (Curtis, 2019). Individually perceived autonomy is vital to DL (Unterrainer et al., 2017), therefore health organisations must develop and support work environments that enable employees to participate in leadership and opportunities to share knowledge and debate innovative ideas.

To promote and nurture DL, communication is essential and required for all components of work, including, change, quality, safety and client-based activities (Wang et al., 2018). Moreover, views and suggestions from employees are imperative for effective communication (Constantin and Baias, 2015) within teams and organisations and therefore must form the basis of any planned communication strategy in healthcare.

Creating positive nurturing relationships at work is a component of social support and essential within healthcare. Having colleagues who can provide guidance and support is useful at any time, but especially during change, innovation and other difficult circumstances (Jackson et al., 2007). Distributed leadership lends itself to such nurturing relationships at work given its three key components: leadership practice, interaction with others and consideration for the situation or context (Spillane, 2006).

Component 2: Talent – *Employees with a range of knowledge and skill mix to provide care and services*
Talent is central to sustaining teams and organisations, therefore every effort should be made to develop work environments that nurture and support talent. Achieving this requires investing in learning and greater participation in leadership (HSE, 2019). Teams and organisations that embrace learning and continuing professional development will inspire innovation and have a positive impact on teamwork and patient care (HSE, 2019). Learning is critical to the success of individuals (van Noy et al., 2016) as well as organisations (Bjork et al., 2013). Learning at work and informal approaches to learning are not new concepts in adult education and work environments offer excellent opportunities for incorporating work-related activities and learning given the range of professional groups and skill mix available (Corrigan and Curtis, 2017). Literature suggests that most of the learning that takes place in the workplace is informal and that the term 'informal' is interpreted as all learning opportunities that discount formal learning (Fahlman, 2013). Learning from one another often takes place at work and

strategies such as mentoring, shadowing and communities of practice are some of the ways this can be achieved (Eljiz et al., 2018).

Leadership, of course, is vital to nurturing individuals, talent and creating nurturing environments (Abramowitz, 2001). All health professionals should acquire skills required for developing caring relationships with colleagues and patients/clients. To overlook this important aspect of work can make it difficult to obtain resources, promote motivation among staff and deliver effective care to patients (Abramowitz, 2001). Similarly, Ribière and Sitar (2003) have suggested that leadership is central to nurturing work environments and culture. Furthermore, they propose that since teamwork is becoming increasingly important within organisations, employers must create work environments that facilitate teamwork. To support such environments, practices that support a concentrated, heroic (single-person) type of leadership will have to change. Leadership must become more participative, inclusive and supportive, with greater emphasis on employees sharing ideas and engaging in decision-making and leadership (Ribière and Sitar, 2003). Distributed leadership lends itself to developing such work environments.

Component 3: Capability – *Acquiring knowledge and skills that will permit reform and improve care practices. Reaffirming the importance of trust and quality care*
The terms capacity and capability are often discussed together but, in this instance, only capability will be addressed. If you were to ask people to identify which organisations or healthcare facilities they have a high regard for, they may be able to identify a few. But if a follow-up question asks how the organisation(s) or healthcare facility(ies) they identified are structured and how they execute their work, few will know or even care. What people tend to remember is not how an organisation or healthcare facility is structured but rather what their capabilities are – aptitude for innovation and change (Ulrich and Smallwood, 2004). These so-called organisational capabilities are intangible assets; they cannot be seen but nevertheless play a huge part in the success or failure of an organisation. Capabilities – combined skills, abilities, expertise in a team or healthcare facility – are promoted or nurtured by investing in training, recruitment, effective communication and other human resources; and refer to how employees and resources can be combined to achieve goals and get work done. These capabilities contribute to the uniqueness or personality of an organisation by outlining what they do and how successful they are at doing it, and arise through the combined abilities and competencies of all individuals in a team or organisation.

While there is no recommended manual of capabilities to suit every team or organisation, there are some features reported in the literature that successful organisations tend to possess. These include talent, collaboration, learning, innovation and leadership. In addition, it would be useful if teams or organisations develop a talent agenda or plan. This can be achieved through lifelong learning, strengthening personal and professional development, and ongoing collaboration (HSE, 2019). Of course, having a leadership brand is essential to sustaining capability. Distributed leadership that emphasises the combining of knowledge, ability and skills to achieve goals lends itself to nurturing and growing organisational capabilities (Ulrich and Smallwood, 2004).

Leadership has always been vital to knowledge development (Lakshman, 2005) but more recent research has shown that DL plays a central role in the knowledge formation process (Von Krogh et al., 2012; Cannatelli et al., 2017). Such findings are exciting indeed and lend support to the implementation of DL in organisations. In addition to everything that has been said about promoting capability, this section would be incomplete without any reference to trust.

Trust is undoubtedly important in healthcare and evidence suggests that it is positively associated with variables such as leadership, organisational citizenship behaviour (helpful activities that employees engage in without being asked), and patient and client care outcomes (Cullen and Curtis, 2017). Creating an ethos of trust is essential to the preservation of human relationships and is the cornerstone of open and honest communication. Trust must begin at the top with senior personnel and is reflected in how individuals communicate and act. This is important since employees' perceptions are formed by what they hear and see at work, and as is well known, perceptions when formed can be very influential (Curtis and Seery, 2017). Other initiatives that can be utilised in creating an ethos of trust include: transparency and honesty with employees, developing shared values (values and beliefs of employees match those of the organisation), and concern and kindness (this signals that the wellbeing of employees is important to the organisation).

Precursors of distributed leadership

Before addressing how distributed leadership could be implemented, it is necessary to first discuss precursors or antecedents of DL. Literature suggests that before attempting to introduce DL these precursors – which include trust and accountability, communication, learning and development, individually perceived autonomy, empowering structures and teams, commitment from senior personnel, and empathy – must be addressed. With research on DL continuing to evolve, the list of precursors presented here is not exhaustive (see Box 16.2).

Box 16.2: Precursors of distributed leadership

1. Trust and accountability
Work environments that are engaging, inspirational and trustworthy must become the norm within every team or organisation, including healthcare (Holt et al., 2017). Trust encourages employees to engage in assigned work and tasks and when team members or employees demonstrate reassurance and gratitude to

others, this can create opportunities for creativity (Carmeli and Spreitzer, 2009). Employees who trust their organisations or colleagues are more likely to have higher levels of dynamism and vigour, participate in work activities and increase their learning at work. Conversely, when there is mistrust or disrespect, employees become exasperated and report psychological distress. Such a negative and discourteous environment can eventually reduce vigour and vitality (Porath and Erez, 2007). Similarly, Jain and Jeppesen (2014) have suggested that a variety of precursors need to be in place for successful distributed leadership (DL) to occur. These include trust, support and engagement as well as cutting-edge approaches to professional development.

Accountability is essential in nursing and healthcare because it supports patient and client safety. Health professionals are accountable to themselves, their profession, colleagues, employers, patients and their relatives, and so accountability must be evident in all aspects of care and patient exchanges. As an example, accountability in nursing is discussed in the document 'Scope of Nursing and Midwifery Practice Framework' (NMBI, 2015). Employers and managers are also accountable to patients and staff, and have a duty to provide a culture that supports safe, compassionate and excellent care. Leadership is regarded as central to shaping organisational culture, therefore managers must ensure that the right kind of leadership flourishes. To achieve this, concentrated heroic forms of leadership must be discarded and replaced with more participative approaches such as DL (de Zulueta, 2016).

2. Communication

In healthcare, communication is essential to all aspects of work, including leadership, change, patient activities, and maintaining high levels of quality and safety (Wang et al., 2018). In fact, communication is often described as the 'lifeblood of an organisation' and compared to the human circulatory system (Sethi and Seth, 2009: 32). Communication that is honest and clear is a precursor to trust and therefore all managers must be clear and truthful when communicating with employees (Curtis and Seery, 2017). Furthermore, the views and opinions of all employees are central to effective internal communication (Constantin and Baias, 2015) in organisations and therefore must be considered when planning any communication strategy in healthcare. Cullen and Gordon (2014) examined the association between leadership and communication of nurse managers and the organisational citizenship behaviour of nurses. Findings indicated that combined leadership and communication skills resulted in a positive correlation with perceived organisational citizenship behaviour of nurses and care assistants. The implication, therefore, is that effective leadership and communication are both necessary for nurses' organisational citizenship behaviours.

3. Learning and development

Healthcare continues to undergo major changes and all disciplines including nursing will have to participate in these transformations (Finkelman, 2012). This of course will require new competencies, knowledge and skills, which can be achieved through carefully planned learning opportunities and specialised continuing professional development (CPD) programmes. Learning and development are essential to the success of all disciplines and therefore should be included on agendas responsible for staff development, employee engagement and retention. For example, ongoing learning and development opportunities are necessary for maintaining patient safety. This view is supported by Sherwood (2015), who suggests that staff must have CPD to acquire new knowledge, skills and attitudes for improving patient safety. Learning opportunities are also important for attracting and retaining staff (Coffey and Collins, 2017), so managers must facilitate the learning and CPD needs of all staff and recognise the ongoing nature of such learning.

4. Individually perceived autonomy

Organisations with flat (few tiers or levels of management) structures offer opportunities for employees to collaborate and inspire implementation of DL. Another advantage of such structures is increased autonomy (Unterrainer et al., 2017). Unterrainer and colleagues found that individual perceptions of autonomy are crucial to DL and that autonomy offers employees the chance to become resourceful and take on leadership functions and roles. Therefore, healthcare facilities should strive to create work environments that offer opportunities for all employees to engage in leadership activities, meetings and discussions that embrace knowledge-sharing and allow individuals to debate ideas and initiate scholarly activities. To achieve this, employers must reduce or revoke work practices that involve excessive routine or tedious tasks and commit to improving communication processes (Curtis, 2010).

5. Empowering structures and teams

Preparation is central to implementing DL and examining work structures is an important precursor. Structures that allow staff members to participate in several work groups or teams are essential. For example, team members could join at least one standing committee that addresses a specific issue or theme (e.g. infection control or patient advocacy), since participating in initiatives such as these can bring about opportunities for joint problem-solving and better decision-making practices (Grenda and Hackmann, 2014). Teamwork is vital to implementing DL, therefore staff members will have to become team players. However, accomplishing this requires a collective approach and contemporary knowledge and skills (Yammarino et al., 2012). Further research suggests that empowered teams are likely to engage in mutual support, sharing of knowledge and information with team members, and that sharing knowledge aids team performance (Jiang et al., 2016). A downside is that empowered teams sometimes experience internal conflict, which can have a negative impact on team performance. Any such intra-group conflict should be addressed immediately to avoid relationships deteriorating.

6. Commitment from senior personnel

Change in healthcare is inevitable and requires that flexibility be the guiding principle during planning and implementation. The goal of any change initiative is to maximise the benefits that emerge from the change and reduce potential barriers and failures. Several obstacles to change are recorded in organisational literature but two that are relevant here are: (a) inadequate or no support from senior management personnel (Franklin and Aguenza, 2016), and (b) lack of readiness for change (Kirrane et al., 2016). The first can sometimes occur when managers see no need to introduce change initiatives while readiness is critical to implementing initiatives successfully. If readiness for change is low, resistance is likely and so too is failure. The importance of readiness for change has resulted in much research to explore its facilitators and barriers, and a key barrier reported by Kirrane et al. (2016) is the attitude of management towards change.

The introduction of DL is dependent upon senior management personnel giving their commitment and support. Furthermore, DL relies on a collaborative mindset and as such senior management personnel must believe in its importance and be willing to work amenably with employees or team members to achieve implementation and subsequent transformation (Grenda and Hackmann, 2014). Management personnel and those in designated leadership roles must be willing to share power and responsibility with team members (employees). This, together with bottom-up discussions can result in employee empowerment, which is consistent with a humanistic approach to management (Dierksmeier, 2016). As well as providing commitment and support, senior management personnel must also be proactive: they must recognise failures in care and through collaborative working formulate plans for putting them right (Kodama and Fukahori, 2017).

7. Empathy

Empathy is essential to leadership and evidence suggests that being able to show empathy is fundamental to effective leadership (Wan Abdul Rahman and Castelli, 2013; Holt et al., 2017). Furthermore, 'empathy plays an essential role in interpersonal relations, including . . . caring for the wellbeing of others, and facilitating cooperation among group members' (Decety and Cowell, 2014: 526). Within healthcare, it is often said that for a caring profession we do not always show compassion or display empathy. This viewpoint is reflected in an integrative review by de Zulueta, who stated: 'In many countries, there is a deep concern that modern health care has lost its moral compass and is struggling to provide safe, timely, and compassionate care to its citizens' (2016: 1). This of course resonates with healthcare delivery in Ireland as well as the UK following prominent incidents of unnecessary patient deaths and unacceptable care practices (Francis, 2013; Áras Attracta Swinford Review Group, 2016). Surely, occurrences such as these strengthen the argument for greater compassion and empathy in healthcare. A similar view from the business field (Natale and Sora, 2010) suggests that a key reason for the last economic recession is that companies or organisations stopped communicating with their stakeholders and recommended that empathy could help resolve problems if it is included in the decision-making process. Holt et al. believe that the link between empathy and service is not unusual given that people who are empathetic can relate to 'the feelings, thoughts and experiences of other individuals' (2017: 16). By doing so, empathetic people are more likely to 'assist and support others' (ibid.). These authors further explained that assistance and support are attributes of service and that this may account for the association between empathy and service. Interestingly, the association between empathy and service seems to apply in the opposite direction too: in addition to empathy leading to greater alignment with service, a strong sense of service also enhances empathy (Holt et al., 2017). Research by Cannatelli and colleagues (2017) reported empathy as an antecedent of DL. These researchers found that empathy aided DL through greater consideration for someone else's perspective, which 'enabled the distribution of leadership to that person because of the increased understanding' (2017: 590).

Approaches to implementing distributed leadership

Bolden (2011) suggests that distributed leadership can be implemented in many ways and offers examples from four authors. He specifies that the frameworks were based on research conducted in schools but that they could be useful in other contexts too. For example, the frameworks of Gronn (2002) and Spillane (2006) both stress interactions with leaders, other employees, the setting as well as other methods of collaborative working to achieve shared goals and outcomes. These are all procedures and ways of working that can be used in many organisations not just schools. Briefly, Gronn suggests three main elements to his framework: 'spontaneous collaboration', 'intuitive working relations' and 'institutionalised practices' (2002: 430). Gronn's framework is suggested as a potential approach for implementing DL in healthcare. It is important to note, however, that this framework is rather aspirational, and no guidelines are offered to assist users. Brief descriptions for each of the three elements to this framework are outlined in Box 16.3.

Box 16.3: A potential framework for introducing distributed leadership in healthcare (after Gronn, 2002)

Element 1: Spontaneous collaboration

Leadership is viewed as distributed practice. This suggests that leadership is apparent in the interaction of several leaders. It is not about what an individual leader or manager 'knows or does'. Rather, it is about concerted or contrived effort (Gronn, 2002: 430). An example of how this can be enacted is to assemble a small group of about three employees with different skills, knowledge and experiences, and from different grades or levels in an organisation to complete a specific task or project or resolve a problem. The group is then dissolved when the task or project is completed. Such opportunities to work in synergy with others can ignite future collaborative work (Gronn, 2002; Bolden, 2011), which can be beneficial for a team or healthcare organisation. This model of working currently exists in some teams and organisations, including healthcare, but for it to succeed, due consideration must be given to issues that can arise from different professions and grades of staff working together and the complexities of health systems.

Element 2: Intuitive working relations
Over time, two or more employees may decide to work jointly (small team) on key initiatives (e.g. develop care standards for infection control). In such cases, leadership develops in the joint working relationship and it is this working relationship that is credited with leadership by other colleagues, and team members see themselves as joint leaders (Gronn, 2002; Bolden, 2011). This is not an unusual scenario in healthcare given the strong emphasis on team and multidisciplinary working. Babiker et al. (2014) suggest that teamwork is essential to reducing adverse events and for the effective and efficient delivery of healthcare.

Element 3: Institutionalised practices
This type of distributed leadership focuses on formalising structures to support DL. New structures may be authorised if necessary or if there is displeasure with the current set-up this may encourage new configurations (Gronn, 2002). For example, new committees or teams can be initiated to enable improved collaborative working (Bolden, 2011).

Benefits and challenges of distributed leadership

Several positive outcomes have been reported regarding distributed leadership, including empowerment of teachers and through this overall school improvement, a positive impact on organisational change (Harris, 2011), decentralisation of power and authority – moving away from positional leadership to greater participation and interaction from those not in formal leadership positions (Jain and Jeppesen, 2014) – improved job satisfaction, and better organisational commitment (Torres, 2019). Despite these positive outcomes of DL (note that the list is not exhaustive) there are challenges too. In many ways, some of the challenges reported in the literature are similar to the precursors/antecedents outlined in Box 16.2, strengthening the argument that precursors should be fulfilled before introducing DL. For example, DL is unlikely to succeed if a culture of trust and supportive structures and practices are not in place (Jain and Jeppesen, 2014). Additionally, further challenges could arise if employees lack motivation and interest in participating in DL activities. Two reasons may contribute to this lack of motivation: first, engaging in DL may be viewed by some employees as outside their work remit or their personal professional goals, and second, they may not have the necessary knowledge and skills to engage meaningfully in distributed leadership (Jain and Jeppesen, 2014). Research reporting the introduction of DL in schools argues that DL is very time-consuming: much time is spent by headteachers inspiring, reinforcing and supporting staff while at the same time fulfilling their own management role – which includes overseeing quality issues (Torrance, 2013). Another key finding from this study is that headteachers are crucial to the introduction of DL in schools, thus suggesting that if those in charge (of schools or healthcare organisations) are not willing to engage in DL, then it is unlikely to take place.

A reasonable question to ask at this point is, has the application of DL in healthcare been effective? Before trying to address this question, it is necessary to stress that few research studies on DL in healthcare were uncovered during literature searches for this chapter, but some of those retrieved are referred to here. Martin et al. reported that participants in their study on the application of DL were 'sceptical about it and there was little accepted evidence that it would bring about a better state of affairs' (2015: 25). In their paper, Currie and Lockett posed the question: 'does the health and social care context promote DL?' (2011: 293). In responding to the question several challenges were raised. Most health and social care organisations operate within a bureaucratic structure which can challenge leadership. For example, influential professionals (e.g. doctors) have considerable voice in how services are delivered, thus offering few opportunities for leadership from other health professional groups (Currie and Lockett, 2011: 293). In addition, bureaucratic structures prevail in most health and social care organisations and the corollary of this is that work is essentially processed using 'paternalistic and authoritarian' methods which are likely to decrease opportunities for leadership by those from other professional groups. Managers employed in publicly funded agencies work within legal boundaries and stringent policy guidelines and are therefore accountable not only for their own work but also that of their employing organisation. Such emphasis on performance and accountability likens the concept of leadership to individualism and concentration instead of collectivism and distribution (Currie and Lockett, 2011: 294), which raises serious challenges for enacting DL in healthcare.

In research conducted in Canada, Chreim and MacNaughton reported that distributing leadership roles to employees did not result in 'comprehensive leadership practices' (2016: 209). In the UK, McKee et al. (2013: 14) examined the views of senior National Health Service (NHS) staff regarding quality and safety issues and the type of leadership needed for improvement. Their results indicated that leadership was indeed important for maintaining 'safe high-quality care' and that although DL is essential to patient safety and quality, they also felt that DL could result in 'confusion about who was in charge' (ibid.). In Denmark, Günzel-Jensen et al. (2018) reported a significant negative association between organisational efficacy and employee participation in DL. This means that if employees perceived high organisational efficacy (collective participation), they were unlikely to participate in DL initiatives. So answering the question posed earlier in this section is not that easy. Some studies demonstrate positive results from introducing DL while others report challenges. Such mixed findings on DL are no different to those of other improvement initiatives and therefore should not deter its implementation provided that precursors of DL are addressed well in advance.

Sustaining the implementation of distributed leadership in healthcare

Literature searches revealed no research studies that addressed the sustainability of distributed leadership in healthcare. This is probably due to the focus of research on DL as well as the limited number of publications on the topic in the health field. Nevertheless, literature on DL continues to grow, so it is possible that the gaps identified in current literature could change soon. Interestingly however, Dambrauskiene (2018: 41) referred to DL as 'a change in organisations', and Harris and Spillane (2008) suggest that literature seems to indicate that DL is positively associated with change and other organisational development initiatives. Consequently, researchers frequently view DL as a method of effecting change successfully. In view of this, literature on sustaining change or improvement initiatives is used to support content for this section of the chapter.

Organisations that are successful are those that introduce and sustain initiatives that improve quality (Maher et al., 2010). Sustainability is defined by Lennox et al. as 'the general continuation and maintenance of a desirable feature of an initiative and its associated outcomes as well as the process taken to adapt and develop in response to emerging needs of the system' (2018: 2). Sustaining change is not an easy process and reports suggest that as many as 70% of change initiatives fail (Beer and Nohria, 2000; Maher et al., 2010), and that in healthcare 33% of good quality initiatives that are evaluated do not survive beyond one year after implementation (Silver et al., 2016). It would appear, therefore, that introducing change initiatives can only be sustained through planning and investment in time. So, the first stage in sustainability is careful planning. This process must start early, and the first step is to determine potential sustainability difficulties. Several models and frameworks (which I will return to later) are available to assist with this, including the NHS Sustainability model (Maher et al., 2010). Alongside the use of a model, several other practical initiatives can be utilised to assist in sustaining new projects. A sustainability plan for distributed leadership may contain but not be limited to the following: uphold and sustain new initiative; brief new staff; ensure work environment supports motivation; keep evaluating and monitoring; share or spread; encourage collective decision-making and ongoing communication; respect, trust, and recognition; and designated time for discussion and reflection. These suggestions for creating a sustainability plan are based on work by Laur et al. (2018), De Brún et al. (2019) and others.

Uphold and sustain new initiative: after an improvement initiative (e.g. implementation of DL) has become embedded into practice it is important that individuals who were central to its implementation keep momentum going and give support to others. Answering questions or addressing difficulties staff are encountering may be required, as will ongoing education and upskilling. This small act may identify slippages and bring people together to help put them right. It is necessary also that innovation and change is seen as part of everyone's job where ongoing improvement and accountability are expected (Laur et al., 2018).

Brief new staff: in some disciplines in healthcare (e.g. nursing) there is a rapid turnover of staff, therefore it is essential that newly appointed employees are briefed about ongoing improvement initiatives within teams or departments they may be allocated to, given time to review and understand what is taking place, and encouraged to become involved. These ongoing improvement initiatives could be discussed as part of the interview process as well as during orientation programmes (Laur et al., 2018).

Ensure work environment supports motivation: motivation is an essential part of every improvement initiative and sustainability plan. Often, however, employers tend to focus on intrinsic motivation (things that are important and meaningful to a person, such as achievement and recognition) without addressing extrinsic motivation (e.g. income, job security, supervision and job promotion). There is no doubt that both intrinsic and extrinsic motivation are important for improving work engagement and evidence suggests that extrinsic motivation does not reduce intrinsic motivation (Putra et al., 2017). Furthermore, employers must create work environments that encourage a relaxed atmosphere and make work meaningful and enriching (Breckenridge et al., 2019), since these variables are all associated with an increase in intrinsic motivation (Putra et al., 2017).

Keep evaluating and monitoring: pivotal to the successful implementation and sustainability of improvement initiatives is ongoing data collection (throughout the implementation phase and beyond completion). Based on data collected, appraisals can be conducted by the implementation team as often as they deem necessary so that gaps can be identified and addressed. Laur et al. (2018) found that these appraisals or reports can be useful for sustaining improvement initiatives and improving motivation. The results from the appraisals or reports can be shared via emails, flyers or posters, and improvement huddles – daily or weekly meetings of between 10 and 15 minutes with all staff to address progress and pre-empt problems (Silver et al., 2016).

Share or spread: the success of an improvement initiative encourages other teams or departments in a healthcare facility to become energised and interested in implementing innovative ideas also. Ways in which spreading can occur include rolling out an implemented initiative to other teams or departments, responding to requests from others, simplifying procedures (having gained experience from implementation it may be possible to shorten some procedures) and, of course, giving support and sharing experiences – for example, alerting others to potential obstacles (Laur et al., 2018).

Encourage collective decision-making and ongoing communication: in a systematic review to examine ways of developing collectivistic leadership approaches, including DL, De Brún et al. (2019) report that leadership is instrumental to organisational culture, therefore supportive leadership behaviours and practices must be adopted if health services are to improve. These authors further suggest that replacing centralised power with collective decision-making practices enables improved job satisfaction, empowerment and staff engagement. Throughout this chapter communication has played an important role; it was identified as essential to nurturing DL and as a precursor to its implementation. Once again, it is called upon to support the sustainability of improvement initiatives such as DL. De Brún et al. (2019) report that improved communication was a key element in many of the studies included in their systematic review and suggest that it had a dual role: first, as a facilitator of collectivistic leadership, and second, as an outcome variable of several research initiatives.

Respect, trust and recognition: collective working has many benefits, including improved roles, goals and better team working. Furthermore, working collectively can bring about mutual respect, trust and support for colleagues, thereby increasing camaraderie and team connectedness. Recognising the efforts and contributions of employees can strengthen collective working; team members feel valued, which in turn strengthens their self-confidence and encourages them to continue participating in debates, discussions and future collective initiatives (De Brún et al., 2019).

Designated time for discussion and reflection: successful implementation and sustainability of improvement initiatives, such as DL, benefit enormously from designated time for teams to come together to share ideas, reflect on current successes and brainstorm future ventures. Sadly, however, health professionals seldom have time for team development or opportunities to link debate with action due to the ever-increasing demands of contemporary health systems. Yet, it is clear from the literature that designated time for sharing ideas and team development are necessary for enacting collectivistic leadership (including DL). Therefore, employers will have to prioritise this essential factor if improvement initiatives are to be successful and sustained beyond implementation (Virani et al., 2009; De Brún et al., 2019).

Acknowledging the need and importance of sustaining new initiatives, several authors have shared their experiences and have put forward suggestions for achieving this. Those proposed in this chapter represent a small portion of available approaches, so further reading is recommended. Such reading includes Breckenridge et al. (2019), whose paper is based on work of the Scottish Improvement Science Collaborating Centre (SISCC); Willis et al. (2016), who explored sustainability of culture change in health systems in Canada; and Virani et al. (2009), who offer a discussion on sustaining change framed around organisational learning. An interesting feature contained in the paper by Willis et al. (2016) is that they identified *fostering distributed leadership* as critical to sustaining improvement (change) initiatives.

Models and frameworks

Various initiatives aimed at improving patient care outcomes have been introduced in recent years, but many never experienced their full potential because they were unable to achieve sustainability. Consequently, several researchers and health professionals have developed models and frameworks to aid sustainability (Lennox et al., 2018). Examples include: the National Health Service (NHS) Sustainability model (Maher et al., 2010) and the Institute for Healthcare Improvement (IHI) Framework for Spread (Massoud et al., 2006). The NHS Sustainability model consists of ten domains: four process domains, four staff domains and two organisation domains. Each of these domains contain descriptions which can be used to identify merits and deficiencies in an innovation or improvement initiative plan. In general education, MacBeath and colleagues (2005) developed a model for sustaining distributed leadership in schools. The model, which consists of three main phases – (a) delegate, (b) develop and (c) support – was developed using case studies of eleven schools in Essex, Suffolk and Hertfordshire in England. For more information on models, frameworks and tools, see the paper by Lennox et al. (2018). These authors carried out a systematic review to identify approaches used for sustaining initiatives in healthcare.

No specific framework or model will be suggested for use, a decision based on several factors. First, this book is about distributed leadership, which supports enabling practices and participation, and so employees should have independence and autonomy to select a framework, model or tool that is appropriate for their needs. This ensures involvement from the beginning and throughout all stages of an improvement initiative. Second, some frameworks are developed with specific users and settings in mind. Therefore, it is important that several frameworks are reviewed so that the most suitable is selected. Third, many frameworks and models are linked to specific theories, so it is perhaps wise to select one that is suitable for the theory underpinning a specific improvement initiative. Furthermore, some frameworks may regard sustainability as a linear process (introduced after implementation), while others view it as operating in parallel with implementation; thus, it is imperative that this decision for selecting a model is made by those involved in the proposed improvement initiative. Fourth, terms and constructs used to describe sustainability in models and frameworks can vary and even accounting for commonality, it is essential that these terms and constructs are examined to determine how each is assessed prior to selecting a framework.

Sustaining improvement initiatives such as distributed leadership is a demanding process but the message from the literature is clear: there is no magic formula – what is required is careful planning, early implementation of sustainability strategies at unit or organisational level, and the use of a framework or model to guide this process. To neglect this could be construed as irresponsible given that many innovative initiatives fail, resulting in the loss of potential benefits such as improving patient care outcomes.

Conclusion

This chapter reminds readers about the importance of leadership in healthcare by calling attention to failures in care standards and unnecessary deaths of patients in healthcare facilities. Some of these incidents led to public enquiries, and subsequent reports highlighted a lack of leadership and an urgent need to address this. These deficiencies together with research evidence have resulted in several authors calling for a different type of leadership in healthcare. One alternative approach proposed is distributed leadership. After clarifying the meaning of the term, a definition of DL was put forward. Nurturing and supporting improvement (change) initiatives such as DL is essential to both implementation and sustainability, thus, ways in which DL can be nurtured were put forward using key themes derived from the Irish Health Services People Strategy Framework (HSE, 2019). Precursors of distributed leadership preceded discussions about implementation frameworks and the benefits and challenges associated with DL application. The implementation of any improvement initiative, including distributed leadership, would be incomplete without reference to sustainability, especially since a large proportion of initiatives fail shortly after implementation. Consequently, the final sections of the chapter offer suggestions for fostering sustainability.

Key concepts discussed

- Leadership has featured in health and social care for decades and continues to play a dominant role in contemporary healthcare, given its role in promoting working relationships, communication, productivity and patient care outcomes.
- Over the last two decades, several reports have highlighted major failures in patient care, and several have emphasised the need for improved leadership practices in hospitals and other care facilities.
- Leadership has generated interest among people for a long time and much has been written about it too. From a research perspective, leadership has been conceptualised in many ways and several theories or approaches to doing leadership are reported in research literature. In healthcare, leadership has traditionally engaged in individual, positional, heroic forms of leadership, with senior clinicians and managers assuming leadership roles and responsibilities in teams and various positions within healthcare facilities.
- More recently, key reports and scholarly literature have emphasised the need for a new kind of leadership in healthcare – one that encourages greater participation and utilisation of talent and skills of all employees. Distributed leadership is one such approach put forward.
- Like most improvement initiatives, application can be difficult, and DL is no exception. Evidence suggests that a nurturing and supporting ethos is critical to the success of any new initiative, therefore the chapter discusses ways in which support can be provided using three themes from the Irish Health Services People Strategy Framework (HSE, 2019).
- Distributed leadership is relatively new within healthcare, so few research studies have been conducted in the field. Nevertheless, nurses, physiotherapists and others at the forefront of care are leading improvement initiatives and this should be nurtured and supported. Frameworks outlining how DL might be implemented are reported in the literature, but the one suggested for use in healthcare in this chapter is by Gronn (2002).
- Successful application of improvement initiatives including DL is dependent on two key factors: (a) ensuring that antecedents are addressed prior to implementation, and (b) that a sustainability plan is developed to enable continuation of the initiative beyond application.

Key readings

- Beirne, M. (2017) The reforming appeal of distributed leadership, *British Journal of Healthcare Management*, 23 (6): 262–270.
  This paper emphasises the importance of distributed leadership in healthcare, identifies enabling and constraining factors that could impact on DL processes, and presents key outcomes from literature reviewed. Findings include (a) clinical staff without formal leadership titles are leading improvement initiatives, and (b) DL is evident in some of these initiatives but constraints are evident too. The paper suggests that more attention is given to educational and continuing professional development modules and programmes, as these may help 'ordinary leaders' in healthcare practice.
- Bennett, N., Wise, C., Woods, P.A. and Harvey, J.A. (2003) *Distributed Leadership: A review of literature*, National College for School Leadership. Available at: http://oro.open.ac.uk/8534/1/ (accessed 21 October 2020).
  This report provides a useful summary of literature on DL, addresses implications for professional development and advises that a research agenda be developed to determine how DL research is developed and how its effectiveness is measured.
- Bolden, R. (2011) Distributed leadership in organisations: A review of theory and research, *International Journal of Management Reviews*, 13 (3): 251–269.
  This paper addresses themes such as the theoretical origins of DL, as well as related concepts, patterns and outcomes of DL.
- Currie, G. and Lockett, A. (2011) Distributing leadership in health and social care: Concertive, conjoint or collective?, *International Journal of Management Reviews*, 13 (3): 286–300.
  An interesting paper that reports on different conceptualisations of DL and explores issues such as (a) whether health and social care settings support DL, and (b) if governments support DL in the public sector.
- Martin, G., Beech, N., MacIntosh, R. and Bushfield, S. (2015) Potential challenges facing distributed leadership in health care: Evidence from the UK National Health Service, *Sociology of Health and Illness*, 37 (1): 14–29.
  This paper begins by referring to failings in care standards and concerns about leadership in Stafford Hospital in England. It informs the reader that DL has been adopted as a key component of policy in the National Health Service (NHS), as a potential solution to dealing with the perceived problems of traditional leadership. The authors argue that while DL supports giving voice to others and embraces empowerment it can also give rise to 'forms of disconnect' which can threaten DL.
- Spillane, J.P. (2006) *Distributed Leadership*, San Francisco, CA: Jossey-Bass.
  A useful resource for those interested in distributed leadership. It is written by a leading author in the field and although intended for school leadership, the key principles can be utilised by other professional groups including those involved in healthcare. The book is composed of four key sections written in a straightforward way which makes it an enjoyable read.

Examples of studies about distributed leadership in healthcare

- Boak, G. (2015) Distributed leadership, team working and service improvement in healthcare, *Leadership in Health Services*, 28 (4): 332–344.
  This study examined the introduction of distributed leadership and teamwork in a physiotherapy department in England. Results showed that DL and teamwork are both compulsory for change and that DL as an approach to working resulted in improved waiting times.
- Chreim, S. and MacNaughton, K. (2016) Distributed leadership in health care: Constellation role distribution and leadership practices, *Health Care Management Review*, 41 (3): 200–212.
  The researchers used a qualitative design to investigate how role boundaries within leadership are understood and how leadership practices relate with team dynamics. Findings showed overlaps in leadership roles and responsibilities in DL, and while this could lead to problems it has advantages too.
- Chreim, S., Williams, B.E., Janz, L. and Dastmalchian, A. (2010) Change agency in a primary health care context: The case of distributed leadership, *Health Care Management Review*, 35 (2): 187–199.
  This study sets out to understand the subtleties of distributed leadership using a qualitative design. The findings demonstrated that distributed leadership was important for influencing difficult and complicated change.
- Fitzgerald, L., Ferlie, E., McGivern, G. and Buchanan, D. (2013) Distributed leadership patterns and service improvement: Evidence and argument from English healthcare, *Leadership Quarterly*, 24 (1): 227–239.
  A multiple case study design was used to examine patterns of leadership in healthcare organisations and their impact on change. Findings showed that DL supports service enhancement and that 'good pre-existing relationships underpin the capacity of distributed leadership to implement service improvements' (2013: 227).
- Martin, G., Beech, N., MacIntosh, R. and Bushfield, S. (2015) Potential challenges facing distributed leadership in health care: Evidence from the UK National Health Service, *Sociology of Health and Illness*, 37 (1): 14–29.
  These researchers investigated the meaning of DL as well as its usefulness in the NHS. Qualitative data was collected from three healthcare organisations that had adopted DL. Findings revealed that on many occasions views put forward by policy-makers were aired while those from staff in clinical areas (e.g. nurses) were unlikely to be addressed. A number of problems with DL were reported in the paper.
- McKee, L., Charles, K., Dixon-Woods, M., Willars, J. and Martin, G. (2013) 'New' and distributed leadership in quality and safety in health care, or 'old' and hierarchical? An interview study with strategic stakeholders, *Journal of Health Services Research and Policy*, 18 (suppl. 2): 11–19.
  Using interviews, this study investigated the views of 107 strategic level stakeholders about leadership for enhancing quality and safety in the NHS in the UK. Findings indicated that leadership is important for upholding quality care. Also, the researchers felt that while there is justification for using DL (all employees play a role in maintaining quality care), participants reported

that DL may lead to confusion regarding who was in charge and had overall responsibility.

- Rydenfalt, C., Johansson, G., Odenrick, P., Akerman, K. and Larsson, P.-A. (2015) Distributed leadership in the operating room: A naturalistic observation study, *Cognition, Technology and Work*, 17 (4): 451–460.
This study was carried out in an operating unit in Sweden using an observational design. The researchers set out to investigate leadership behaviours in an operating theatre and to establish how leadership is distributed across different professions. Several leadership behaviours were reported but this was whittled down to nine. Analysis revealed that surgeons provided most of the leadership but that others, including nurse anaesthetists and scrub nurses, also participated in leadership. Interestingly, leadership activities or behaviours that were associated with patient safety 'appeared to be more distributed' (2015: 451).

Useful websites

- Books on distributed leadership available at: www.amazon.com
- European School Heads Association: www.esha.org
A website for headteachers that offers information about distributed leadership, projects and other material useful for those working in education.
- General Medical Council Guidance on Leadership: www.gmc-uk.org
This website contains a document entitled leadership and management for all doctors. It provides guidance relating to leadership and management in the workplace. No reference is made to DL.
- Health Service Executive Ireland – Leadership and management development: www.hse.ie
This website provides information about short leadership and management courses. Courses or modules on distributed leadership are not cited.
- James Spillane, author of several articles on distributed leadership, has a website that offers useful information for those working in education: www.distributedleadership.com.au
This website offers a literature review on distributed leadership, other publications and a benchmarking framework for distributed leadership.
- The King's Fund: www.kingsfund.org.uk
Offers a selection of publications and material on various topics and policy issues including leadership.
- A few scholarly articles on distributed leadership are available at the distributed leadership site at Leeds University, UK at the following link: https://scholar.google.com/scholar?q=research+on+distributed+leadership++site:leeds.ac.uk&hl=en&as_sdt=0&as_vis=1&oi=scholart

References

Abramowitz, P.W. (2001) Nurturing relationships: An essential ingredient of leadership, *American Journal of Health-System Pharmacy*, 58 (6): 479–484.

Ahmed, N., Ahmed, F., Anis, H., Carr, P., Gauher, S. and Rahman, F. (2015) *An NHS Leadership Team for the Future*, London: Reform Research Trust.

Áras Attracta Swinford Review Group (2016) *What Matters Most*, Dublin: Health Service Executive. Available at: https://static.rasset.ie/documents/news/aasrgwhatmattersmost.pdf (accessed 5 March 2020).

Babiker, A., El Husseini, M., Al Nemri, A., Al Frayh, A., Al Juryyan, N., Faki, M.O. et al. (2014) Health care professional development: Working as a team to improve patient care, *Sudanese Journal of Paediatrics*, 14 (2): 9–16.

Beer, M. and Nohria, N. (2000) Cracking the code of change, *Harvard Business Review*, 78 (3): 113–141, 216.

Bennett, N., Wise, C., Woods, P.A. and Harvey, J.A. (2003) *Distributed Leadership: A review of literature*, National College for School Leadership. Available at: http://oro.open.ac.uk/8534/1/ (accessed 11 February 2020).

Bennis, W. (2007) The challenges of leadership in the modern world, *American Psychologist*, 62 (1): 2–5.

Bjork, I.T., Toien, M. and Sorenson, A.C. (2013) Exploring informal learning among hospital nurses, *Journal of Workplace Learning*, 25 (7): 426–440.

Bolden, R. (2011) Distributed leadership in organisations: A review of theory and research, *International Journal of Management Reviews*, 13 (3): 251–269.

Breckenridge, J.P., Gray, N., Toma, M., Ashmore, S., Glassborow, R., Stark, C. et al. (2019) Motivating change: A grounded theory of how to achieve large-scale, sustained change, co-created with improvement organisations across the UK, *BMJ Open Quality*, 8: e000553. Available at: https://doi.org/10.1136/bmjoq-2018-000553 (accessed 21 October 2020).

Bubb, S. (2014) *Winterbourne View – Time for Change: Transforming the Commissioning of Services for People with Learning Disabilities and/or Autism*. A report by the Transforming Care Commissioning Steering Group. Available at: https://www.england.nhs.uk/wp-content/uploads/2014/11/transforming-commissioning-services.pdf (accessed 5 March 2020).

Cannatelli, B., Smith, B., Giudici, A. and Jones, J. (2017) An expanded model of distributed leadership in organizational knowledge creation, *Long Range Planning*, 50 (5): 582–602.

Carmeli, A. and Spreitzer, G.M. (2009) Trust, connectivity and thriving: Implications for innovative behaviours at work, *Journal of Creative Behaviour*, 43 (3): 169–191.

Chreim, S. and MacNaughton, K. (2016) Distributed leadership in health care: Constellation role distribution and leadership practices, *Health Care Management Review*, 41 (3): 200–212.

Coffey, D. and Collins, M. (2017) Learning organisations and leadership, in E.A. Curtis and J.G. Cullen (eds.) *Leadership ad Change for the Health Professional*, London: Open University Press, 52–65.

Constantin, E.C. and Baias, C.C. (2015) Employee voice: Key factor in internal communication, *Procedia Social and Behavioural Sciences*, 191: 975–978.

Corrigan, S. and Curtis, E.A. (2017) Facilitating informal learning in nursing, *British Journal of Healthcare Management*, 23 (1): 22–27.

Cullen, C.P. and Gordon, P.A. (2014) The relationship between leadership and communication skills of nurse managers and the organizational citizenship behaviours of medical-surgical nurses and nursing assistants, *Management and Organisational Studies*, 1 (2): 23–29.

Cullen, J.G. and Curtis, E.A. (2017) Introduction: A broad overview, in E.A. Curtis and J.G. Cullen (eds.) *Leadership and Change for the Health Professional*, London: Open University Press, 1–6.

Cullen, J.G. and O'Connell, R. (2017) Leadership in nursing and healthcare: An overview of theory, research and practice, in E.A. Curtis and J.G. Cullen (eds.) *Leadership and Change for the Health Professional*, London: Open University Press, 67–80.

Currie, G. and Lockett, A. (2011) Distributing leadership in health and social care: Concertive, conjoint or collective?, *International Journal of Management Reviews*, 13 (3): 286–300.

Curtis, E.A. (2010) Work motivation, in A.M. Brady (ed.) *Leadership and Management in the Irish Health Service*, Dublin: Gill & Macmillan, 205–230.

Curtis, E.A. (2019) Distributed leadership: An alternative approach for intellectual disability?, in F. Sheerin and E.A. Curtis (eds.) *Leadership for Intellectual Disability Service: Motivating Change and Improvement*, New York: Routledge, 47–84.

Curtis, E.A. and Seery, A. (2017) Trust and leadership, in E.A. Curtis and J.G. Cullen (eds.) *Leadership and Change for the Health Professional*, London: Open University Press, 112–127.

Dambrauskiene, D. (2018) Challenges for the distributed leadership development of education institutions in a hierarchical national culture, *Management of Organisations: Systematic Research*, 79 (1): 38–53.

De Brún, A., O'Donovan, R. and McAuliffe, E. (2019) Interventions to develop collectivistic leadership in healthcare settings: A systematic review, *BMC Health Services Research*, 19: 72. Available at: https://bmchealthservres.biomedcentral.com/articles/10.1186/s12913-019-3883-x (accessed 25 March 2020).

Decety, J. and Cowell, J.W. (2014) Friends or foe: Is empathy necessary for moral behaviour?, *Perspectives on Psychological Science*, 9 (5): 525–537.

Department of Health and Children (2008) *Building a Culture of Patient Safety: Report of the Commission on Patient Safety and Quality Assurance*, Dublin: Stationery Office. Available at: https://www.gov.ie/en/publication/5d9570-building-a-culture-of-patient-safety-report-of-the-commission-on-pat/ (accessed 13 February 2020).

De Zulueta, P.C. (2016) Developing compassionate leadership in health care: An integrative review, *Journal of Healthcare Leadership*, 8: 1–10.

Dierksmeier, C. (2016) What is humanistic about humanistic management?, *Humanistic Management Journal*, 1 (1): 9–32.

Eljiz, K., Greenfield, D., Molineux, J. and Sloan, T. (2018) How to improve healthcare? Identify, nurture, and embed individuals and teams with 'deep smarts, *Journal of Health Organisation and Management*, 32 (1): 135–143.

Fahlman, D. (2013) Examining informal learning using mobile devices in the healthcare workplace, *Canadian Journal of Learning and Technology*, 39 (4): 1–21.

Feng, Y., Hao, B., Iles, P. and Bown, N. (2017) Rethinking distributed leadership: Dimensions, antecedents and team effectiveness, *Learning and Organisation Development Journal*, 38 (2): 284–302.

Finkelman, A. (2012) *Leadership and Management for Nurses*, Boston, MA: Pearson Education.

Francis, R. (2013) *Report of the Mid Staffordshire NHS Foundation Trust Public Enquiry: Executive Summary*, London: HMSO. Available at: https://www.gov.uk/government/publications/report-of-the-mid-staffordshire-nhs-foundation-trust-public-inquiry (accessed 14 October 2020).

Franklin, U.E. and Aguenza, B.B. (2016) Obstacles, resistance and impact of change in organisations: An examination of the Saudi Telecommunication Company (STC), *International Journal of Academic Research in Business and Social Sciences*, 6 (4): 23–37.

Grenda, J.P. and Hackmann, D.G. (2014) Advantages and challenges of. Distributing leadership in middle-level schools, *National Association of Secondary School Principals (NASSP) Bulletin*, 98 (1): 53–74.

Gronn, P. (2002) Distributed leadership as a unit of analysis, *Leadership Quarterly*, 13 (4): 423–451.

Günzel-Jensen, F., Jain, A. and Kjeldsen, A. (2016) Distributed leadership in health care: The role of formal leadership styles and organizational efficacy, *Leadership*, 14 (1): 110–133.

Harris, A. (2011) Distributed leadership: Implications for the role of the principal, *Journal of Management Development*, 31 (1): 7–17.

Harris, A. (2013) Distributed leadership: Friend or foe, *Educational Management Administration and Leadership*, 41 (5): 545–554.

Harris, A. and Spillane, J. (2008) Distributed leadership through the looking glass, *Management in Education*, 22 (1): 31–34.

Health Service Executive (HSE) (2013) *Investigation of Incident 50278 from time of patient's self-referral to hospital on the 21st of October 2012 to the patient's death on the 28th of October 2012*. Available at: https://www.lenus.ie/bitstream/handle/10147/293964/nimtreport50278.pdf?sequence=1&isAllowed=y (accessed 5 March 2020).

Health Service Executive (HSE) (2019) *Health Services People Strategy 2019–2024*, Dublin: Human Resource Division, Health Service Executive. Available at: https://www.hse.ie/eng/

staff/resources/hrstrategiesreports/health-services-people-strategy-2019-2024.pdf (accessed 4 March 2020).

Holt, S., Marques, J., Hu, J. and Wood, A. (2017) Cultivating empathy: New perspectives on educating business leaders, *Journal of Values-Based Leadership*, 10: 3. Available at: https://core.ac.uk/download/pdf/208613563.pdf (accessed 21 October 2020).

Hughes, R.L., Ginnet, R.C. and Curphy, G.J. (2006) *Leadership: Enhancing the Lessons of Experience*, Boston, MA: McGraw-Hill.

Jackson, D., Firtko, A. and Edenborough, M. (2007) Personal resilience as a strategy for surviving and thriving in the face of workplace adversity: A literature review, *Journal of Advanced Nursing*, 60 (1): 1–9.

Jain, A.K. and Jeppesen, H.J. (2014) Conceptualising and implementing the distributed leadership practices in Indian organisations, *Journal of Management Development*, 33 (3): 258–278.

Jiang, X., Flores, H.R., Leelawong, R. and Manz, C.C. (2016) The effect of team empowerment on team performance: A cross-cultural perspective on the mediating roles of knowledge sharing and intra-group conflict, *International Journal of Conflict Management*, 27 (1): 62–87.

Kaufman, G. and McCaughan, D. (2013) The effect of organisational culture on patient safety, *Nursing Standard*, 27 (43): 50–60.

Kirrane, M., Lennon, M., O'Connor, C. and Fu, N. (2016) Linking perceived management support with employees' readiness for change: The mediating role of psychological capital, *Journal of Change Management*, 17 (1): 47–66.

Kodama, Y. and Fukahori, H. (2017) Nursing managers' attributes to promote change in their wards: A qualitative study, *Nursing Open*, 4 (4): 209–217.

Lakshman, C. (2005) Top executive knowledge leadership: Managing knowledge to lead change at Central Electric, *Journal of Change Management*, 5 (4): 429–446.

Laur, C., Bell, J., Valaitis, R., Ray, S. and Keller, H. (2018) The Sustain and Spread Framework: Strategies for sustaining and spreading nutrition care improvements in acute care based on thematic analysis from the More-2-Eat Study, *BMC Health Services Research*, 18: 930. Available at: http://doi.org/10.1186/s12913-018-3748-8 (accessed 21 October 2020).

Lennox, L., Maher, L. and Reed, J. (2018) Navigating the sustainability landscape: A systematic review of sustainability approaches in healthcare, *Implementation Science*, 13: 27. Available at: https://doi.org/10.1186/s13012-017-0707-4 (accessed 21 October 2020).

MacBeath, J., Oduro, G. and Waterhouse, J. (2005) Distributed leadership: A developmental process, paper presented at the 'Leadership for Learning' symposium at the *18th International Congress for School Effectiveness and Improvement*, Barcelona, 2–5 January. Available at: https://www.leraar24.nl/app/uploads/macbeath_et_al05.pdf (accessed 5 March 2020).

Maher, L., Gustafson, D. and Evans, A. (2010) *Sustainability Model and Guide*, Coventry: NHS Institute for Innovation and Improvement. Available at: https://www.england.nhs.uk/improvement-hub/wp-content/uploads/sites/44/2017/11/NHS-Sustainability-Model-2010.pdf (accessed 3 April 2020).

Martin, G., Beech, N., MacIntosh, R. and Bushfield, S. (2015) Potential challenges facing distributed leadership in health care: Evidence from the UK National Health Service, *Sociology of Health and Illness*, 37 (1): 14–29.

Massoud, M.R., Nielsen, G.A., Nolan, K., Nolan, T., Schall, M.W. and Sevin, C. (2006) A framework for spread: From local improvements to system-wide change, Institute for Healthcare Improvement (IHI) Innovation Series White Paper, Cambridge, MA: IHI. Available at: http://www.ihi.org/resources/Pages/IHIWhitePapers/AFrameworkforSpreadWhitePaper.aspx (accessed 7 April 2020).

McKee, L., West, M., Flin, R., Grant, A., Johnston, D., Jones, M. et al. (2010) *Understanding the Dynamics of Organisational Culture Change: Creating Safe Places for Patients and Staff.* Report for the National Institute for Health Research Service Delivery and Organisation programme, London: HMSO. Available at: http://www.netscc.ac.uk/hsdr/files/project/SDO_FR_08-1501-092_V01.pdf (accessed 13 February 2020).

McKee, L., Charles, K., Dixon-Woods, M., Willars, J. and Martin, G. (2013) 'New' and distributed leadership in quality and safety in health care, or 'old' and hierarchical? An interview study with strategic stakeholders, *Journal of Health Services Research and Policy*, 18 (suppl. 2): 11–19.

Natale, S. and Sora, S. (2010) Ethics in strategic thinking: Business processes and the global market collapse, *Journal of Business Ethics*, 94 (3): 309–316.

Nursing and Midwifery Board of Ireland (NMBI) (2015) *Scope of Nursing and Midwifery Practice Framework*, Dublin: NMBI.

Oduro, G.K.T. (2004) Distributed leadership in schools: What English headteachers say about the pull and push factors, paper presented at the *British Educational Research Association Annual Conference*, University of Manchester, 16–18 September. Available at: http://www.leeds.ac.uk/bei/Education-line/browse/all_items/136829.html (accessed 11 February 2020).

Porath, C.L. and Erez, A. (2007) Does rudeness matter? The effects of rude behaviour on task performance and helpfulness, *Academy of Management Journal*, 50 (5): 1181–1197.

Putra, E.D., Chow, S. and Liu, J. (2017) Extrinsic and intrinsic motivation on work engagement in the hospitality industry: Test of motivation crowding theory, *Tourism and Hospitality Research*, 17 (2): 228–241.

Regan, S., Laschinger, H.K. and Wong, C.A. (2016) The influence of empowerment, authentic leadership, and professional practice environments on nurses' perceived interprofessional collaboration, *Journal of Nursing Management*, 24 (1): E54–E61.

Ribi re, V.M. and Sitar, A.S. (2003) Critical role of leadership in nurturing a knowledge-supporting culture, *Knowledge Management Research and Practice*, 1 (1): 39–48.

Sethi, D. and Seth, M. (2009) Interpersonal communication: Lifeblood of an organisation, *IUP Journal of Soft Skills*, 3 (3/4): 32–41.

Sherwood, G. (2015) Perspectives: Nurses' expanding role in developing safety culture: Quality and safety education for nurses – competences in action, *Journal of Research in Nursing*, 28 (8): 734–740.

Silver, S.A., McQuillan, R., Harel, Z., Weizman, A.V., Thomas, A., Nesrallah, G. et al. (2016) How to sustain change and support continuous quality improvement, *Clinical Journal of the American Society of Nephrology*, 11 (5): 916–924.

Spillane, J.P. (2006) *Distributed Leadership*, San Francisco, CA: Jossey-Bass.

Torrance, D. (2013) The challenges of developing distributed leadership in Scottish primary schools: A catch 22, *International Journal of Primary, Elementary and Early Years Education*, 41 (3): 330–345.

Torres, D.G. (2019) Distributed leadership, professional collaboration and teachers' job satisfaction in U.S. schools, *Teaching and Teacher Education*, 79 (March): 111–123.

Ulrich, D. and Smallwood, N. (2004) Capitalizing on capabilities, *Harvard Business Review*, 82 (6): 119–127.

Unterrainer, C., Jeppesen, H.J. and Jonsson, T.F. (2017) Distributed leadership agency and its relationship to individual autonomy and occupational self-efficacy: A two wave-mediation study in Denmark, *Humanistic Management Journal*, 2 (1): 57–81.

Van Noy, M., James, M. and Bedley, C. (2016) *Reconceptualizing Learning: A Review of the Literature on Informal Learning*, Piscataway, NJ: Rutgers Education and Employment Research Centre, State University of New Jersey.

Virani, T., Lemieux-Charles, L., Davis, D.A. and Berta, W. (2009) Sustaining change: Once evidence-based practices are transferred, what then?, *Healthcare Quarterly*, 12 (1): 89–96.

Von Krogh, C., Nonaka, I. and Rechsteiner, L. (2012) Leadership in organizational knowledge creation: A review and framework, *Journal of Management Studies*, 49 (1): 240–277.

Wan Abdul Rahman, W.A. and Castelli, P.A. (2013) The impact of empathy on leadership effectiveness and business leaders in the United States and Malaysia, *International Journal of Economics Business and Management Studies*, 2 (3): 83–97.

Wang, Y.Y., Wan, Q.Q., Lin, F., Zhau, W.J. and Shang, S.M. (2018) Interventions to improve communication between nurses and physicians in the intensive care unit: An integrative literature review, *International Journal of Nursing Studies*, 5 (1): 81–88.

West, M., Armit, K., Loewenthal, L., Eckert, R., West, T. and Lee, A. (2015) *Leadership and Leadership Development: The Evidence Base*, London: The King's Fund.

Willis, C.D., Saul, J., Bevan, H., Scheirer, M.A., Best, A., Greenhalgh, T. et al. (2016) Sustaining organisational culture change in health systems, *Journal of Health Organisation and Management*, 30 (1): 2–30.

Wong, C.A. (2015) Connecting nursing leadership and patient outcomes: State of the science, *Journal of Nursing Management*, 23 (3): 275–278.

Yammarino, F.J., Salas, E., Serban, A., Shirreffs, K. and Shuffler, M.L. (2012) Collective leadership approaches: Putting the 'we' in leadership science and practice, *Industrial and Organisational Psychology*, 5 (4): 382–402.

Yukl, G. (1998) *Leadership in Organizations*, 4th edition, Upper Saddle River, NJ: Prentice-Hall.

Yukl, G. (2013) *Leadership in Organizations*, 8th edition, London: Pearson Education.

17 Strategic, regulating and enabling initiatives: Conducive organisational changes

Patrick Gibbons and Ruifang Wang

Chapter topics

- The environmental issues facing healthcare
- Organisational health
- The antecedents to distributed leadership
- The practices of effective leadership
- Exploitation and exploration
- Political skills

Introduction

The concept of distributed leadership in healthcare settings suggests that traditional notions of management need to be supplemented with an increased focus on leadership practices and behaviours to effect organisational 'health' (Keller and Schaninger, 2019). Distributed leadership addresses the duality of managerial and leadership practices by highlighting that leadership activity and practice can be diffused throughout the organisation. Kotter (1990) sees management as an activity that is based on positional power and emphasises the activities of planning, budgeting, controlling and organising. Management is about an individual's position in a hierarchy who is charged with keeping the cogs in the bureaucratic machine turning, focusing on efficiency. Leadership, on the other hand, is very much focused on a more emergent and social dynamic, emphasising direction-setting, motivating people and organisational effectiveness. Thus, leadership can be displayed at any level in the organisation.

This chapter starts with a discussion of the key environmental trends that influence the healthcare setting and as a result the need for distributed leadership. Some organisational prerequisites for the animation of distributed leadership are then discussed. Particular attention is directed at the concepts of psychological safety and organisational slack.

Then, issues and ingredients of organisational health are identified with a view to surfacing the organisational requirements for distributed leadership. A particular focus will be placed on the twin activities of exploration and exploitation as behaviours to animate organisational wellbeing, with the former directed at developing new capabilities and the latter at deploying existing capabilities. The chapter then outlines the key leadership behaviours in exploration and exploitation. In exploration, the key roles are championing – where the individual advances new initiatives upwards to more senior levels, aimed at developing new organisational capabilities – and facilitating – the influence that leaders have in encouraging and soliciting new initiatives and developing new capabilities in their immediate areas of responsibility. Then, in terms of exploitation, the twin roles of synthesising and implementing become apparent. Synthesising involves upward influence and generation of reports, briefings and presentations on collating information about performance and progress. Ultimately, implementing – typically the crucial role of most leaders – involves the deployment and management of resources in pursuit of organisational objectives.

Each of these roles will be outlined and recent research on appropriate ways to execute these roles will be developed. For instance, facilitating and implementing can be heavily informed by recent research on progress, specifically the critical importance of supporting and encouraging employees in the achievement of even small increments in progress for motivation and job satisfaction. Moreover, the behaviours associated with effective leadership practices are also identified. In addition, for championing and synthesising, the critical political skills required will be outlined. These comments are made to reflect the call from Gosling et al. (2009) that understanding and therefore deploying a distributed leadership perspective requires the recognition and understanding of the social, political and power relationships within organisations.

Background

The appropriateness of organisational forms designed in the twentieth century is increasingly challenged by a number of factors. The US War College has referred to the modern age as reflecting a VUCA environment. Rates of change (*volatility*) have increased, as evidenced in the volume and magnitude of change. *Uncertainty* has increased, in terms of our knowledge of causal linkages across environmental changes and the appropriate choice of organisational responses. *Complexity* has increased as the number of stimuli and signals that the organisation responds to have exploded! This is particularly true in the areas of technology and regulatory change. Finally, *ambiguity*, meaning the mixed interpretations of issues has developed further. The response has been to call for the development of agile organisations. At the same time, peoples's expectations of their working conditions are shifting dramatically. Traditional command and control, hierarchical organisations are being replaced by holocracies (Bernstein et al., 2016), constituted of flat structures that foster flexibility and engagement that yield productivity and efficiency.

The relentless pace and volatile rate of technological change with the emergence of artificial intelligence, big data and communications technologies is transforming the way work is being done. More complex regulatory regimes have emerged as technologies have changed. Unanticipated events such as Covid-19 have transformed societies and economies. In the healthcare setting, demographic changes resulting in increasing demands have combined with fiscal pressures to place a burden on healthcare capacity. At the same time, ongoing advances in treatment have complicated delivery with increased specialisation and differentiation. In addition to these macro trends, a specific series of environmental issues are confronting healthcare organisations.

In terms of financing, the development and introduction of expensive new treatments, based on cell and gene therapy, offering more customised treatments will materially affect the demand for care. Moreover, as the understanding of genomics expands, it is possible that patients who have not yet contracted a disease, but who have been identified as susceptible based on their genetic makeup, will receive treatment. As these cost pressures increase, achieving scale economies in healthcare settings will become more important (Saxena et al., 2019). As scale increases, the traditional organisational response to increasing the height of the hierarchy by adding more and more layers of administrative and managerial oversight will undermine operating efficiencies. So, a new organisational paradigm is required.

While the underlying life sciences are developing, other emerging technologies in the digital sphere also offer significant opportunities to revolutionise healthcare delivery (Singhal and Carlton, 2019). The new technologies developed for healthcare systems and providers are increasingly characterised by open innovation models. Some analysts point out that digital leaders in the healthcare space require extensive changes and education of the healthcare workforce. Specifically, they highlight that the adoption of digital therapeutics is heavily influenced by healthcare providers' understanding of the benefits and difficulties of these technologies. Once more, the increased complexity of the technological environment requires increased complexity and therefore differentiation within the organisation. Once more, the integration and coordination of this increased differentiation can be solved through hierarchy, but at the costs of both lengthier response and increased cost.

In terms of service delivery, there are continuing changes in models of delivery, with increased emphasis on out-of-hospital delivery models. These out-of-hospital delivery models include home-care, the provision of local services for children and alternatives to acute hospital admission (Bartlett et al., 2017). Bartlett and colleagues claim that alternative delivery models will require more innovative workforce models. In particular, they point out that the breadth and depth of expertise available in healthcare settings needs to be appropriately deployed and that clinicians work, as they say, 'to the top of their licence'. This might suggest that leadership roles based on expertise and technical competence will become more widely diffused, hence the attention to models of distributed leadership.

Beirne (see Chapter 1) points out that leadership failures have challenged the traditional notions of hierarchical, top-down leadership and organisational cultures in many jurisdictions. These threats to the legitimacy of healthcare providers highlight the significant reputational risk that accrues to leadership failure. Expanding leadership capacity in healthcare settings therefore becomes vital.

Organisational antecedents to distributed leadership

A related literature recognising middle managers' strategic influence started in the 1970s. Bower (1970) was among the earliest and provided a detailed case study about middle managers' involvement in strategy definition and implementation. Specifically, he found that resource allocations were based on which resource requests that middle managers considered they should provide impetus to. The role of senior management was to provide the 'context' for initiatives to be advanced through structural mechanisms such as incentive scheme design and organisational climate.

Two important aspects of organisational context are the extent to which organisational members can give 'voice' to their concerns and perspectives and the facility with which new ways of doing things can be supported. One clear pathology in organisations is silence (Morrison and Milliken, 2000). Employees who feel that their organisational context is inimical to their contributions can negatively affect organisational decision-making and contribute to catastrophic failure. Examples from the *Challenger* disaster at NASA to the responses to the Chernobyl disaster all point to the negative consequences of silence. Morrison and Milliken (2000) contend that silence has negative organisational and individual consequences. At the individual level, employees won't feel valued and will perceive a lack of control over their work. At the organisational level, there will be an absence of variety in decision inputs and an absence of critical analysis of decisions. This may be particularly problematic in healthcare settings (Yurdakul et al., 2016). By way of contrast, therefore, one of the key antecedents to distributed leadership is the existence of psychological safety. This refers to a climate of openness and open inquiry in an organisation. Edmondson (2019) and her colleagues, in a variety of studies, have identified the positive consequences of psychological safety. These positive outcomes include enhanced organisational learning as there is a free-flow of ideas and contributions. Diverse perspectives are aired and assumptions are openly challenged. In addition, employees are more engaged as their contributions are listened to.

Another key organisational antecedent to the enactment of distributed leadership is organisational slack. Slack refers to the availability of resources in an organisation (Cyert and March, 1963). The availability of slack resources facilitates the exercise of experimentation and learning. Slack resources enable the commitment of discretionary resources to new initiatives. In addition, slack reduces the impact of failure costs, which can be an important source of learning. Specifically, if slack exists, the cost of failure can be more easily absorbed.

These are antecedents to the practice of distributed leadership. In terms of contribution, we see distributed leadership as contributing to organisational health.

Organisational health

Assessment of organisational health is increasingly being addressed as a complement to assessments of organisational performance. While traditionally organisational performance has focused on issues of efficiency and effectiveness, a focus on organisational health takes a more dynamic perspective on ensuring that the organisation possesses the critical ingredients for ensuring that it survives over the longer term and is adaptable to ever-changing environments. Recent work by the consultants McKinsey & Co. has identified a number of 'health frameworks' that guide organisational health (Keller and Schaninger, 2019). These include:

- *Direction*: a clear sense of the target and strategic intent of the organisation and the ability of employees to translate that direction into meaningful implications for their roles.
- *Leadership*: the extent to which leaders inspire the actions of others, to enhance and contribute to organisational performance. This is the social impact that leaders have, as discussed by Kotter (1999).
- *Work environment*: the shared beliefs and quality of cooperative interactions within and across organisational units. The overall level of trust and the extent to which creativity and innovation are encouraged.
- *Accountability*: the extent to which employees understand what is expected of them, have sufficient authority to act and feel a sense of ownership for the delivery of results.
- *Coordination and control*: the use and application of standards of performance, the evaluation of performance and risk, and addressing opportunities and risks as they arise.
- *Capabilities*: the availability of organisational skills, the acquisition and development of talent and its deployment.
- *Motivation*: the overall level of enthusiasm that employees feel for the organisation and its mission and values.
- *Innovation and learning*: the quality and flow of new ideas and the organisation's ability to adapt. The balance of top-down and bottom-up initiative generation. The extent of knowledge-sharing in the organisation.
- *External orientation*: the level and quality of engagement with key external publics such as clients, suppliers and regulators.

It is argued that the notion of distributed leadership can help address many of these indicators of health. This is particularly so in healthcare settings where power is diffuse; multiple, sometimes divergent objectives are being pursued; and, as we saw earlier, the environment is extremely complex (Currie et al., 2009). Specifically, distributed leadership can enhance the sense of direction, the work environment, accountability, capability development, motivation and innovation/learning, provided the leaders display effective leadership behaviours.

One particularly practical approach to leadership is to engage in the five practices of effective leadership, as outlined by Kouzes and Posner (2017). These practices include: Modelling the way, Setting a clear vision, Challenging the process, Enabling others to act and, finally, Encouragement. Box 17.1 seeks to link the characteristics of organisational health with the five practices of effective leadership.

Box 17.1: Linking organisational health to the five practices of effective leadership

Organisational health indicator	Leadership practice contribution
Direction	*Modelling the way* and *Setting the vision*: providing clarity around organisational values and enlisting others in the pursuit of commonly held aspirations
Work environment	*Modelling the way*: engendering trust and openness through the display and example of trusting and open behaviours
Accountability	*Modelling the way*, *Challenging the process* and *Enabling others to act*: the extent to which employees understand what is expected of them, have sufficient authority to act and feel a sense of ownership for the delivery of results
Capability development	*Challenging the process* and *Enabling others to act*: the acquisition and development of talent and its deployment through providing challenge and delegation
Motivation	*Enabling others to act* and *Encouragement*: the overall level of enthusiasm that employees feel for the organisation and its mission and values
Innovation/ learning	*Challenging the process* and *Enabling others to act*: The quality and flow of new ideas and the organisation's ability to adapt

One of the key ways a culture is sustained in an organisation is through the demonstrated behaviours of leaders in that organisation. Nearly all organisations have identified 'values' to support the achievement of the organisation's objectives. Typically, these values are espoused to guide organisational members' behaviours. One of the critical signals that all organisational members receive is the observed behaviours and examples provided by leaders. Leaders who model the values of the organisation help translate these values from merely espoused values to values-in-use. It is the modelling of the behaviour that transmits a signal to other organisational members as to what is valued.

One of the critical roles of a leader as identified by Kotter (1990) is the articulation of a vision. Identifying a picture of the 'future' that is compelling is typically presented as a key element in change programmes. The presumption is that organisational members are willing to engage in change if the future can be depicted as a 'better' situation compared to the status quo. The articulation of a vision, the ability to remind people of the purpose of their endeavours, and the outcome that can be delivered by the organisation can serve as an important motivator. This is particularly true if the vision speaks to the shared aspirations of the organisation's members.

Challenging the process involves the respectful questioning of the status quo to ensure continuous improvement. A key aspect of a leader's role is to enhance organisational performance. Challenging commitment to the status quo and introducing new ways of doing things aimed at improving operations is a contribution to organisational learning, where acceptance of diversity and a willingness to experiment are hallmarks of learning organisations. Moreover, contributing to organisational members' ability to achieve their goals by introducing improved work practices is itself a powerful motivator. This has been further demonstrated by Amabile and Kramer (2011) in discussing the Progress Principle. They demonstrates that making progress, even small progress in 'meaningful work', is a spur to an enhanced inner work life. Moreover, an enhanced inner work life is associated with increased levels of productivity, organisational commitment and job satisfaction. As the authors discuss, meaningful work means that the work contributes to the wellbeing of some group or community that the worker identifies with. From a healthcare perspective, therefore, meaningful work is typically assured.

Enabling others to act speaks to the art of delegating and facilitating others to complete tasks. A crucial aspect of leadership is to contribute to the development of others. One developmental activity is the provision of ongoing feedback on tasks. Feedback is directed at enhancing competence.

Encouragement is about celebrating successes. However, the celebration is directed at recognising, at the individual level, contributions to task achievement and objective attainment. At the organisational level, celebrating success facilitates the reinforcement of organisational values by linking objective attainment to the display and deployment of organisational values.

Exploration and exploitation

As outlined above, a key activity for leaders at all levels in the organisation is the development, advancement and animation of initiatives. Such initiatives can be classified into exploitative initiatives and exploratory initiatives (March, 1991). Exploitative initiatives deploy the organisation's capabilities in a manner that is consistent with the organisation's strategy. Exploratory initiatives deploy the organisation's capabilities in seeking to develop new avenues of endeavour and innovations that extend the organisation's strategy.

Floyd and Wooldridge (1994) analysed middle managers' strategic roles by considering the direction of their influence (upward vs. downward) and their cognitive nature (divergent vs. convergent), and classified the roles into four categories: implementing deliberate strategy, synthesising information, facilitating adaptability, and championing strategic alternatives. We would contend that the cognitive nature of the initiative is consistent with exploration (divergent) and exploitation (convergent). Moreover, as we contend that leadership can occur anywhere in the organisation, we suggest that all leaders can engage in these behaviours.

Implementation of a deliberate strategy is widely seen as a key strategic role. It is often simply thought of as a mechanical process, which follows top-level strategic direction. Leaders below the apex of the organisation translate goals into operational plans and associate them with individual objectives. The reality is, however, much more complicated. The environment is dynamic. It is extremely difficult, if not impossible, to have a perfect strategy that does not require updating or revision. Therefore, implementation is understood as a series of interventions, including organisational structures, key personnel actions and control systems, that follows top-level deliberate plans on the one hand, and then adjusts strategic focus along with emergent challenges on the other (Floyd and Wooldridge, 1994, 1996).

Floyd and Wooldridge (1996) believed that middle managers have the potential to encounter more different types of stakeholders than anyone else in this network given their unique positions located in the centre among both vertical and horizontal levels. In a distributed leadership context, therefore, distributed leaders are in the best place to receive very diverse information and are required to combine the strategic objective-oriented information with operational means-oriented information (Nonaka, 1988). Digesting this information through the prisms of their specialist background, experiences, knowledge and capabilities, distributed leaders synthesise raw information in a structured, meaningful and subjective way. External threats and opportunities, and internal organisational strengths and weaknesses are often important inputs from them. They provide digested facts for their superiors' reference, which lays the foundation for further strategic agenda-setting (Dutton and Jackson, 1987). They are by no means absolutely objective channels for seeking the facts, but the value of their information processing derives from their personal understanding and evaluation. There are also interpersonal skills involved by which middle managers perform this role by interacting with their top managers, peers and subordinates. Synthesising information is therefore defined as 'a subjective process by which middle managers inject strategic meaning into operating and strategic information and communicate their interpretations to others' (Floyd and Wooldridge, 1996: 69).

Organisations are re-engineering from traditional hierarchical structures and require flexible and fast-updated dynamic capabilities to be more responsive. Organisational flexibility is critical in dealing with day-to-day surprises and organisational inertia. Flexibility is derived from new experimental trials and innovations. Identified within an organisation (often in its operating level), original ideas of innovation are inspired by outside stakeholders (such as its clients, suppliers and consultants) (Floyd and Wooldridge, 1996). Distributed leaders often find themselves involved in this initiative evaluation process. Potentially valuable embryonic ideas are selected, and further nurtured and developed to fit organisational needs. The continued facilitating process requires resources and a healthy climate. Distributed leaders tend to be positioned to identify what resources are needed, and where and how to get them (Kuratko et al., 2005). Deployment of resources is also part of their job. Moreover, as stated before, a reasonable amount of organisational slack is extremely valuable in this context to afford individuals the required time and needed resources to develop these extra projects apart from their daily routines (Cyert and March, 1963; Bourgeois, 1981). An effective facilitator is also keen to promote a climate within their department, which encourages team working skills, promotes interpersonal mutual trust, shares a common strategic understanding, and values innovative inputs. In such conditions, employees are more inclined to share their knowledge, challenge the existing status quo, and try new ways. The facilitating role is thus defined as 'the nurturing and development of experimental programs and organizational arrangements that increase organizational flexibility, encourage organizational learning, and expand the firm's repertoire of potential strategic responses' (Floyd and Wooldridge, 1996: 84).

Championing, defined as 'the persistent and persuasive communication of proposals that either provide the firm with new capabilities or allow the firm to use existing capabilities differently' (Floyd and Wooldridge, 1996: 55), is fundamentally a form of upward influence. Burgelman (1983a, 1983b) described how middle managers play champions for new strategic initiatives developed from operating levels in new venture divisions. Their roles centre on discrete proposals, and they try to make them potentially visible and aim to influence the organisational top management to adjust or reshape its current strategic focus. Distributed leaders do much work relating to how new strategic initiatives take shape. Once the proposed initiates are in good shape, it is time to sell upwards. Different issue packaging techniques (such as issue content framing, issue presentation, issue bundling) and selling process factors (such as choice of channel, breadth of involvement, timing and other tactics) contribute to influencing various decisions from top management (Dutton and Ashford, 1993; Dutton et al., 2001; Ren and Guo, 2011). This role is often obscured partly because championing often happens as a consequence of synthesising, implementing and facilitating behaviours. It is also confused with other types of upward influence behaviours (such as 'the malcontent' behaviour, and the 'reactive manager' behaviour), some of which (such as 'empire building') are often self-interested (Floyd and Wooldridge, 1996: 61–65). This confusion undermines the goodwill and benefit that championing behaviours could potentially achieve. Despite the obscurity and confusion associated with the championing role, it is regarded as one of the most fundamental ones for innovative deployment of organisational capabilities. The final question, then, is if a key aspect of distributed leadership is the deployment and activation of implementing, synthesising, facilitating and championing behaviours, then what are the skills and competencies required to engage in these behaviours?

Political skills

An ongoing awareness of the interpersonal nature of managerial work has animated research attention on the effects of interpersonal skills on managers' performance (Semadar et al., 2006). Specific types of interpersonal skills involve empathy, social insights, persuasiveness, oral communication ability and network-building among others. Such skills enable managers to respond to interpersonal cues with more sensitivity and flexibility; build well-connected networks; and understand and influence others in an effective manner (Yukl, 2012). Managers depend heavily upon their interpersonal skills to broaden their strategic behaviours. Within the interpersonal skill category, political skills are identified as an ideal indicator. Defined as 'the ability to effectively understand others at work and to use such knowledge to influence others to act in ways that enhance one's personal and/or organizational objectives' (Ferris et al., 2005: 127), political skills involves social astuteness, interpersonal influence, networking ability and apparent sincerity dimensions:

1. *Social astuteness.* Politically skilled individuals observe others with a more astute and sensitive eye. They interpret others' behaviours and understand social interactions well.
2. *Interpersonal influence.* Individuals who possess political skill have a powerful influence style and capability to adapt and calibrate their behaviour to different targets of influence and various social settings.
3. *Networking ability.* Individuals with political skill are good at identifying a wide range of contacts and building diverse social networks.
4. *Apparent sincerity.* Politically skilled individuals appear to others as being sincere, genuine and authentic. This characteristic is vital, as it enhances the success of influence attempts since the perceived intention of the behaviour is less likely to be interpreted as manipulative or coercive.

Managers generally require political skills to perform their organisational activities successfully, as the organisational context is socially based and requires strong social astuteness, verbal facility and interpersonal skills. The organisation is inherently a political area (Mintzberg, 1983; Pfeffer, 1992), wherein the acquisition and control of resources is largely facilitated by personal political skills (Ferris et al., 2007). While a general mental ability contributes greater job knowledge to an individual's job performance, political skills enhance performance through alliance formation and cooperation, thus facilitating opportunity access and resource acquisition (Hochwarter et al., 2006). Political skill, therefore, represents a key personal competence that enables distributed leaders to envision joint opportunities for exploitation and exploration, obtain the necessary resources and support to pursue these agendas, and create the flexibility and bandwidth in their schedules to engage in these joint activities.

Conclusion

The advance of distributed leadership requires changes to organisational contexts, where psychological safety and the availability of slack resources are required. However, perhaps the biggest obstacle is the development of leadership skills across a broad swathe of the organisational membership. We believe that developing the practices of effective leadership and encouraging the development of political skills are prerequisites to the animation and deployment of diffused leadership.

Key concepts discussed

- Psychological safety refers to a climate of openness and open inquiry in an organisation. There are a number of positive organisational consequences of psychological safety, including enhanced organisational learning and employee engagement. The existence of psychological safety enhances the distributed leadership.

- Another key organisational antecedent to the enactment of differentiated leadership is organisational slack, which refers to the availability of resources in an organisation.
- McKinsey & Co. has identified a number of 'health frameworks' that guide organisational health. These include: direction, leadership, work environment, accountability, coordination and control, capabilities, motivation, innovation and learning, and external orientation.
- Five practices of effective leadership include modelling the way, setting a clear vision, challenging the process, enabling others to act and encouragement.
- Middle managers' four strategic roles include championing, facilitating, synthesising and implementing.
- Political skills refers to 'the ability to effectively understand others at work and to use such knowledge to influence others to act in ways that enhance one's personal and/or organizational objectives' (Ferris et al., 2005: 127). It includes social astuteness, interpersonal influence, networking ability and apparent sincerity dimensions.

Key readings

- Edmondson, A. (2019) *The Fearless Organization: Creating Psychological Safety in the Workplace for Learning, Innovation, and Growth*, New York: Wiley.
  This book offers practical guidance for teams and organisations to succeed in the modern economy. It explores psychological safety, and provides a blueprint for bringing it to life.
- Ferris, G.R., Davidson, S.L. and Perrewé, P.L. (2005) *Political Skill at Work: Impact on Work Effectiveness*, Mountain View, CA: Davies-Black.
  This book explains what political skill is and delivers the 'how' to influence at work, not just the 'what'. It also provides ways to measure and enhance this powerful ability.
- Kouzes, J.M. and Posner, B.Z. (2017) *The Leadership Challenge*, 6th edition, Hoboken, NJ: Wiley.
  This book offers insight into leadership's critical role in organisational health and navigate the shift towards team-oriented work relationships.
- Tian, M., Risku, M. and Collin, K. (2016) A meta-analysis of distributed leadership from 2002 to 2013, *Educational Management Administration and Leadership*, 44: 146–164.
  This article provides a meta-analysis of research conducted on distributed leadership from 2002 to 2013.

Examples of studies

- Currie, G. (1999) The influence of middle managers in the business planning process: A case study in the UK NHS, *British Journal of Management*, 10: 141–155.
- Currie, G., Lockett, A. and Suhomlinova, O. (2009) The institutionalization of distributed leadership: A 'catch-22' in English public services, *Human Relations*, 62: 1735–1761.

- Jønsson, T., Unterrainer, C., Jeppesen, H.J. and Jain, A.K. (2016) Measuring distributed leadership agency in a hospital context, *Journal of Health Organization and Management*, 30: 908–926.
- Yurdakul, M., Bosen, M. and Erdogan, S. (2016) The organisational silence of midwives and nurses: Reasons and results, *Journal of Nursing Management*, 24: 686–694.

Useful websites

- McKinsey & Company: https://www.mckinsey.com/industries/healthcare-systems-and-services/our-insights
  Provides information on the Insights on Healthcare Systems & Services.
- HSE Workplace Health and Wellbeing Unit: https://www.hse.ie/eng/staff/workplace-health-and-wellbeing-unit/
  Offers a range of support services and programme specifically tailored for healthcare staff to help support you physically and emotionally throughout your working life.
- Irish Health Agencies: https://www.citizensinformation.ie/en/health/health_system/health_service_agencies.html
  Provides a number of agencies and bodies that have a role in delivering health services in Ireland.

References

Amabile, T. and Kramer, S. (2011) *The Progress Principle: Using Small Wins to Ignite Joy, Engagement, and Creativity at Work*, Boston, MA: Harvard Business Review Press.

Bartlett, R., Dash, P., Markus, M., McKenna, S. and Streicher, S. (2017) *New Models of Healthcare*, McKinsey & Company. Available at: https://www.mckinsey.com/industries/healthcare-systems-and-services/our-insights/new-models-of-healthcare (accessed 21 October 2020).

Bernstein, E., Bunch, J., Canner, N. and Lee, M. (2016) Beyond the holacracy hype, *Harvard Business Review*, 94 (7/8): 38–49.

Bourgeois, L.J.I. (1981) On the measurement of organizational slack, *Academy of Management Review*, 6: 29–39.

Bower, J.L. (1970) *Managing the Resource Allocation Process*, Cambridge, MA: Harvard University Press.

Burgelman, R.A. (1983a) Corporate entrepreneurship and strategic management: Insights from a process study, *Management Science*, 29: 1349–1364.

Burgelman, R.A. (1983b) A process model of internal corporate venturing in the diversified major firm, *Administrative Science Quarterly*, 28: 223–244.

Currie, G., Lockett, A. and Suhomlinova, O. (2009) The institutionalization of distributed leadership: A 'catch-22' in English public services, *Human Relations*, 62: 1735–1761.

Cyert, R.M. and March, J.G. (1963) *A Behavioral Theory of the Firm*, Englewood Cliffs, NJ: Prentice-Hall.

Dutton, J.E. and Ashford, S.J. (1993) Selling issues to top management, *Academy of Management Review*, 18: 397–428.

Dutton, J.E. and Jackson, S.E. (1987) Categorizing strategic issues: Links to organization action, *Academy of Management Review*, 12: 76–90.

Dutton, J.E., Ashford, S.J., O'Neill, R.M. and Lawrence, K.A. (2001) Moves that matter: Issue selling and organizational change, *Academy of Management Journal*, 44: 716–736.

Edmondson, A. (2019) *The Fearless Organization: Creating Psychological Safety in the Workplace for Learning, Innovation, and Growth*, New York: Wiley.

Ferris, G.R., Treadway, D.C., Kolodinsky, R.W., Hochwarter, W.A., Kacmar, C.J., Douglas, C. et al. (2005) Development and validation of the Political Skill Inventory, *Journal of Management*, 31: 126–152.

Ferris, G.R., Treadway, D.C., Perrewé, P.L., Brouer, R.L., Douglas, C. and Lux, S. (2007) Political skill in organizations, *Journal of Management*, 33: 290–320.

Floyd, S.W. and Wooldridge, B. (1994) Dinosaurs or dynamos? Recognizing middle management's strategic role, *Academy of Management Executive*, 8: 47–57.

Floyd, S.W. and Wooldridge, B. (1996) *The Strategic Middle Manager: How to Create and Sustain Competitive Advantage*, San Francisco, CA: Jossey-Bass.

Gosling, J., Bolden, R. and Petrov, G. (2009) Distributed leadership in higher education: What does it accomplish?, *Leadership*, 5: 299–310.

Hochwarter, W.A., Witt, L.A., Treadway, D.C. and Ferris, G.R. (2006) The interaction of social skill and organizational support on job performance, *Journal of Applied Psychology*, 91: 482–489.

Keller, S. and Schaninger, B. (2019) *Beyond Performance 2.0: A Proven Approach to Leading Large-Scale Change*, 2nd edition, Hoboken, NJ: GWiley.

Kotter, J.P. (1990) What leaders really do, *Harvard Business Review*, 68: 103–111.

Kotter, J.P. (1999) *What Leaders Really Do*, Boston, MA: Harvard Business School Press.

Kouzes, J.M. and Posner, B.Z. (2017) *The Leadership Challenge*, 6th edition, Hoboken, NJ: Wiley.

Kuratko, D.F., Ireland, R.D., Govin, J.G. and Hornsby, J.S. (2005) A model of middle-level managers' entrepreneurial behavior, *Entrepreneurship Theory and Practice*, November: 699–716.

March, J.G. (1991) Exploration and exploitation in organizational learning, *Organization Science*, 2: 71–87.

Mintzberg, H. (1983) *Power in and around Organizations*, Englewood Cliffs, NJ: Prentice-Hall.

Morrison, E.W. and Milliken, F.J. (2000) Organizational silence: A barrier to change and development in a pluralistic world, *Academy of Management Review*, 25: 706–725.

Nonaka, I. (1988) Toward middle-up-downmanagement: Accelerating information creation, *Sloan Management Review*, 3: 9–18.

Pfeffer, J. (1992) *Managing with Power: Politics and Influence in Organizations*, Boston, MA: Harvard Business School Press.

Ren, C.R. and Guo, C. (2011) Middle managers' strategic role in the corporate entrepreneurial process: Attention-based effects, *Journal of Management*, 37: 1586–1610.

Saxena, S., Holobinko, N., Liu, C. and Porwal, A. (2019) *Preparing for a New Kind of Shakeup in Health Care*, Boston Consulting Group, Perspective. Available at: https://www.bcg.com/publications/2019/shakeup-health-care (accessed 2 November 2020).

Semadar, A., Robins, G. and Ferris, G.R. (2006) Comparing the validity of multiple social effectiveness constructs in the prediction of managerial job performance, *Journal of Organizational Behavior*, 27: 443–461.

Singhal, S. and Carlton, S. (2019) *The Era of Exponential Improvement in Healthcare?*, McKinsey & Company. Available at: https://www.mckinsey.com/industries/healthcare-systems-and-services/our-insights/the-era-of-exponential-improvement-in-healthcare (accessed 21 October 2020).

Yukl, G. (2012) *Leadership in Organizations*, Upper Saddle River, NJ: Pearson.

Yurdakul, M., Bosen, M. and Erdogan, S. (2016) The organisational silence of midwives and nurses: Reasons and results, *Journal of Nursing Management*, 24: 686–694.

18 Epilogue: Where are we now and what is to be done?

Elizabeth A. Curtis, Martin Beirne, Siobhán Corrigan, John Cullen and Ruth Northway

Chapter topics

- Closing remarks
- The richness of the collection and range of contributions
- Recognising practitioner concerns and the appeal of distributed leadership
- Reinforcing the case for change
- The core message and prominent themes
- The current situation and value of subsequent work
- Priorities for further research, advocacy and developmental initiatives

Introduction

The message to be taken from this book is clear: leadership is central to the performance of work organisations, yet is much maligned, frequently inadequate and applied on the basis of assumptions that are often unrealistic. Leadership in healthcare has, quite rightly, been subjected to biting criticism and regular revelations about scandalous failures that prominent investigators, researchers and commentators often attribute to the influence of ideas and senior figures brought in from the commercial sector. The appetite for change, and for breaking free from the restrictions of traditional leadership thinking, is substantial.

This collection has brought together a range of insights and reference material on a topic that attracts enthusiastic support among health professionals, and which deserves to be taken seriously in strategic and operational initiatives to improve the performance of health organisations. This, of course, is distributed leadership, an approach which the contributors to this book suggest has real potential to restore confidence, improve patient care outcomes, and create supportive and innovative working environments. The future of healthcare leadership is far from clear, though what it involves and requires to be effective is too important to be left to unreflective endorsements of conventional wisdom and the blind reproduction of orthodox theories and traditional assumptions. Many healthcare systems continue to function through anachronistic combinations of concentrated authority and quasi-heroic forms of top-down leadership that complicate, curtail and devalue the contributions of frontline clinicians and other health workers. A substantial number of researchers and practitioners, including those who delivered the chapters in this collection, consider this to be inadequate for health organisations in the twenty-first century.

Planning, writing and editing the chapters in this book was a privilege, and we are delighted that so many expert scholars agreed to work with us. We hope that health professionals, students, researchers and practitioners from related disciplines find some encouragement in the collection to more actively question taken-for-granted notions and challenge the lingering leadership conventions that stifle collaborative working, inhibit the application of local knowledge and restrict shared decision-making. The resilience and self-empowering leadership interventions of frontline clinicians that so many of the chapters here commend provide an alternative way forward for healthcare providers, although most of those who occupy places in their managerial and professional hierarchies seem reluctant to recognise or harness this potential. Expanding and protecting the space for distributed leadership is important for both the quality of care services and for health employment, yet this is likely to be an uphill struggle. If this book helps to broaden the appeal of distributed leadership, to build momentum and translate the practitioner interest that it already attracts into wider and stronger forms of advocacy and intervention, then everyone involved with this collaboration will have good reason to be satisfied with their efforts.

What have we learnt?

What can be gleaned from the theory, evidence, evaluative commentary and lines of argument covered in this book? A number of major themes and conclusions are worth keeping in mind.

First, distributed leadership is not a new idea, concept or movement. The recent interest and expanding literature fit into a much longer trajectory of both detached and applied scholarship, especially in the field of education. The genesis of distributed leadership can evidently be traced back to 1250, making it one of the oldest reference points for leadership learning and improvement. Despite this pedigree, several writers have expressed concerns about competing interpretations and the absence of an agreed definition. The term carries different meanings and expectations, with some writers using it rather loosely as a 'catch-all' means of capturing a broad collection of writing about shared and collaborative leadership (Harris, 2013).

Within healthcare, ideas about principled and effective behaviour are frequently fused together in appeals for distributed leadership. Functional arguments about the service benefits that can flow from suitably supported local leadership at the level of clinical teams are intertwined with demands for more inclusive and respectful forms of engagement, and a greater awareness of the self-empowering agency and frontline influence of health professionals. Many of the chapters in this book suggest that the growing complexity of the health sector, and the evolving contextual conditions which affect patient care, underline the importance of distributed leadership initiatives, and provide a clear push in this direction. Progress is far from straightforward, however, and by no means assured. The available evidence points to constraints as well as opportunities, and to reluctance and negativity at senior levels as a counterweight to grassroots demands for a more distributed approach.

Reactions from the health professionals who attended the engagement events that provided the inspiration for this book tempered enthusiasm with a candid appreciation of the obstacles to distribution, often with expressions of frustration. They were acutely aware of potential gains, though also the difficulty of realising these in practice. Nonetheless, a catalogue of insights, initiatives and anecdotal evidence emerged from our nine years of hosting leadership seminars and a conference at Trinity College Dublin, demonstrating that distributed leadership is, in fact, occurring as an everyday feature of healthcare, enacted by nurses, doctors and local managers, regardless of whether their collective influence is actually labelled as such. Further evidence to support this is contained in the case information reported in this book. Of course, additional research is needed to document the full extent of distributed leadership within health organisations, to record the details, outcomes, challenges and issues that affect the diffusion of exemplary practices on this front. Our collection provides a considered step towards this agenda, though more is needed to support its utility and translate the theory, evidence and advocacy into effective forms of practice and development across the sector. Persevering with established approaches to the leadership of health professionals and their organisations is simply too costly, risky and myopic. Leadership represents more than the actions of those in senior positions, though concentrated approaches are unlikely to give way or to accommodate distributed thinking easily and without sustained arguments for change (Ahmed et al., 2015; West et al., 2015).

The second key point to take from this collection is that support for distributed leadership should not be equated with a denial of the significance of positional influence. It is orthodox thinking that is in the firing line, and elitist preoccupations with executive authority, directive control and assumptions about the exclusive qualities of those who reach the highest levels of managerial and professional hierarchies. Positional leaders can have a positive or negative impact, and a recurring theme is that supportive senior figures are often praised and highly valued by clinical staff, with appreciative comments registered about their ability to stimulate beneficial collective contributions to overall performance. This can vary enormously across units, departments and populations of executives and managers, however, and is relatively rare overall, with the balance of employee opinion pointing to limiting, damaging and corrosive behaviour within executive teams. More constructive combinations of distributed and concentrated leadership are still required, and should be set as a priority for organisational design and personal development programmes over the next decade. The latest research on creative configurations and hybrid forms of leadership can help with this, and signpost useful ways of engaging multiple leaders, regardless of whether their contributions are formal or informal, regular or variable, local or hierarchical.

Where are we now?

In terms of evaluative and applied research, particularly in healthcare, the stock of knowledge about distributed leadership remains underdeveloped. Nevertheless, there appears to be widespread enthusiasm for it, especially among nurses and within frontline clinical teams. A research plan that taps into this and is able to sustain it by prioritising work that is capable of addressing practitioner concerns will be vital if progressive change is to be achieved. Several chapters in this collection have highlighted viable areas for rapid development, although these are not presented as an exhaustive list. Since there are very few truly integrated studies of leadership in healthcare, establishing constructive ties for an expansion of cross-disciplinary collaboration is important, especially for applied work, including action research that is capable of anticipating, testing and evaluating distributed leadership policies, projects and developmental initiatives. Greater use of mixed-methods research, longitudinal investigations and comparative studies is required to generate reliable insights into the specifics of distribution, and to cast light on conditions and interventions that promote sustainability, longer-term engagement and further detail on outcomes across the full range of healthcare sites and contexts.

It will be clear by now that much of our learning about the logic and applied relevance of distributed leadership has come from the educational sector. There is a close correspondence between health and education in terms of professional orientations and commitments, with nurses and teachers sharing an ethic of care, for instance. While the path-breaking research on distributed leadership in education has generated valuable information and guidance for developmental work in healthcare, caution is required when straddling the boundaries between contexts and professions. Attending to the specifics of the health sector is vitally important, with all of the chapters in this collection magnifying the complexity of health services and underlining the need for custom-built approaches to distributed leadership that are suitably aligned with service requirements and the demands of the workplace. This is crucial, requiring grounded research and a cautious approach to learning from elsewhere. Some of our contributing authors have expressed concerns about the propensity of health organisations to import leaders and ideas about leadership from the commercial sector. Their cautionary message reaches beyond conventional leadership theories and the orthodoxy to encourage reflective engagement with education and the ostensibly more attractive emphasis on distribution in that sector.

Leadership preparation and continuing professional development (CPD) programmes are critical for the future of distributed leadership. This has been a recurring theme through the collection, with chapter authors calling for more research on the nature and delivery of viable developmental initiatives for both formal and local leaders. There is an evident demand among health professionals for this sort of provision, and hence an urgent need for researchers and educators to devise and deliver attractive and accessible development schemes that can nurture and support distributed leadership on a wide scale. Exactly how these are to be implemented could be decided locally, via more active collaborative work between academics and CPD staff within health organisations and third-party agencies. The editors have some experience with such work as they created a distributed leadership network a few years ago to share ideas with colleagues across Europe, hosting seminars and a research conference for health professionals, and also creating a capacity-building module to facilitate practitioner engagement in 'live' projects. Further work is needed on this front to extend the reach, refine the content and improve the effectiveness of CPD for distributed leadership, and to ensure that this is available to every health worker on demand, regardless of their grade or position.

To achieve such ambitious research and educational agendas, several key considerations are worthy of note. The limitations of concentrated, leader-centric approaches to leadership, along with reductions in public funding, have encouraged some governments to move towards policies that favour, or at least open doors for, distributed leadership. The publication of the *Modernising Government* White Paper in England in 1999 (Cabinet Office, 1999) stressed the importance of improving leadership in public services, including health and social care. Furthermore, the National Health Service in the UK singled out distributed learning as a key element of leadership policy, resulting in several new initiatives, including the setting up of the NHS Leadership Academy in England, Northern Ireland, Scotland and Wales (Martin et al. 2015). This is very encouraging indeed, and if other countries were to take a similar stance support for distributed thinking would likely increase.

Another key factor to consider is that many healthcare facilities still subscribe to a bureaucratic, hierarchical prototype. Such models are generally characterised by paternalistic and byzantine practices which frequently constrain the implementation of distributed leadership beyond powerful groups of executives and senior managers. To further compound this problem is the question of funding and time for health professionals to engage with relevant research and cultivate their own local arrangements for enacting or sustaining distributed influence among care teams. A cursory search of online funding opportunities revealed the use of terms such as 'future leaders' fellowships', 'investment in research leaders' and 'future research leaders' by funders, clearly demonstrating that the emphasis continues to be placed on key individuals (current and short-listed formal leaders) rather than promoting or extending communities of leadership.

We know only too well how difficult it is to secure funding, nationally and internationally, for the promotion and adoption of distributed leadership. This is frustrating and inadequate given the demands for leadership innovation in healthcare. Research evidence and several high-profile reports support the call for progress with distribution, yet funders seem to be unresponsive, and possibly locked-in to the old orthodoxy. Progress is urgent, and practitioner frustrations with the restrictive impact of top-down leadership inclinations are growing. Success with the implementation and sustainability of any improvement initiative, and certainly with distributed leadership schemes, requires designated time for practitioners and support groups to come together to brainstorm ideas and work out the detail of their initiatives. Sadly, however, health professionals are seldom given time and space for team development, or opportunities to translate their collective ideas into explicit leadership arrangements, norms and agreed conventions (De Brún et al., 2019). Distributed leadership is founded upon collaboration, discussion and purposeful interaction among teams of knowledgeable workers, and without that degenerates to little more than spin or empty rhetoric. This is where positional influence can be indispensable in defending and protecting space and time for distribution to be taken seriously and to have a chance of becoming established as regular leadership practice.

What can be done?

The consensus view among a substantial number of researchers, policy-makers and practitioners is that distributed leadership provides a viable route to organisational improvements and an effective means of curtailing the dysfunctional consequences of elitist leading and directing from the top of health organisations (Rafic-Berjaoui and Karami Akkary, 2019). This book has powerfully reinforced this message. While there are encouraging signals that distributed leadership is taking place in some disciplines in healthcare, this is frequently as an undercurrent and informal antidote to official accounts of how health organisations function. For reasons already addressed in this chapter and throughout the book, concentrated, heroic leadership theories and practices are unreliable, ill-considered and anachronistic (Thoroughgood et al., 2018). A more holistic definition of leadership is required, as well as an acknowledgement that leadership and its outcomes are not the preserve of elite groups. This is the summative view of the editors, and a key message for healthcare professionals who make valuable leadership contributions on an everyday basis, without this being acknowledged or supported to any reasonable degree.

During the writing of this book, the Covid-19 pandemic crisis emerged and threw the world into chaos. People were dying, others lost their jobs and were worried about their families. Anecdotally, people were questioning how this happened, how to get out of the crisis and how to secure their future. While this may court controversy, our view is that the pandemic shone a spotlight on the difficulties with established approaches to leadership and the need for more distributed thinking and practice. Effective leadership requires open collaboration, consultation, interaction, honesty, empathy and the pooling of ideas between different agencies, groups and interests. The complexity of the Covid-19 situation tested top-down leadership inclinations across many countries and institutions, and found them wanting to a remarkable extent. Progress was contingent upon de facto and often voluntary leadership interventions at multiple levels, with these revealing tensions as well as inspirational and telling contributions. The picture that emerged from saturation media coverage and initial reports on the wisdom or otherwise of key decisions from different actors, the most senior to responsive local people who made a difference within their own communities, revealed the wisdom of conceptualising leadership in hybrid terms. Distributed leadership was evident in everyday attempts to deal with the pandemic on medical, social and economic fronts, and to compensate for inconsistencies and widely reported weaknesses with the measures introduced by official leaders in various governments around the world, who were regularly criticised for their inability to apply a decisive and independent influence against this dreadful virus.

Looking to the future, we are hopeful that leadership lessons will be learned from the Covid-19 pandemic and that these will make it easier to claim space for distributed thinking and practice. Several research and innovation funding calls have emerged which have a bearing upon this, notably from the World Health Organization (WHO, 2020) and Science Foundation Ireland (2020). These prioritise work in epidemiology, clinical management and vaccine development, though suggest also that research on leadership will carry greater weight. In light of the scholarship invested in this collection, distributed leadership must figure prominently in any emerging agenda for the future of healthcare research and practice, with particular attention given to the following issues:

- considering how to reconfigure structures so that they support autonomy and increase professional discourse
- prioritising continuing professional development (CPD) and learning, both individually and collectively since these contribute to growth and longer-term organisational success
- creating better work environments so that employees feel safe, empowered and motivated to practise leadership
- increasing employee 'voice' so that health professionals feel able to participate meaningfully in decision-making and speak out about concerns without fear of reprisal
- reworking internal structures and procedures to facilitate and encourage leadership regardless of formal position or role
- promoting dignity and respect while encouraging healthy scepticism, critical reflection and an appreciation for debate and disagreement.

Conclusion

We are collectively very proud of this collection, which, to the best of our knowledge, is the first of its kind in healthcare. The combination of scholarship, advocacy and commitment to practitioner engagement is distinctive, and hopefully compelling in the way that it speaks to the expressed concerns of health workers and encourages resilience under difficult conditions. To varying degrees, the crisis of leadership in healthcare lingers on, with dysfunctional behaviour recurring and capturing too many media headlines. We appreciate that there is a long way to go before the contributions of informal local leaders are generally and sufficiently appreciated, and longer still for distributed leadership to be integrated into the formal structures of health organisations. However, the cautious and pessimistic elements of this book are counterbalanced by numerous detailed insights into the realities of distributed leadership in healthcare and the benefits that local leaders deliver for their patients and colleagues.

References

Ahmed, N., Ahmed, F., Anis, H., Carr, P., Gauher, S. and Rahman, F. (2015) *An NHS Leadership Team for the Future*, London: Reform Research Trust.

Cabinet Office (1999) *Modernising Government*, White Paper, Cm 4310, London: HMSO.

De Brún, A., O'Donovan, R. and McAuliffe, E. (2019) Interventions to develop collectivistic leadership in healthcare settings: A systematic review, *BMC Health Services Research*, 19: 72. Available at: https://doi.org/10.1186/s12913-019-3883-x (accessed 21 May 2020).

Harris, A. (2013) Distributed leadership: Friend or foe, *Educational Management Administration and Leadership*, 41 (5): 545–554.

Martin, G., Beech, N., MacIntosh, R. and Bushfield, S. (2015) Potential challenges facing distributed leadership in health care: Evidence from the UK National Health Service, *Sociology of Health and Illness*, 37 (1): 14–19.

Rafic-Berjaoui, R. and Karami-Akkary, R. (2019) Distributed leadership as a path to organizational commitment: The case of a Lebanese school, *Leadership and Policy in Schools*. Available at: https://doi.org/10.1080/15700763.2019.1637900.

Science Foundation Ireland (SFI) (2020) *COVID-19 Rapid Response: Research and Innovation Funding*, Dublin: SFI. Available at: https://www.sfi.ie/funding/funding-calls/covid19-rapid-response/.

Thoroughgood, C.N., Sawyer, K.B., Padilla, A. and Lunsford, L. (2018) Destructive leadership: A critique of leader-centric perspectives and toward a more holistic definition, *Journal of Business Ethics*, 151 (3): 627–649.

West, M., Armit, K., Loewenthal, L., Eckert, R., West, T. and Lee, A. (2015) *Leadership and Leadership Development: The Evidence Base*, London: The King's Fund.

World Health Organization (WHO) (2020) *A Coordinated Global Roadmap*, Geneva: WHO. Available at: https://www.who.int/publications/m/item/a-coordinated-global-research-roadmap (accessed 21 October 2020).

Index